200 veg-growing basics

hamlyn | **all colour gardening**

200 veg-growing basics

Richard Bird

An Hachette Livre UK company
www.hachettelivre.co.uk

First published in Great Britain in 2009 by
Hamlyn, a division of Octopus Publishing Group Ltd
2–4 Heron Quays, London E14 4JP
www.octopusbooks.co.uk

Richard Bird asserts the moral right to be
identified as the author of this work

ISBN: 978-0-600-61833-1

A CIP catalogue record for this book is available
from the British Library

Printed and bound in China

10 9 8 7 6 5 4 3 2 1

contents

introduction

Anyone who grows their own vegetables will agree that they taste far better than anything you can buy. Commercial growers choose varieties that travel well, are uniform in appearance and ripen at the same time. Gardeners, however, can choose varieties purely for flavour.

It's not just a question of choosing the best varieties, however – flavour is also about freshness. Many vegetables, including sweetcorn and peas, contain sugars that contribute to their wonderful taste. As soon as they are picked, the sugars begin to convert to starch and the flavour deteriorates. This is why supermarket produce can't compete with a handful of the sweetest peas picked a few moments before cooking.

Another good reason to grow your own is one of practicality. If you feel like adding a few spring onions to a salad you have them to hand. If unexpected visitors arrive you can gather a few extra parsnips for lunch.

If you also take into account the satisfaction you feel, the beneficial exercise and the fact that you know exactly what has been put on your vegetables, you will soon realize that home-grown is best. All you need to get started is a small area of soil or a few containers on the patio and a little time. This handy book contains over 200 invaluable hints and tips on growing your own vegetables; in fact, everything you need to know to get growing.

getting started

organic or non-organic?

Much has been said in the media about what we should or should not eat, and whether organic food is better for our health than non-organic produce. Similarly, there is also a debate about organic gardening – should we be using chemicals on our vegetable plots and allotments?

what does organic mean?
Non-organic gardeners use artificially manufactured chemical fertilizers, pesticides and weedkillers. Organic gardeners avoid chemicals altogether because of their impact on the environment and on beneficial wildlife, although some may resort to pesticides derived from plants and other natural ingredients.

developing the right philosophy
To a good gardener, however, organic versus non-organic need not become an issue. Making and using your own compost is not a question of belief, but one of good gardening practice. In addition, having a mixture of flowers as well as vegetables is largely a matter of common sense (see page 24). Beneficial insects as well as pests are attracted to the garden and there is a balance that rarely needs interference. By practising good husbandry (see page 40), you shouldn't need to use any treatments to keep pests at bay. And if a problem does arise, you can simply remove the crop and discard it, then have another go next year. This is one great advantage that growing vegetables has over other more permanent plants, such as trees and shrubs.

soil

Soil is the very stuff of gardening. Get it right and you stand a good chance of producing a fine array of vegetables. You may have an old garden that has near-perfect soil or you may have a new garden still full of builder's rubble. No matter what your starting point, a little effort is all it will take.

the ideal soil

The ideal soil is fertile and free-draining yet moisture-retentive. The second two terms may seem to contradict one another, but what they mean are that a soil retains enough water for the plants to thrive but does not become waterlogged in wet weather.

improving the texture

The soil in new gardens built over solid clay is among the worst you may encounter. However, after carefully cultivating the soil for even as little as two years, you can transform it into something quite respectable. The key is to add plenty of well-rotted organic material (humus) in the form of garden compost, mushroom compost, farmyard manure or commercial soil conditioners. Any of these will help to break down the soil and encourage worms, which will condition it even further.

Horticultural grit is also valuable for improving the drainage and soil texture. Dig some into the soil at the same time as the organic matter. For more details on soil preparation see page 22.

improving the fertility

As well as improving soil texture, well-rotted organic material will also provide nutrients to feed the plants. Add plenty of well-rotted organic material, such as garden compost or farmyard manure, to the soil when you are digging it at the end of autumn, so that it has a chance to break down before sowing and planting in the spring. Some plants – parsnips for example – do not like newly composted ground, so plant these crops in areas that have been treated the previous year. Mention is made under individual plants when this is required.

With permanent crops, such as asparagus, apply a layer of well-rotted manure or compost around the plants at the beginning of each season. There is no need to dig it in – the worms will take it down for you.

Other fertilizers, such as bonemeal, seaweed meal or organic poultry fertilizer, can be used to give a boost to soil fertility. Sprinkle them on the surface of the soil and rake in before planting. If there are already plants growing in the soil, sprinkle the fertilizer on the soil surface and water in. Always follow the instructions on the packet.

soil pH

On the whole, vegetables are a tolerant lot, but the acidity or alkalinity of the soil can be important. Generally speaking, vegetables prefer a neutral soil – that is, a pH of 7 – but some crops, such as brassicas, prefer a slightly alkaline soil. To check the pH (the measure of acidity/alkalinity) of your soil, buy a soil-testing kit at a garden centre. They are simple to use and will tell you the pH value of your soil.

Acidic soils can be made more neutral by adding lime (ground limestone or dolomitic limestone), while alkaline soils can be made more neutral by adding compost and manure on a regular basis. Extremely alkaline soil is the most difficult to rectify, and if you have this type of soil you might have to grow vegetables in raised beds or containers.

making compost

In the vegetable garden we tend to remove plants as they are ready to eat, so the soil is gradually impoverished. Making compost is a way of storing decaying plant matter until it has rotted down. It can then be returned to the soil, to add nutrients, improve soil texture and help drainage.

compost bins

Compost bins can be made at home using wood, old pallets or bricks, or you can buy a range of bins, usually in plastic. Wood is the best material because it keeps the compost warm to help it rot and allows it to breathe. It is best to have three bins: one that you are filling up, another that is rotting down and a third that is ready to use.

what to compost

- Use all garden waste and vegetable matter. Woody material will need to be shredded or chopped first.
- Use raw kitchen vegetable waste, including tea, coffee and egg shells.
- Include newspaper, wood ash, torn cardboard, animal hair and straw.
- Avoid perennial weed roots, such as couch grass or ground elder and weed seeds.
- Avoid cooked food or non-vegetable food scraps, which will attract rats.

making compost

Pile all the material into the bin — the more you can put in at once, the more heat will build up to help rot the material. After a few weeks, fork the material out onto a plastic sheet, turn it to mix the contents, then pile it back in the bin. Repeat this from time to time until the compost is brown, crumbly and sweet-smelling. It is then ready to use.

where to grow vegetables

The traditional vegetable plot where the plants are arranged in long rows with bare soil in between is still popular, but there are two other methods that are perhaps better suited to beginners. The first is to grow vegetables in blocks instead of rows, and the second is to use raised beds.

block planting

Block planting is where the plants are arranged in blocks rather than long rows one plant deep. This allows closer planting and makes the ground more productive. Although the individual vegetables produced tend to be smaller, the overall yield is higher. The blocks should be a maximum of 1.2 m (4 ft) across to allow you to reach all the plants without stepping on the soil. The disadvantage is that air circulation is better with rows, which helps prevent mildews and rust (see pages 42 and 44).

raised beds

Raised beds, with sides made from bricks or wooden boards, allow the soil to be deeply cultivated so that roots can go down a long way, not only providing extra stability but also increasing their chance of finding moisture in dry periods. Construct the beds no more than 1.2 m (4 ft) wide so that you can reach all parts of the bed without walking on it. This maintains the structure of the soil and avoids the need for digging once the bed has been prepared.

Raised beds are good for gardens with poor soil because much of the mixture is brought in, allowing you to create a good, compost-rich, free-draining soil for your vegetables. If you have a raised bed across which you can easily reach it makes sense to use block planting.

preparing beds

The only way to prepare a bed properly is to dig it, removing weeds, stones and pests as you go. Autumn is a good time because the frosts will break down the soil. Any remaining weed fragments that regrow can be removed before you start planting in the spring.

where to site your vegetables

Don't just design your garden on paper. Have a good look at it and select a place for the vegetables beds that is open to the sun and the air, avoiding shady places under trees. Choose a warm spot away from frost hollows. You also need to check the soil to make certain that the drainage is good enough. If the soil does not drain freely, find another position because you will never successfully grow vegetables on waterlogged soil. Ideally, the soil should be rich, crumbly and fertile, though this is less important as it can be improved and will be over the years of use.

clearing the ground

The next job is to remove any rubbish left over from previous uses or from the builders. It is also important to get rid of any weeds. If you have a light soil remove weeds by hand, but on heavier, clay soils this is near impossible. You have two choices: to cover the ground with black polythene or an old carpet until the weeds give up (this will take some months and in the case of perennial weeds, at least a year) or to use a weedkiller. If used properly, you should need to use a weedkiller only once.

digging the beds

Dig the soil thoroughly to a depth of at least 30 cm (12 in), but preferably more. Remove any remaining weeds as you go and any rubbish you find buried. At the same time, dig in plenty of well-rotted organic material (see page 12). The deeper this goes the better because it will hold the moisture down near the roots, even when the top of the soil dries out. If the soil is very heavy, incorporate a lot of horticultural grit to improve the drainage.

last-minute preparation

Autumn is the best time to prepare the bed. This gives winter frosts the chance to break down the soil, making it easier to work with. It will also allow any remaining weed fragments to grow big enough to be seen, giving you the opportunity to remove them before you sow in the spring.

In the spring rake over the dug bed, breaking down the soil into a fine tilth and levelling the surface. Just before planting, rake in a general fertilizer, such as blood, fish and bone, following the instructions on the packet to tell you how much to use. Until you can recognize deficiencies in the soil from the appearance of the plants, it is best to check the soil with a good soil testing kit and add fertilizers accordingly. You are now ready to start planting.

during the year

When you are replacing finished crops, such as lettuces, there is no need to do a full preparation before replanting. Remove all weeds and clear away any old leaves or remains of the previous crop. Lightly fork over the soil and rake it back to a fine tilth. On light soils, particularly in dry conditions, it may just be sufficient to rake the surface over so that the soil is not disturbed, which will cause further moisture loss. At the same time, rake in a light dressing of fertilizer for the more hungry crops. In dry conditions, water well before replanting

decorative vegetables

Most gardeners choose to keep their flowers and vegetables
separate, but there is no reason why this should be so.
Vegetables can be extremely decorative in their own right,
so why not enjoy them in the garden as well as on your plate.

cottage garden charm

Cottage gardeners of old blurred the edges between decorative gardening
and vegetable growing and often grew their vegetable plants and herbs in
the flower beds. This was partly for practical reasons of limited space, but
also for the aesthetic benefits. Wigwams of runner beans with their scarlet
flowers, or globe artichokes with their bold silver foliage are just two great
choices for the flower beds.

formal potagers

The idea of decorative vegetable gardens, or potagers, holds the most
interest today. Here, the vegetables are not simply arranged in groups but
are used in decorative patterns, with the textures, colours and shapes of
the plants exploited to make a satisfying picture. The shapes of the beds
are often intricate, with formal paths between them and trained fruit trees
adding permanent structure. Within the overall layout the vegetables are
planted in rows, blocks or even singly to create the desired pattern.

elegant edibles

If you want to make the most of the decorative qualities of vegetables,
choose some of the following: scarlet-stemmed ruby chard; bushy pepper
and chilli plants; bush courgettes with green or yellow fruits; runner beans
with prolific flowers in scarlet, white or pink; and tomato plants with bright
shiny fruits in red, orange or yellow.

vegetables in containers

You don't need a big garden to grow vegetables. Even people
with just a balcony can grow a few edibles because, with the
right care, most are perfectly successful in containers.

choosing containers

Most containers are suitable. Large plastic or ceramic pots, plain or
decorative, are ideal and will look good on the patio or balcony. Less
attractive, but cheap and practical, are old dustbins (ideal for potatoes), or
even dump bags in which building materials have been delivered. The other
possibility is to build your own wooden containers, but whatever you choose
bear in mind the bigger the better. The larger the container, the less quickly
it will dry out and the cooler the compost will be around the plant's roots.

getting the compost right

A soil-based compost is the best choice, because peat-based composts are
too light and are difficult to rewet once they have dried out. Mix in plenty of
humus in the form of well-rotted garden compost or manure (see page 12),
and improve the drainage by adding horticultural grit. Put the container in
place before filling as it will be heavy once it is full of moist compost.

where to stand them

Choose an open, sunny position in which to stand the containers. The
permanent shade of a tree or tall building will not provide ideal conditions.

container care

Vegetables growing in containers will need regular watering to keep the
compost just moist at all times. The watering will, however, leach (wash)
the nutrients out of the compost, so apply a liquid feed once a week
when the plants are growing.

what and when to plant

If you have an enormous garden and a healthy appetite,
you can grow plenty of different varieties, but most of
us are restricted in some way, usually by space or time.

choosing vegetables

Concentrate on vegetables that are not easily available from greengrocers
or supermarkets, such as fresh peas or Jerusalem artichokes. Those that
you use only in small quantities, such as spring onions, are also good
choices. But perhaps the best to choose are those that taste so much
better when they are fresh and home grown, such as sun-ripened
tomatoes or waxy, yellow new potatoes.

getting maximum yield

The key to vegetable gardening is to get the maximum out of your plot.
If space is limited, select varieties that don't take up much space – globe
artichokes, for example, take up a lot of space for what they produce.
Intercropping also maximizes yield; this is when you plant fast-growing
crops, such as lettuces and radishes between slower vegetables, like
Brussels sprouts or broccoli. The lettuces grow and are harvested
before the brassicas need the extra space.

   Catchcropping, where you sow another crop in the space as soon
as you have harvested the first, is another way of maximizing yield.

don't overdo it

Resist the temptation to use all the seed in the packet. Only sow what
you can eat. It is better to sow a few lettuces, followed three weeks later
with another few, than to sow a large number all at once, which may
produce more than you require.

crop rotation

It is best not to grow the same crops each year in the same piece of soil, as the pests and diseases that attack specific crops will build up in the soil and become a problem. To avoid this, gardeners practise what is known as crop rotation.

how does it work?

Vegetables can be divided into four basic groups (see below), the members of which attract the same pests and diseases. Rotation involves dividing the space allotted to vegetables into four areas. You grow all the root vegetables or all the brassicas (the cabbage family) on one plot one year, then move them to the next plot the following year and so forth, returning to the original plot in the fifth year. You don't actually have to have four individual plots – it can be the same large bed – but you move each crop to a different part of it each year. If you are growing vegetables in containers, change the compost every year to avoid a build-up of pests.

what are the groups?

• **The legumes:** dwarf beans, broad beans, climbing beans and peas.
• **The brassicas:** broccoli, calabrese, cauliflower, Brussels sprouts, cabbage, kale, kohlrabi, swedes and turnips.
• **The root crops:** potatoes, carrots, parsnips, celeriac, Florence fennel, plus a few other related crops, including tomatoes, aubergines, peppers, chillies and celery.
• **The onion family and the squashes:** garlic, leeks, onions, shallots, spring onions, cucumbers, courgettes, marrows, pumpkins and squashes.
Other vegetables can be slotted in with any of the groups where there is space, while permanent crops, such as rhubarb, asparagus and seakale, can have a space of their own.

propagation

Many gardeners start their vegetables off as young plants bought from a nursery or garden centre. This is by far the quickest way, but raising your own vegetables from seed is straightforward, satisfying, more economical, and you'll get a much bigger selection of varieties from which to choose.

getting started

The vast majority of vegetables are grown from seed. The exceptions are globe artichokes, rhubarb, potatoes and Jerusalem artichokes (see page 34).

Buy seed fresh each year from a garden centre or a seed merchant's catalogue. Seed merchants offer a much more exciting selection of varieties, and their catalogues are often useful sources of information. Seed can either be sown direct into the soil outside or in pots until the young plants are ready for planting out.

sowing seed in the soil

Avoid sowing seed too early; wait until the soil has warmed up and dried out to prevent the seed rotting before it germinates. The ground is ready when the soil will break up into a fine, crumbly tilth. Use a fork to turn over the soil, then rake it lightly to a fine tilth, standing on boards if necessary to avoid compacting the soil.

Use a cane to mark out drills (narrow depressions) into which to sow the seed, consulting the seed packet to tell you how deep the drills should be. If the weather is dry, water the drills before sowing. Now sprinkle the seed thinly in the drills, cover by carefully drawing soil back to fill the drill and firm down the soil gently with the back of your rake. Water well, using a fine spray to avoid dislodging the seed.

larger plants

Seeds of larger vegetables, such as parsnips, should be station sown to avoid wasting seed. This means sowing two or three seeds where each of the mature plants will grow. Remove the excess seedlings at each station, leaving just one strong plant. Another method is to sow the seeds as normal in a drill, then transplant the resulting seedlings into their permanent growing positions when they are large enough to handle.

sowing in pots

Seed can be sown in pots or modules, indoors or in a greenhouse. This means that the seed can be sown earlier and by the time the soil is warm enough outside, the plants will be ready for planting out. Sowing in pots also stops mice eating the seed before it germinates.

Fill the pots with compost and shake them to settle the soil. Sow the seed thinly on top, before covering with a little more compost. Individual modules are a good idea as there is less root disturbance when you plant out. If you use modules, sow two or three seeds in each and thin to one seedling as soon as they emerge.

hardening off

Seedlings that have been grown under cover will need to be hardened off. This means slowly getting them used to the colder temperatures, before planting out. Stand the seedlings outside for a few hours the first day, then bring them back indoors. Repeat, increasing the time spent outside for the next few days. After a week or so, the seedlings can be planted out.

other forms of propagation

Potatoes and Jerusalem artichokes are grown from tubers which should be laid in trenches rather than drills and spaced according to the variety.

Globe artichokes and rhubarb are increased by division. In early spring lift a clump and break it into smaller sections, each with roots and at least one bud, which can be found around the edges of an old clump. Remove broken roots and replant clumps in new positions at the same depth as before.

feeding your plants

Bed preparation is all-important because it is at this stage that the nutrients are added to the soil. If you have prepared the ground thoroughly, there is rarely any real need to feed during growth, unless the plants are in containers.

why feed?
It is best, however, to feed your plants occasionally. Plants will not only grow bigger and be more prolific, but they will also be healthier and less susceptible to disease. This is important because preventing disease is better than curing it, especially if you want to avoid using chemicals.

all-important organic matter
The most important thing is to add organic material to the soil on a regular basis. This can be well-rotted garden compost or farmyard manure, both of which contain a good range of nutrients, as well as working wonders with the soil structure and encouraging all sorts of beneficial creatures, such as worms. Add organic matter when preparing beds each spring, and you may not need any other fertilizer.

other fertilizers
Most gardeners, however, supplement organic matter with a general fertilizer, such as a seaweed feed or blood, fish and bone. Liquid feeds are also useful, especially for container-grown plants, and for giving a quick boost as plants, such as tomatoes, are coming into fruit. There are organic liquid feeds available, too.

If you are worried about nutrient or mineral deficiencies in your soil, use a soil-testing kit to highlight any problems and remedy them by carefully choosing the right fertilizer.

watering

Water is essential for all plants, but especially for those producing vegetables. Indeed, all vegetables contain a large percentage of water. Deprive plants of water and at worst they die; at best the vegetables are small and woody.

conserving water

Conserving water in the soil is the key, because the more you can conserve, the less you will have to add, saving time, money and hard work. Adding organic material to the soil really helps hold moisture, so dig in as much as you can (see page 12). Organic material also works well as a mulch to prevent moisture evaporating from the soil surface – add a layer of well-rotted garden compost, leafmould or even straw on the surface of bare soil. Inorganic mulches, such as black polythene, also serve to prevent evaporation, but they are not especially attractive and they don't help to improve the soil.

how and when to water

Most water is provided by rain, but during prolonged periods of drought it may be necessary to water your crops, even when the soil is well mulched. Rainwater collected in butts is best, but tapwater is a good alternative. When watering, use a watering can or hose to soak the ground thoroughly. Sprinklers are very wasteful, but hand-held sprays or lances attached to a hose pipe can be economical. Water when the surface of the soil is dry. Evening is the best time to water; avoid the heat of the day as the water will evaporate as soon as it hits the ground.

Containers dry out very quickly, especially small ones, so water when the surface of the compost is dry. In very hot weather, this will be once or even twice a day.

pests and diseases

Most gardeners get through life without much more than the occasional outbreak of blackfly or a mild case of mildew, and vegetable gardening is no different. Serious diseases in the vegetable garden are not common, especially if you practise good husbandry.

avoiding trouble

If you spot any diseased plants, it is usually easier to dig them up and burn them rather than trying to rescue them with doses of chemicals. Vegetables are short-term plants, so you can simply try again. On pages 42–44, there is a list of the most common pests and diseases. Remember that just because they are listed, it does not mean that your vegetables will suffer from them. With good husbandry and common sense they won't.

The key to success is to keep plants healthy and they won't be susceptible to problems like pests and diseases.

If you are not growing from seed, buy young plants from a reputable source and never plant what may look like diseased plants, especially brassicas. Always make certain that the plants have optimum growing conditions: plenty of light, plenty of air (but not strong winds), plenty of water and nutrients. Don't allow the growth of your plants to be checked in dry weather: mulch the ground and water regularly to keep the plants moist and growing strongly.

Another important factor is to keep a well-balanced garden. Many pests have their own natural predators: for example, ladybirds, lacewings and hoverflies demolish vast numbers of aphids, while ground beetles eat slugs and underground larvae. If you have flower beds with a wide range of plants, you are likely to attract many different creatures to the garden. These will create a balance, and you should rarely have problems.

Aphids There are hundreds of different types of these sap-sucking pests, including greenfly and blackfly, but they rarely cause serious problems. If you have a large infestation, rub the stems through your fingers to squash them or blast them away with a jet of water.

Birds Pigeons in particular, attack young seedlings. Use bird scarers or netting. A wire cage is the only way to keep them away with any certainty.

Blight A problems only with tomatoes and potatoes, this infectious disease causes brown marks on the tops of leaves and stems and white spores underneath. Prevent it by buying resistant strains and good-quality seed potatoes. Space plants widely for good air circulation. Remove and burn affected plants; do not add them to the compost.

Cabbage rootfly This serious pest affects mainly brassicas. The adults lay eggs near the plants, and the pupae burrow into the soil to eat the roots, causing wilting and poor growth. Prevent the pupae from burrowing by planting young plants through a layer of fleece or fine netting on the soil, or surround each plant with a 10 cm (4 in) diameter collar of carpet underlay after planting.

Caterpillars Caterpillars affect many crops, but mainly brassicas. Cover the crops with fleece to prevent butterflies laying eggs or simply pick off the caterpillars as they appear.

Clubroot A serious disease of brassicas and some root vegetables, clubroot causes distortion and swellings on the roots. If your brassicas are inexplicably wilting, dig one up and check the roots. If you find clubroot, dig up and burn the entire crop. Prevent the disease by rotating crops (see page 30), and making your soil slightly alkaline (above pH7). Buy young plants from a reputable source or grow your own from seed.

Downy mildew A fungal disease causing discoloured patches on leaf surfaces and fluffy white or grey growth beneath. It thrives in warm, damp conditions. Remove and destroy affected leaves, improve air circulation and water at the base to avoid spreading it.

Top left: Aphids. Top right: Blight.
Bottom left: Caterpillars. Bottom right: Clubroot

Flea beetles These small, shiny, jumping beetles leave tiny holes in leaves and stems, and the larvae eat the roots, weakening plants. Prevent an attack by growing crops under cloches or fleece. If they appear, dust the plants with Derris, which can also be a preventative measure.

Mice Mice will eat peas and beans from the soil after sowing. Either trap the mice or sow extras to allow for some losses.

Powdery mildew A whitish, powdery fungal growth appears on leaves and stems. Keep plants well watered, and make sure there's plenty of air circulation to prevent it. If it appears, remove and burn affected leaves.

Red spider mite Rarely a problem in the open garden, but more commonly seen in greenhouses. The tiny red or brown mites suck the sap and cause leaves to become silver, then yellow. They thrive in dry conditions, so keep the atmosphere moist and humid by misting the plants and by regularly watering the greenhouse floor.

Rust This fungal disease attacks only a few plants, including leeks and beans, causing yellow or brown pustules on the foliage. Ignore it as it does not cause any problems.

Slugs and snails Probably the most severe problem for many gardeners. The best method to clear them is to go out at night with a torch and destroy any you find. If you don't mind using chemicals, slug pellets are also effective.

Viruses There are many different types, all incurable. They usually appear as stunting and distortion of the plants, with unusual colour changes or patterning on the leaves, such as mottling or mosaic patterns. Viruses are spread by aphids or by the gardener and his tools. Keep aphids at bay and buy resistant stock. If viruses occur, remove and burn affected plants.

Whitefly Rarely a problem in the open garden, more of a problem in the greenhouse, these tiny sap-sucking insects can be controlled using sticky yellow fly traps or a biological control.

Top left: Flea beetles. Top right: Powdery mildew.
Bottom left: Rust. Bottom right: Whitefly

protecting crops

There are several ways to protect crops from cold and marauding pests. A barrier of glass or clear plastic brings them on much earlier than those in the open garden, and fleece or netting will keep flying pests at bay.

Greenhouses Vegetable plants can be grown in a greenhouse in the same way as they are in the garden. It is also a good place to grow tomatoes, aubergines and other tender crops, which benefit from the protection and raised temperatures. A heated greenhouse can be used to germinate and raise seeds before it is warm enough to sow them outside.

Cold frames Cold frames are like small, low greenhouses. They can be covered with old carpet at night to maintain a good temperature. They are also useful for hardening off young plants (see page 34).

Cloches These are transparent covers used to cover single plants or whole rows in the garden, keeping the soil and air around the plants a little warmer. Glass cloches are the best but are more expensive than their plastic equivalents. When growing plants under protection, remember they need circulating air to prevent fungal diseases. Be sure to water regularly as the soil will dry out more quickly.

Horticultural fleece This light, woven fabric is used to protect plants from frosts, especially in late spring. It is also a good choice for preventing insects getting at young seedlings.

Micromesh This is a fine netting used to protect crops from insect pests, such as caterpillars and carrot fly. It allows light to reach the crops so it can be used as permanent protection.

harvesting and storing produce

The moment you pick your first home-grown produce is always exciting, but the first taste is even more of a thrill.

when to harvest

As a general rule, the less time between harvesting and eating the better as the flavour and vitamin content start to deteriorate when vegetables are picked.

It is usually obvious when vegetables are ready to harvest, and many are even sweeter if you pick them while they are small, so there's no harm if you are a little early. If you are unsure whether they are ready, pick a handful and try them.

Many vegetables have a definite end to their harvesting season, and they become tough or woody as they age, so be sure to harvest them before this point and store the produce while it is in peak condition.

Some vegetables, including leeks, cabbages and cauliflowers, can be left in the ground until you are ready to use them. Most root crops will tolerate at least some winter weather, so dig them up when you need them. Parsnips actually taste a little better after a frost, so leave them until you have had a cold snap.

storing produce

After harvesting, store vegetables in a cool but frost-free place, preferably with air circulating round them. Open boxes or mesh sacks are ideal. Some root vegetables, including carrots and potatoes, should be surrounded by sand or peat.

Most vegetables can be frozen after harvesting. Bottling and pickling are also great ways to preserve vegetables, which can be enjoyed later in the year. Specific details of when and how to harvest can be found under the entry for each vegetable.

getting growing

garlic

Garlic is a vital ingredient in many cuisines around the world and presents few problems to the grower. One of the advantages of growing your own is that you can harvest some of the heads while still green and juicy, to appreciate their fresh flavour in your spring cooking.

	J	F	M	A	M	J	J	A	S	O	N	D
Plant		*									*	*
Harvest						*	*					

From planting to harvest 26–36 weeks

Site & soil Garlic does best in a sunny, open site and a light soil. If your soil is heavy, dig in plenty of organic matter and grit to improve the drainage. It needs a moderately rich soil, so plant in ground to which manure was added for the previous crop earlier in the spring or the autumn before. Avoid recently manured ground.

Sowing & planting Garlic is grown by planting individual cloves split from a bulb. It is best to buy a specific cultivar from a specialist seed merchant that suits your conditions. For best results plant cloves in late autumn so they get two months at a temperature of 1–10°C (32–50°F). Garlic can also be planted in late winter.

Plant individual cloves with the flat basal plate at the bottom of a small hole, with the pointed tip about 2.5 cm (1 in) or so below the soil surface. Space at 15 cm (6 in) intervals, with about 30 cm (12 in) between rows, or 20 cm (8 in) each way if you are planting in blocks (see page 18).

Care Keep the area free from weeds. It is best to weed by hand to avoid damaging the bulbs with a hoe.

Problems Garlic is generally trouble free, although it may suffer from various fungal diseases. The most common are rust (see page 44) and onion white rot, which causes the leaves to turn yellow and wilt. If you lift a bulb you will see fluffy white fungus with little black specks on the roots. It can stay in the soil for a considerable time, so be sure to rotate crops (see page 30). If disease does occur, remove infected plants and burn them. If it is close to harvest time, however, ignore any rust, but remove all infected parts of the plant when you lift the bulbs.

Harvesting Harvest autumn-planted garlic in early or mid summer as the leaves turn yellow, late winter-planted garlic a bit later. Dry the bulbs and remove any soil before storing. If you want fresh green garlic, lift the immature bulbs while the leaves are still green.

Storing Store in a cool, dry place with good air circulation, for example in string sacks or bags. The bulbs can be tied in decorative strings, but don't hang them in a warm kitchen as they will not last long. Some varieties store longer than others, so check the suppliers' catalogues when you buy.

Good choices Elephant, Solent Wight, Early Purple Wight, Giant Wight, Purple Moldovan, Lautrec Wight

leeks

Leeks are among the mainstays of the winter kitchen, perfect for warming soups and stews. They can be left in the ground until required and with the right selection of cultivars you could be pulling fresh leeks from autumn through to the spring.

	J	F	M	A	M	J	J	A	S	O	N	D
Sow		*	*	*	*							
Plant			*	*	*	*						
Harvest	*	*	*	*						*	*	*

From sowing to harvest 16–20 weeks

Site & soil The ideal site is open, with well-drained, water-retentive soil, which does not become waterlogged in winter. Try raised beds (see page 18) with plenty of humus.

Sowing & planting Leeks can be sown in pots under cover and then planted out, or sown directly in the soil and then transplanted. Sow thinly in trays or modules in a good-quality seed compost and keep in a cool greenhouse. Harden off (see page 34) and plant out when they are 20 cm (8 in) tall. Make holes 12–15 cm (5–6 in) deep and lower the leeks into them. Do not refill the holes with soil, but fill with water. Space the leeks 10–15 cm (4–6 in) apart in rows 30 cm (12 in) apart. Alternatively, grow in blocks with leeks set 15–23 cm (6–9 in) apart.

If sowing direct, sow seed in drills (see page 32) from early spring and transplant to their permanent positions in the same way as pot-grown plants.

Care Once the leeks have filled their planting holes, they can be earthed up to blanch the stems by gently drawing soil up around the leeks to exclude light. Keep the area weeded by hand to avoid damaging the leeks with a hoe.

Problems Leek rust (see page 44) is the most common, seen as a golden powder on the leaves. It is not serious and can be ignored. Keep the leeks watered in dry weather and avoid close planting to prevent it. Plants may bolt, that is produce flower stems which result in a hard centre to the leeks. Again, watering in dry weather will prevent this.

Harvesting Leeks can be left in the ground until they are required. Some early cultivars may go soft as the winter progresses, so sow later crops as well to give a long period of good-quality leeks.

Storing Leeks are best left in the ground; they do not keep well once lifted.

Good choices Early croppers: Titan, Carlton, Swiss Giant – Zermatt, Einstein
Maincroppers: Musselburgh, Apollo, Autumn Giant – Porvite, Neptune
Baby leeks: Amor, Edison, King Richard

onions

Onions are probably the most useful vegetable in the kitchen, and if you grow your own you will always have plenty to hand and a choice of different sizes. Onions can be grown from seed or from small bulbs called sets.

	J	F	M	A	M	J	J	A	S	O	N	D
Sow	*	*	*	*					*			
Plant	*	*	*	*					*	*		
Harvest						*	*					

From sowing/planting to harvest 18–42 weeks, depending on method

Site & soil Onions prefer an open, sunny site. The soil should be well drained and reasonably fertile. Incorporate manure into the soil in autumn for spring planting, and spring for autumn planting.

Sowing & planting Onions can be grown from seed, or planted as small bulbs called sets. Sow seed in trays or modules under glass in winter, then plant out the seedlings in spring. Alternatively, sow direct into the soil in shallow drills (see page 32) in spring, or in late summer for an early crop.

   Plant sets in late winter if the soil is not waterlogged, or in early spring. Space them 10 cm (4 in) apart in rows 30 cm (12 in) apart, or 15 cm (6 in) apart if you are planting in blocks (see page 18). The tips should be just visible above the soil. You can also buy sets for autumn planting that produce earlier crops.

Care Weed the area carefully by hand to prevent bulb damage. Be careful not to loosen the bulbs in the soil while weeding.

Problems Onions can suffer from onion white rot (see page 54), downy mildew (see page 42) and onion neck rot, which doesn't usually appear until after the bulbs have been harvested. They become soft and a grey fluffy mould develops around the neck. All these can be prevented by crop rotation (see page 30) and good hygiene. They can also be reduced by ensuring a good flow of air round the plants by wide spacing. Removal of infected plants will help prevent spread. Seedlings seem to be less susceptible than sets. Onion fly may also be a problem, as the maggots bore holes into the bulbs and eat the roots. Avoid onion fly by covering with fleece soon after the sets have been planted.

Harvesting Allow the leaves to fall over and die back, then carefully loosen the bulbs from the soil. Leave them lying in the sun for a few days for the skins to ripen.

Storing Keep in a cool, dry place, preferably hanging in nets or string bags, or tie into ropes so that the air can circulate between bulbs. Do not hang ropes in a warm kitchen, unless you use them quickly, as they will soon shrivel. Open wooden boxes with slatted sides are another good choice.

Good choices Brown-skinned onions: Ailsa Craig, Marco, Bedfordshire Champion, New Fen Globe, Show Master, Setton, Kelsae, Autumn Gold Improved
Red-skinned onions. Red Baron, Red Pearl, Long Red Florence
White-skinned onions: White Prince, Albion F1, Snowball

shallots

Shallots grow in little clusters of bulbs, smaller and milder than regular onions. They are invaluable in slow-cooked casseroles and are deliciously sweet when roasted. They are also used in oriental dishes and raw in salads. Stored well, they will last throughout the winter.

	J	F	M	A	M	J	J	A	S	O	N	D
Sow			*	*								
Plant	*	*	*									
Harvest						*	*	*				

From sowing/planting to harvest 20–28 weeks

Site & soil Shallots prefer an open, sunny situation, but will tolerate a little shade. The soil should be free draining and reasonably fertile. Ground that was manured for a previous crop is ideal. Alternatively, manure the ground in the autumn before planting.

Sowing & planting Shallots are usually grown from small bulbs called sets. Plant the sets in late winter or early spring. In warm, dry areas it can be earlier, even late autumn or early winter. Push the sets into holes in the soil, so that the tips are just above the soil surface. Plant at 15 cm (6 in) intervals with rows 25 cm (10 in) apart. Space 20 cm (8 in) apart if you are growing in blocks (see page 18).

Shallot seed is now also available, but it will produce single bulbs rather than clusters. Sow in shallow drills (see page 32) and thin seedlings to 5 cm (2 in) apart.

Care Keep the area well weeded, preferably by hand to avoid damaging the bulbs with a hoe. Take care not to dislodge the bulbs at the same time as the weeds. Water in dry weather when the bulbs are swelling.

Problems Shallots can suffer from the same problems as onions (see page 62), but on the whole they are less troublesome. At the early stages, the newly planted bulbs may pop out of the ground, either pushed out by the emerging roots or by sparrows looking for nesting material. Make certain that bulbs are planted up to their tips, and replant any that come lose.

Harvesting Let the foliage die back naturally, then lift the clusters of bulbs. As with onions, lay them in the sun for a few days for the skins to ripen. Once they rustle when rubbed, split the clusters into individual bulbs.

Storing Keep over winter in a cool, dry place, storing them in net or string bags, or in slatted, open boxes. The air must be able to circulate round them. They can also be plaited into ropes, but avoid hanging in a warm kitchen as they won't keep well.

Good choices Round varieties: Pikant, Golden Gourmet, Springfield, Red Sun, Topper
Long varieties: Jermor, Pink Viganor, Mikor
Seed: Ambition F1, Prisma F1

spring onions

Spring onions, also known as bunching onions, make a crisp and flavoursome addition to salads. They can also be used in sauces and cooked dishes, particularly in Oriental cuisine. Pickling onions are grown in the same way, except they form small bulbs.

	J	F	M	A	M	J	J	A	S	O	N	D
Sow	*	*	*	*	*	*						
Harvest							*	*	*	*	*	*

From sowing to harvest **8 weeks**

Site & soil Spring onions like an open, sunny site, although they can be grown in the lee of a tall hedge as long as it does not overhang them. They like an open, free-draining soil that is not too fertile; soil that has been manured for a previous crop is ideal. Pickling onions can be grown in poorer soil. Raise early crops under cover in a cold frame or greenhouse if you have one. Spring onions are also good subjects for containers.

Sowing & planting Sow outside from early spring into early summer, or under cover from mid winter to late summer. They should be sown thinly in shallow drills (see page 32) about 1 cm (½ in) deep, with the rows about 15 cm (6 in) apart. If the soil is dry, water along the drill before sowing.

Thin the seedlings to about 2 cm (¾ in) apart when they appear. If you are growing in blocks (see page 18), thin to 2 cm (¾ in) apart in both directions.

Care Little attention is required, other than weeding. Take care not to disturb the spring onions as they can easily be pulled up with the weeds. Water during dry weather.

Problems Spring and pickling onions can suffer from the same pests and diseases as onions (see page 62), but as the crop matures quickly these are rarely a problem. If disease does strike, remove the crop and start again in new soil. The onions can become tough if they become too dry, so water in dry weather.

Harvesting Spring onions can be harvested as soon as they are large enough to use. They can usually be pulled from the ground by hand, but in heavier soils they may require a hand fork to lift them. Pull alternate onions and allow the neighbours to continue growing. Pickling onions should be left until the foliage dies down, then lifted.

Storing Leave in the ground until required; they do not store well for more than a couple of days. Pickling onions can be dried and stored for a short time before pickling.

Good choices Spring onions: Guardsman, Lilla, Ishikuro, White Lisbon, White Lisbon Winter Hardy, Vigour King **Pickling onions:** Barletta Silverskin, Purplette, Paris Silverskin

purple sprouting broccoli

Purple sprouting broccoli is a wonderful mainstay for winter cooking, although the season can last from autumn until spring. The tender young flower heads stand the frost well and make a delicious treat or side dish drizzled with butter or anchovy dressing.

	J	F	M	A	M	J	J	A	S	O	N	D
Sow			*	*	*							
Plant					*	*						
Harvest	*	*	*							*	*	*

From sowing to harvest 8–12 months

Site & soil Choose an open, sunny site protected from the wind, as this can loosen the large, heavy plants. They will grow in any reasonably fertile soil; soil that has been manured the previous autumn is ideal. If your soil is acid, add some lime to bring the pH up to 6.5–7 (see page 14).

Sowing & planting Sow seed in spring under cover in trays or modules, or in the open ground. In the open ground, sow in drills about 1 cm (½ in) deep, then thin the seedlings to about 5 cm (2 in) apart in the row.

When the seedlings are 12 cm (5 in) tall, transplant to their permanent positions. Those grown under cover should be hardened off first (see page 34). Water the plants the evening before transplanting. Plant deeply in rows or blocks with 60 cm (24 in) between plants. Make certain the plants are firmly planted by pressing down the soil with your heel. Keep watered until established.

Care As with all vegetables, keep the ground free of weeds. As this is a long-term crop, mulch to prevent weeds and to conserve water (see page 38). Water during dry periods, especially as the heads form.

Problems Cabbage rootfly (see page 42) can be troublesome; cover the seed beds and young transplants with fleece or a transparent mesh to avoid it. Caterpillars (see page 42) can be a real nuisance; cover the plants with mesh or pick off the caterpillars as they appear. Clubroot (see page 42) is a problem with all brassicas. It is difficult to cure so prevention is important – only buy plants from a reliable source or grow your own to avoid infection.

Harvesting Pick the young spears as they appear. The flowers should be in tight bud – once they start to show yellow they are opening and no longer suitable for picking.

Storing Pick the broccoli spears as you require them as they are difficult to store fresh for more than a few days. If you have to keep them, stand the spears in a jug of water and keep in a cool place. Broccoli freezes well.

Good choices Early season: Summer Purple, Bordeaux F1, Tenderstem Green Inspiration
Mid season: Extra Early Randolf, Red Arrow
Late season: Claret F1, Late Purple Sprouting, Redhead
White-flowered: Early White Sprouting

calabrese

Known by most people as 'broccoli', calabrese is similar
to sprouting broccoli but the flower heads are much larger
and arranged in a smooth, rounded head. Romanesco
has heads made up of pointed whorls of flower buds.
Both are highly nutritious and flavoursome vegetables.

	J	F	M	A	M	J	J	A	S	O	N	D
Sow			*	*								
Plant					*							
Harvest								*	*	*		

From sowing to harvest 14–20 weeks

Site & soil As with most brassicas, these vegetables need
a sunny, open site protected from the wind to avoid root
movement. Calabrese will tolerate a less fertile soil than
broccoli; soil manured the previous year is ideal. Add lime
to the soil (see page 14) to bring the pH to around 6.5–7
to help reduce the chances of clubroot (see page 42).

Sowing & planting Calabrese resents root disturbance, so
it cannot be sown in rows and then transplanted. Sow in
modules or fibre pots, or station sow in open ground (see
page 34). Sow seed in spring. Space plants 15 cm (6 in)
apart in rows 30 cm (12 in) apart, or if you are growing in
blocks (see page 18), space plants 23 cm (9 in) apart.

Care Keep the area weeded, but avoid disturbing the
plants. It is important to water during prolonged dry
spells, especially as the heads begin to develop.

Problems Calabrese suffers from the same diseases and pests as other brassicas. Keep watered in dry weather and do not plant too close together to avoid downy mildew (see page 42). Caterpillars (see page 42) can be prevented by covering plants with a fine mesh or by picking off by hand. As calabrese is a short-lived plant, either ignore other diseases, or remove and burn plants.

Harvesting Cut off the central head, including some stem, as the buds form but before they open into flowers. Side shoots will develop into smaller heads, and these can be harvested as required.

Storing Remove heads as required. They can be kept for a few days by placing the cut stem into a jug of water and keeping it in a cool place. Calabrese freezes well.

Good choices Calabrese: Fiesta F1, Belstar F1, Kabuki, Volta, Samson, Ironman, Beaumont F1, Crown and Sceptres
Romanesco: Celio, Veronica, Natalino

cauliflower

With their beautiful white curds, cauliflowers look like no other vegetable. Home-grown cauliflowers are crisper and sweeter than their shop-bought equivalents, and there are many different varieties from which to choose, including yellow, purple and green forms.

	J	F	M	A	M	J	J	A	S	O	N	D
Sow		★	★	★	★	★	★	★	★	★		
Plant				★	★	★	★	★	★			
Harvest	★	★	★						★	★	★	★

From sowing to harvest 16–40 weeks

Site & soil Choose an open, sunny site away from strong winds. As some varieties overwinter outside, avoid frost pockets. The soil should be of medium fertility, perhaps manured for a previous crop. If your soil is acid, add lime to bring the pH to 6.5–8 (see page 14).

Sowing & planting Varieties of cauliflower for harvesting at different times of the year all need sowing at different times. Their planting distances also differ, so when buying seed check the recommended times and distances.

Seed can be sown in trays or modules under cover, or outside in the open ground in 1 cm (½ in) drills. Thin seedlings to 5 cm (2 in) intervals when they appear.

Transplant young plants to their permanent positions, spacing at the distance recommended on the packet, or to 60 cm (24 in) apart. Use your heel to push the earth down to firm well around the plants. Water well.

Care Keep the area weeded. Water well during dry spells or the heads may be encouraged to flower quickly and become lose. Mulching will help retain moisture in the soil (see page 38). As the heads begin to mature, break the leaves so they cover the head to keep the curds white.

Problems Cauliflowers suffer from the same pests and diseases as other brassicas, clubroot (see page 42) being the most serious. Rotate crops (see page 30) and either buy plants from reliable sources or grow your own to avoid it. Caterpillars (see page 42) can be picked off by hand, or cover plants with a fine mesh to prevent butterflies laying eggs. Cabbage rootfly (see page 42) can be prevented with cabbage rootfly mats, or by keeping the plants covered with fleece or fine mesh.

Harvesting Cut the head when the curds are tight and white. Once they begin to open, they are past their best. Once the head has been cut, remove the whole plant as it will not produce further heads.

Storing Use soon after cutting, or store for a few days in a refrigerator and use before the heads start to become discoloured. Heads can also be hung upside down in a cool place for two weeks or so. Alternatively, break the heads into florets and freeze.

Good choices Gipsy, Pavilion, Mayflower F1, Aviso F1, Regata F1, White Excel F1, Winter Aalsmeer, All Year Round, Sydney F1
Mini-cauliflowers: Fremont F1, Candid Charm F1
Coloured cauliflowers: Cheddar (yellow-orange), Graffiti F1 (purple), Emeraude F1 (green)

brussels sprouts

When freshly picked, lightly boiled and drizzled with butter, Brussels sprouts are a revelation. There are many different varieties providing a range of flavours, including sweet ones which particularly appeal to children.

	J	F	M	A	M	J	J	A	S	O	N	D
Sow			*	*								
Plant				*	*	*						
Harvest	*	*	*								*	*

From sowing to harvest 9–12 months

Site & soil As with most vegetables, sprouts prefer an open, sunny site. Choose an airy position to prevent mildew, but protect from wind as this can blow the plants over. Brussels sprouts can be grown in any reasonable soil with an average fertility, perhaps manured from a previous crop. Add lime to raise the pH to 6.5–7 to help prevent clubroot.

Sowing & planting Sow in trays or modules under cover, or in a seed bed in the open garden. For early crops, sow under glass in early spring, followed by the maincrop in spring to early summer. Outside, sow in drills 1 cm (½ in) deep and thin plants to 5 cm (2 in) once the seeds have germinated. Plants are ready for transplanting five–six weeks after sowing. Harden off (see page 34) those raised under cover before planting out at 60 cm (24 in) intervals In rows 75 cm (30 in) apart. If growing in blocks (see page 18) space 60 cm (24 in) apart. Plant in firm ground and use your heel to push the earth down firmly around the plants.

Care Generally, Brussels sprouts need little care apart from weeding around them. Remove any yellow or dying leaves and remove some of the green leaves as the sprouts mature to improve air circulation.

Problems Besides the problems seen in other members of the cabbage family (see page 90), Brussels sprouts can suffer from bolting, where the heads become very loose and open. Planting in firm, not loose, soil helps. Also plant the young plants deeply, up to the first leaf, to deter cabbage rootfly (see page 42) and cover with fleece. Pick off any caterpillars by hand. White mealybugs can cause problems: the fluffy, white bugs stick on the stems and sprouts. Treat with insecticidal soap or pyrethrum. Aphids can also be a problem (see page 42).

Harvesting Pick when the sprouts are big enough, removing the leaves to make it easier. Snap the sprouts downwards to free them, starting at the bottom of the stem. Most varieties taste better after a frost. The cluster of leaves at the top of the stem also makes good eating.

Storing Brussels are best used as soon as they are picked. They can be kept a few days, but loose their freshness. The whole stem can be picked and hung in a cool place, or stood in water, for up to a week. They freeze well for longer storage.

Good choices Early croppers: Brilliant F1, Bosworth F1, Nelson F1, Cromwell, United
Later croppers: Clodius F1, Exodus F1, Agincourt F1, Rovongo F1, Borwick, Montgomery F1, Topline
Purple sprouts: Red Bull, Red Rubine, Falstaff

cabbage

Whether it's a dark green, curly Savoy or a colourful red, cabbage is as delicious as it is healthy. There are many different varieties, varying with the type of head, the time of harvest and the colour – it's well worth growing a selection.

	J	F	M	A	M	J	J	A	S	O	N	D
Sow		*	*	*	*			*				
Plant			*	*	*	*			*			
Harvest	*	*	*	*	*	*	*	*	*	*	*	*

From sowing to harvest 20–40 weeks

Site & soil Chose an open, sunny site protected from strong winds. Cabbages can be grown in most soils, but preferably those that have not recently been manured. Ground enriched for a previous crop is ideal. The pH should be around 6.5–7 (see page 14), so add lime if your soil is acidic.

Sowing & planting The different types of cabbage are sown at different times of the year, so follow the instructions on the packet. For example, spring cabbage is sown in late summer.

Sow in trays or modules under cover, or thinly in 1 cm (½ in) deep drills in the open ground. Thin seedlings to 5 cm (2 in) apart when they emerge. When the plants are large enough to handle, transplant into rows or blocks, following the planting distances recommended on the packet. Firm the soil around them with your heel.

Care Ensure the area is kept free of weeds. Refirm the
ground if the cabbages are rocked by the wind. Water
regularly in prolonged dry spells and mulch if necessary
to retain moisture (see page 38).

Problems Cabbages are more troublesome than most
other vegetables, but you probably won't encounter any
serious pests and diseases. Caterpillars (see page 42)
can be a problem – remove them by hand or cover plants
with fleece to prevent egg laying.

Take preventive action against clubroot (see page 42)
by liming the soil to raise the pH (see page 14), and either
growing your own plants or obtaining them from a reliable
source. Protect overwintering plants against birds using
netting. Cabbage rootfly (see page 42) can be prevented
by using rootfly mats or pieces of felt on the ground around
the bases of the plants.

Harvesting Cut the cabbages as they are required. Lift the
whole plant or cut the stem just below the head. Spring
cabbages should be cut from the stem, as these may
produce a second crop.

Storing Winter cabbages are bred to withstand cold
weather, so leave them in situ until required. Once cut they
can be kept in a cool place for several days. Some of the
dense winter varieties will last several weeks, even months,
hung in nets in cool, airy conditions protected from frost.

Good choices Spring: Peter, Hispie Pixie, Durham Elf
Summer: Greyhound, Hispie, Derby Day, Primo 2, Puma
Autumn: Stonehead, Sherwood Picador, Minicole
Winter: Tundra, Highland, Holland Winter White Extra
Savoys: Clarissa, Wintessa, Tarvoy, Alaska, Endeavour
Red cabbages: Red Rookie, Red Flare, Red Jewel

kale

Available in a range of vivid colours and strange shapes, kale makes an attractive addition to the flower garden. It can be substituted for cabbage or spinach. Kale is a very hardy plant that withstands cold winter temperatures, and is extremely rich in vitamins.

	J	F	M	A	M	J	J	A	S	O	N	D
Sow		*		*	*							
Plant				*	*	*						
Harvest	*	*	*	*		*				*	*	*

From sowing to harvest 7–40 weeks

Site & soil Choose an open, sunny site with good air circulation. Avoid a windy position for the larger varieties, as wind rock can be a problem. Most garden soils are suitable, as long as they are not too rich — perhaps pick a plot manured for a previous crop. Add lime (see page 14) to bring the pH to 6.5–7.5 if necessary.

Sowing & planting Sow crops for summer harvesting in trays or modules under cover in late winter; transplant in spring when they are large enough.

Sow autumn and winter crops in spring in the open garden in 1 cm (½ in) deep drills, then thin the emerging seedlings to about 5 cm (2 in) apart. They can also be sown in trays or modules undercover. Transplant the young plants into their permanent positions, spacing them 60–75 cm (24–30 in) apart, or at about half this distance for dwarf kale or if you intend to harvest the leaves when young.

Care As with all vegetables, ensure that weeds are kept at bay. Mulching (see page 38) helps to suppress weeds as well as retain moisture in the soil during dry periods. Water well during prolonged dry spells.

Problems During late summer and autumn, caterpillars can be a threat: pick them off by hand or cover plants with netting. Birds can be a problem in winter, especially pigeons – again protect with netting. Cabbage rootfly (see page 42) can be avoided by using rootfly mats or pieces of felt to cover the soil around the bases of the plants. Kale can also suffer from cabbage whitefly: the tiny, white adults fly away when disturbed, while the brown young stay on the undersides of the leaves. They result in sticky honeydew and sooty moulds on the foliage but are rarely serious. Wash light infestations from the plant with a spray of water; for more serious outbreaks spray with insecticidal soap.

Harvesting Pick the leaves as they are required, either while they are young and fresh, or more mature and flavoursome. They sometimes have more taste after a frost.

Storing Kale is very hardy and will withstand most winters, so don't harvest until required. The leaves do not store well, but they can be frozen successfully.

Good choices Dwarf Green Curled, Darkibor, Storbor, Winnetou
Black varieties: Black Tuscany
Red varieties: Redbor, Red Russian

broad beans

With their fresh, distinctive flavour, broad beans are delicious in a wide range of dishes, including risotto and warm salads. The fresher they are the better they taste, so growing your own gives you a distinct advantage. They can also be successfully grown in containers.

	J	F	M	A	M	J	J	A	S	O	N	D
Sow	·	*	*	*	*					*	*	*
Harvest						*	*	*				

From sowing to harvest 12–30 weeks

Site & soil Broad bean plants require an open, sunny site. Autumn-sown crops will have to stand through the winter so may need protection from strong winds to prevent wind-rock problems. Broad beans will grow well in most garden soils as long as they are not too wet or too dry. The soil should be reasonably fertile and will benefit from being manured.

Sowing & planting Sow in late autumn for early crops the following year, if your climate is not too wet. Otherwise sow from late winter to late spring, depending on the variety. Make a shallow trench about 4 cm (1½ in) deep and 15 cm (6 in) wide, and sow two staggered rows in the trench, spacing the beans about 15 cm (6 in) apart. Trenches should be 60 cm (24 in) apart. If you are planting in blocks (see page 18), space the beans 25 cm (10 in) apart. You can also sow them in individual pots and plant the young plants out at the same distances.

Care Protect autumn-sown beans against the wind and cover with cloches in wetter areas. Weed carefully, being certain not to disturb the beans' roots. Taller varieties may need strings along either side of the row to hold the plants upright.

Problems Watch out for mice stealing the sown beans. Cover the rows with wire netting, or grow the beans in pots and plant out as young plants, or trap the mice. Black aphids (see page 42) may also occur on the young tips of the plants around flowering time. The best remedy is to pinch these tips out, either before the problem arrives or after they are infested. The other possible problem is rust (see page 44). This looks bad but rarely causes a problem. However, remove plants immediately after harvesting and clear away any remains to help prevent recurrence.

Harvesting You can begin harvesting as soon as the beans are big enough. Smaller beans have a better flavour, and the larger they get the more floury they become. You can also eat the young pods of some varieties.

Storing Broad beans are best eaten straight from the plant while at their maximum sweetness. They do not keep well once picked, as they lose their flavour. They freeze well (do this straight after picking). Alternatively, allow the beans to dry in the pods on the plants, then store them in an airtight jar.

Good choices Autumn-sown beans: Aquadulce, Aquadulce Claudia, Super Aquadulce
Tall varieties: Bunyards Exhibition, Express, Witkiem Manita, Jubilee Hysor, Green Windsor, Giant Exhibition, Imperial Green Longpod
Short varieties: The Sutton

dwarf beans

Probably the most versatile beans for cooking, dwarf beans come in a range of exciting colours, from green and yellow to purple. These are plants that grow to only 30 cm (12 in) or so high, including French beans and thin Kenya beans. They are nutritious and perfect for stir-fries and salads.

	J	F	M	A	M	J	J	A	S	O	N	D
Sow			*	*	*	*						
Harvest						*	*	*	*	*		

From sowing to harvest 7–14 weeks

Site & soil Choose an open, warm, sunny site protected from strong winds. They can be grown in most garden soils, but a rich, light soil suits them best. Enriching the soil with manure or compost in spring helps produce a good crop. They can also be grown very successfully in containers.

Sowing & planting Wait until the soil and air temperature has warmed up. Low temperatures below 10°C (50°F) will inhibit germination and cause the seedlings to die. If you want an early crop, sow in pots under cover and transplant once temperatures rise, or grow in containers under glass.

To sow outside, make a shallow trench about 4 cm (1½ in) deep and 15 cm (6 in) wide, and sow two staggered rows in the trench, spacing the beans about 15 cm (6 in) apart. Trenches should be 60 cm (24 in) apart. If you are planting in blocks (see page 18), space the beans 20 cm (8 in) apart. You can also sow in individual pots and plant the young plants out at the same distances.

Care Weed carefully around the plants as they can be easily uprooted. Protect in windy areas to prevent root disturbance. The taller varieties are best supported by twiggy sticks or lines of strings held on canes.

Problems There is a long list of diseases from which dwarf beans can suffer, but unless you are unlucky most rarely seem to cause trouble. One of the most likely is the seed being stolen by mice. Cover the seed bed with wire netting, or sow in pots and then plant out as young plants to overcome the problem. Slugs and snails may eat the emerging shoots, but once the plants are mature they should not present such a problem.

Harvesting Pick the beans as they become large enough, with the little stalk still on the bean. The more you pick, the more they will produce. Old beans become tough, but they can be dried.

Storing Beans are best cooked and eaten straight from the plant. They will keep for a few days, but soon start to lose their quality. For long-term storage, blanch and freeze them. Some varieties will produce beans inside the pods if allowed to mature: dry them and store in an airtight jar until required.

Good choices Delenel, The Prince, Speedy, Tendergreen, Atlanta, Montano, Sunray, Nomad
Purple varieties: Purple Queen, Purple Teepee
Yellow varieties: Golddukat, Orinoco Golden Bean, Golden Teepee, Sonesta
Kenya beans: Safari, Ferrari, Opera
Beans for drying: Yin Yang, Borlotto
Dwarf runner beans: Hestia

climbing beans

Runner beans have been joined by an increasing number of climbing French beans, which have the advantage of being 'stringless'. Runner beans and climbing French beans each have their own distinctive flavour, so it is well worth growing a few of each. Both are simple to grow.

	J	F	M	A	M	J	J	A	S	O	N	D
Sow			*	*	*	*						
Harvest						*	*	*	*			

From sowing to harvest 14–26 weeks

Site & soil Choose an open, sunny site away from strong winds, as once trained up a support, the plants cover a large area. The soil should be fertile, but any good garden soil will do, especially if you dig a trench the previous autumn and add a layer of manure. Avoid more recently manured ground as this can encourage foliage at the expense of flowers and beans. Climbing beans grow well in containers if you can provide the supports.

Sowing & planting Climbing beans need warmth to germinate and grow, so don't sow them before the soil and weather warms up. If you are impatient, sow in pots under cover a couple of weeks before it is warm enough outside, and plant out when they are big enough and the weather allows. Sow the beans in pairs about 5 cm (2 in) deep. If both germinate, remove the weaker seedling. Plants should be spaced 15 cm (6 in) apart, either in a single or double row or round a wigwam of canes.

Care Climbing beans need support. Erect a double row of bean canes, a wigwam of canes or use a framework of supporting strings. They need to be at least 2 m (6 ft) high. The plants are self-supporting, but may need to be trained at the start. Keep watered in dry weather.

Problems On the whole, runner beans are fairly trouble free. See page 102 for problems affecting French beans. Poor flower set may be a problem, due to the weather keeping pollinating insects away or birds pecking the flowers. Water shortage can also cause flower drop, so keep watered in dry weather.

Harvesting Pick the beans as soon as they are big enough to eat. The more you pick the more they will produce. Runner beans can become 'stringy' and tough if they get too old, so pick regularly, even if it means giving the beans away as there are too many for your own use. Discard any beans that have got too big.

Storing Cook as soon as possible after picking for the best flavour. They will keep a couple of days in a cool place, but not more than that. If you want to store them for winter use, blanch and freeze them, or try salting runner beans by slicing them and packing layers into airtight jars with layers of salt in between. With some varieties of French bean, you can allow the pods to mature and produce beans inside, which can be dried (see page 102).

Good choices Runner beans: White Lady, Red Rum, Celebration, White Apollo, Enorma, Polestar, Aintree, Desiree, Lady Di, Achievement Merit, Scarlet Emperor, Wisley Magic
Climbing French beans: Cobra, Algarve, Sultana, Mantra, Blue Lake, Isabel

peas

Peas are among the most popular of vegetables, yet surprisingly few people grow them. Eaten raw straight from the pod, fresh home-grown peas are far sweeter than any you can buy. Peas are easy to grow, as are mangetout and sugar snaps, which are treated in the same way.

	J	F	M	A	M	J	J	A	S	O	N	D
Sow			*	*	*	*	*				*	*
Harvest						*	*	*	*			

From sowing to harvest 12–16 weeks

Site & soil An open, sunny site is ideal, although peas will also tolerate a little shade. Since the plants are often tall, avoid windy positions. The soil should be well drained but moisture retentive, preferably with a reasonable amount of humus in it (see page 12). Shorter varieties of pea can be grown in containers.

Sowing & planting For an early crop, sow in late autumn in warm areas, ensuring that the soil is not waterlogged. Otherwise, sow in spring once the soil has started warming.

If you want to start early, or if you have problems with mice, sow in pots or modules under cover and plant out as young plants with as little root disturbance as possible.

In the open ground, sow in a single or double staggered row at 5 cm (2 in) intervals. Double rows should be 23 cm (9 in) apart with at least 60 cm (24 in) between rows. Only short varieties are suitable for planting in blocks (see page 18).

Care Peas need support – choose branched pea sticks (often hazel), plastic netting or wire netting. Short varieties can be grown up the same supports, or just stretch horizontal strings on either side of the row. Water in dry weather.

Problems Mice and birds can eat the peas before they germinate: cover the rows with wire netting, but remove it before the young plants become entangled in it. Mildew (see pages 42–44) can be a problem if air circulation is poor, but ignore it unless it is very severe. Pea moths may be troublesome, revealed as maggots in the pods. Sow early and late to avoid them, and cover the row with fleece when plants are in flower.

Harvesting Pick the peas once they have swelled in the pod, and keep picking to encourage a continuous supply. Peas become floury and hard if they are left too long on the plant. Pick mangetout as the pods develop and reach an edible size, sugar snaps when the pods swell.

Storing Cook or eat immediately after picking if possible. The quality deteriorates the longer they are stored, so use within a couple of days at most. Peas often produce sudden gluts that provide too many to eat, so freeze the excess. Peas can be left on the plant until the pods become dry and the peas rattle in them – pick them, dry them and store in a jar until required for soups and casseroles.

Good choices Earlies: Ambassador, Misty, Little Marvel, Meteor, Kelvedon Wonder, Meteor, Feltham First
Maincrop: Alderman, Endeavour, Onward, Hurst Green Shaft, Rondo, Starlight, Ambassador
Mangetout: Oregon Sugar Pod, Carouby de Maussane, Delikata, Reuzensuiker
Sugar snaps: Sugar Ann, Jooey, Sugar Snap, Dolikott

asparagus

Asparagus is an easy and trouble-free plant to grow at home, and is so much sweeter and more delicious straight from the garden than from the supermarket. Drizzle with melted butter, or serve with poached eggs and shavings of Parmesan. It is also wonderful in risotto, pasta dishes and salads.

	J	F	M	A	M	J	J	A	S	O	N	D
Sow		*	*	*								
Plant				*	*	`						
Harvest					*	*	*					

From sowing to harvest 3 years; planting to harvest 1 year

Site & soil Choose an open, sunny site away from strong winds, as the fully grown plants can suffer from wind rock. The soil should be free draining and not too rich; most garden soils are suitable. Once planted, asparagus can remain in the soil for many years so prepare the beds well before planting, improving drainage if necessary and removing all traces of perennial weeds.

Sowing & planting Asparagus can be grown from seed or from crowns, which are the fleshy roots. Crowns produce spears earlier and they are often more reliable plants. Sow seed under cover in late winter in modules, then plant out the young plants into their final positions in early summer. Alternatively, sow in drills outside in spring, thinning seedlings to 15 cm (6 in) apart.

Plant crowns or young plants into their final positions in spring. Make a 25 cm (10 in) deep trench with a ridge

down the middle. Rest the crowns on the ridge with their roots spread out on either side. Cover the crowns with 10 cm (4 in) of soil and add more as the plants grow until they reach soil level.

Care Make certain that the area is kept free from weeds, but be careful not to damage the plants' roots. Remove all old foliage as it turns yellow.

Problems Generally asparagus does not suffer from any problems although asparagus beetle can be a nuisance by eating foliage and stunting growth. The beetles overwinter in plant debris so clear up well around the plants. Handpick the larvae or in case of a more severe infestation use derris. Slugs can also be a nuisance and should be cleared using your preferred method. Violet root rot can also be a problem. Dig up and burn any affected plants.

Harvesting Allow the plants to develop for the first couple of years, picking only a few spears. From the third year after planting, harvest more heavily. Cut all spears during the harvest period (about eight weeks) so that there is a constant renewal. Harvest the spears when they are 15 cm (6 in) above the surface, cutting them off up to 5 cm (2 in) below soil level.

Storing Asparagus is wonderful when eaten really fresh, so delay picking until just before cooking. It will keep in the refrigerator for a couple of days with the bases of the spears in water, but the flavour deteriorates after picking. Any excess can be frozen.

Good choices Backlim, Grolim, Gijnlim, Crimson Pacific Purple, Ariane, Connover's Colossal, Sorbonne, Lucellus

globe artichokes

Cutting your own artichokes is one of the great luxuries of vegetable gardening. As well as producing something delicious to eat, these are also very attractive plants and add stature to the vegetable patch or flower bed. They are a pleasure to grow, with very few problems.

	J	F	M	A	M	J	J	A	S	O	N	D
Plant			*									
Harvest							*	*	*			

From planting to harvest 16–36 weeks

Site & soil Choose a sunny, open site, although they will tolerate a little shade. Protect from high winds. Artichokes will grow in most garden soils, but avoid wet soils and those waterlogged in winter. They appreciate a relatively rich soil, so dig in manure before planting. Since the plants will be in the ground for a number of years, be sure to remove all traces of perennial weeds before planting.

Sowing & planting Globe artichokes can be grown from seed but the resulting plants are very variable. It is much better to buy young plants. Plant in mid spring with a distance of about 1 m (3 ft) between plants, and trim the leaves back to about 15 cm (6 in).

Plants will be productive for three or four years, so after the third year dig up one plant and split it up into divisions, replanting the best ones into a new bed. Remove the other old plants once the new ones are established. Repeat every three or four years.

Care The most important thing is to keep the area well weeded, especially being vigilant for perennial weeds. Mulch (see page 38) to prevent the plants drying out in warm weather, and in colder climates add a winter mulch to protect against frost.

Problems Globe artichokes are not subject to pests and diseases. The weather can be the only real problem – high winds may damage the plants but this can be prevented by choosing a sheltered site or adding some form of protection. Waterlogged soils also cause problems, which again can be avoided by choosing the right site, or improving drainage before planting.

Harvesting Cut the flower heads when they are large enough to eat, removing around 10 cm (4 in) of stem with them. Only harvest when the scales are still tight to the heads – it is too late when the scales become loose or the flowers begin to open.

Storing Pick the artichoke heads as required. They will keep for a couple of days in a cool place but are much better when fresh. If you have a glut, cut off the scales and freeze the hearts.

Good choices Green Globe, Romanesco, Violetta di Chioggia, Purple Globe, Vert de Laon

kohlrabi

With a crisp texture and a delicate flavour somewhere between a cabbage and a turnip, kohlrabi can be grated raw into salads, or steamed and used as a summer alternative to turnips. There are varieties with green and purple skins, some of them growing very large.

	J	F	M	A	M	J	J	A	S	O	N	D
Sow			*	*	*	*			*			
Harvest	*						*	*	*	*		*

From sowing to harvest 5–8 weeks

Site & soil Choose a sunny, open position outdoors, or grow under cover, in a greenhouse or cloche, for an early crop. They do best in light soils, particularly those that are not too rich – a plot manured for a previous crop is ideal. They also do well in containers or growing bags.

Sowing & planting For an early crop, sow in modules under cover in late winter. When they are 5 cm (2 in) tall, plant out in a greenhouse or under a cloche, or out in the open garden when the weather is not too cold or wet.

Alternatively sow outdoors in 1 cm (½ in) deep drills, in rows 30 cm (12 in) apart. Thin the seedlings to 15–18 cm (6–7 in) apart as they emerge. If planting in blocks (see page 18), space plants 25 cm (10 in) apart.

Sow further crops under cover in early autumn for winter use. Choose purple-skinned varieties as these are hardier.

Care Kohlrabi should be kept in continuous growth, so water regularly in dry weather if necessary. Keep the area weeded, but be careful not to disturb the roots.

Problems Although it is the swollen stem that is eaten, kohlrabi is in fact a member of the cabbage family although it is not so susceptible to the diseases from which brassicas tend to suffer. It is a relatively quick crop so fairly trouble-free, although kohlrabi may become tough if allowed to dry out too much. Control slugs (see page 44) while the plants are small, and check for flea beetles (see page 44) at the same time.

Harvesting Pull up the kohlrabi as you need it. It is best while small; once it gets older and larger it can become woody and tough. Some of the purple-skinned varieties can grow very big without this toughness.

Storing If possible, use the vegetable as soon as you harvest it. It will store for some days after pulling, but its freshness soon deteriorates. Late crops can be stored for a couple of months in slightly damp sand in a frost-free place, or be left in the soil until required if they are growing under cover.

Good choices Purple-skinned kohlrabi: Kolibri F1, Purple Danube, Blusta, Azur Star
Green-skinned kohlrabi: Lanro, Quickstar F1, Olivia F1

swede

Swede is a true winter treat when added to soups and casseroles, or made into a golden mash oozing with butter and black pepper. They survive well in the ground over winter, so are always on hand when you need some fresh vegetables.

	J	F	M	A	M	J	J	A	S	O	N	D
Sow					*	*						
Harvest	*	*	*							*	*	*

From sowing to harvest 24 weeks

Site & soil Like most vegetables, swedes do best in an open, sunny site. They prefer a light, well-drained soil, but will grow well on most garden soils as long as they are not waterlogged. The soil should not be too rich – a plot manured for a previous crop would be ideal. Avoid freshly turned soil, as swedes prefer to be sown in a firm soil. Trample it down if you have just dug it.

Sowing & planting Don't be tempted to sow too early: late spring is early enough. Sow in 2 cm (¾ in) deep drills in rows 38 cm (15 in) apart. Sow in ground that has been firmed down, not in loose soil. While the seedlings are still small, thin them out to about 23 cm (9 in) apart. If sowing in blocks (see page 18), space the plants 30 cm (12 in) apart. If you intend to harvest crops when the swedes are still quite small, they can be grown closer together.

Care Keep the area well weeded as swedes are often in the ground for nearly a year and weeds can build up during this time. Water regularly and consistently during dry weather, otherwise they become tough and woody, and a sudden resumption of watering may lead to cracking.

Problems Swede belongs to the cabbage family and can suffer from all the same pests and diseases (see page 90), but it is generally free from trouble. Flea beetle (see page 44) can be a problem with young seedlings, so sow seed under fleece. Slugs can also be troublesome while plants are young. If you have clubroot (see page 42) in the garden, the swedes are likely to catch it. Try to prevent infection by raising all your own brassicas from seed rather than buying plants. Mildew (see pages 42–44) can also be a problem, so ensure the plants have air circulating between them and keep watered.

Harvesting Swedes can be lifted as required as soon as they are big enough. The swollen root grows above ground and can easily be pulled.

Storing Swedes are perfectly winter hardy and can be left where they are until required. However, in late winter they tend to become woody, especially in mild weather, so it is often best to lift them. Store in net bags or boxes in a shed, or leave in piles in the garden covered with a good layer of straw.

Good choices Marian, Magres, Invitation, Best of All, Virtue, Bora, Helenor, Angela, Ruby

turnips

Like kohlrabi and swede, turnips belong to the cabbage
family. They are mainly grown for their crisp white roots,
perfect for casseroles and stir-fries, but the young leaves
(the turnip tops) can be used as a delicious spring green,
at a time when fresh vegetables are in short supply.

	J	F	M	A	M	J	J	A	S	O	N	D
Sow			*	*	*	*	*	*				
Harvest	*						*	*	*	*	*	*

From sowing to harvest 6–12 weeks

Site & soil Unlike most vegetables, turnips will tolerate a
little shade. The soil should be moisture retentive because
they can become woody and tough if they dry out too much.
Choose a plot manured for a previous crop, because they
prefer a soil that is not too rich.

Sowing & planting Turnips should be sown in situ as they
do not transplant well. For early crops, sow under cover in
containers or in covered beds in early spring. Alternatively,
sow outside from mid spring onwards.

Sow early varieties until late spring, maincrop varieties
after that. Sow a batch every three weeks for a continuous
crop if you use a lot of turnips. Sow in 2 cm (¾ in) deep
drills in rows about 30 cm (12 in) apart. Thin the seedlings
to 15 cm (6 in) apart as they emerge, slightly closer for
quick-maturing varieties. For block planting (see page 10),
space plants 15 cm (6 in) apart.

Care Ensure turnips are watered regularly during a dry spell or they will become hard and woody. They are also likely to bolt. Keep the area weeded as weeds will take up moisture.

Problems Turnips are prone to many of the same pests and diseases as other brassicas. Generally, however, they suffer few troubles, especially if they are pulled young before any problems develop. Flea beetles (see page 44) may be a problem for young seedlings – cover the seed bed with fleece or dust with derris in the event of an attack. Slugs may also be a problem at this stage.

Harvesting Harvest as soon as soon as the roots are big enough to eat. They are best pulled while still relatively small as the bigger they get, the tougher and more woody they become. Harvest the leaves as greens when the plants are young, or remove all growth from turnips still in the ground in late winter to promote new leaves that are excellent for eating.

Storing Leave turnips in the ground until they are required. In colder areas, however, they can be lifted and stored in a cool shed in net bags or boxes. Alternatively, make them into a neat pile outside and cover with straw.

Good choices Oasis F1, Snowball, Market Express, Primera, Aramis, Atlantic, Purple Top Milan

parsnips

These sweet, starchy root vegetables are a great winter stand-by and will happily stay in the ground until you fancy a buttery mash, a warming soup or some crisp roasted chunks. Or if you can't wait, pull them as mini-vegetables and steam them whole to enjoy their fresh flavour.

	J	F	M	A	M	J	J	A	S	O	N	D
Sow			*	*								
Harvest	*	*	*							*	*	*

From sowing to harvest 24 weeks

Site & soil Choose a sunny, open site. The soil should be light and not too rich – one manured the previous year is ideal. Make sure the soil is deeply tilled and as stone-free as possible, otherwise the parsnips will be forked and stunted, rather than the classic cone shape, making them more difficult to deal with in the kitchen.

Sowing & planting Buy seed fresh each year for a good germination rate. Parsnips are slow to germinate, so sow some radishes thinly in the same drill to mark the row and make weeding easier. Parsnips can be sown from late winter to late spring, but early spring is the best time.

Sow in 2 cm (¾ in) deep drills in rows 30 cm (12 in) apart. Station sow (see page 34) three seeds at 12–15 cm (5–6 in) intervals. Thin seedlings to one per station as they emerge. For block planting, thin seedlings to 15–20 cm (6–8 in) in each direction.

Care As parsnips are in the ground for a long period, keep the area free from weeds. Be careful in the early stages as the seedlings are easily disturbed.

Problems Canker is probably the most serious problem, causing brown woody patches on the roots. To prevent it, avoid sowing seed too early, make certain the soil is not too rich and add lime if conditions are too acid, aiming for a pH of 6.5–7.5. If parsnips do get canker, cut off the cankerous bit and eat the rest. Carrot fly (see page 142) may also attack, but rarely damages large parsnips very much. Covering the seed with fine micromesh after sowing will reduce the problem.

Harvesting Dig up the parsnips as they are required. For the best flavour, wait until after the first frost. If you want mini-parsnips, however, pull when they are the desired size.

Storing Leave the parsnips in the ground until they are required. In areas with severe frosts, cover the rows with straw to keep the soil from freezing so that you can dig them up. When they start shooting in the spring, however, they should be discarded so dig the remainder before then, cut into battens, blanch and freeze them.

Good choices Tender & True, Countess F1, Gladiator F1, Patriot F1, Excalibur F1, Javelin F1, White Gem, Avonresister

beetroot

Whether long or round, red, yellow or white, beetroot is a joy in the kitchen, for salads, soups, purées, risotto and casseroles. It is also simple to grow and suffers very few problems. This is a great plant for containers.

	J	F	M	A	M	J	J	A	S	O	N	D
Sow			*	*	*	*						
Harvest						*	*	*	*	*	*	*

From sowing to harvest 8 weeks

Site & soil Beetroot prefers an open, sunny site. It will grow in most garden soil, but does best in light, rich conditions. Soil that has been manured for a previous crop is ideal. Beetroot can be grown under cover in containers for early crops, or in containers on the patio.

Sowing & planting Most packets of beetroot seed contain small clusters of seeds, producing groups of seedlings that need thinning early on to prevent too much root disturbance of the remaining plant.

They can be sown early under cover in modules and planted out, but it is easier to sow in situ. Sow in 1 cm (½ in) deep drills in rows about 30 cm (12 in) apart. Station sow (see page 34) the seed in twos at 10 cm (4 in) intervals. Thin seedlings as soon as possible, leaving one at each station. For block planting (see page 18), thin to 15 cm (6 in) apart. Continue to sow at three-week intervals to produce a continuous crop of small beetroot.

Care Keep the area weeded but be careful not to disturb the roots at an early stage of their growth. If a prolonged dry spell sets in, keep the plants watered so they continue to grow steadily.

Problems Beetroot is generally trouble free and easy to grow. Slugs may be a problem when the plants are still young, and they can also damage beetroot overwintering in the ground.

Harvesting Beetroot are easy to harvest – simply pull them from the ground as you require them as soon as they have reached the desired size. Smaller ones are more succulent, but larger ones are still edible although they tend to get tough as winter progresses.

Do not cut off roots or leaves as this will cause the beetroot to bleed when cooked. Remove the leaves by twisting them off about 5 cm (2 in) above the globe. Remove the root after cooking.

Storing Usually it is possible to leave the beetroot in the ground until required, but they may become tough. Slugs may also attack them. Cover with straw in the rows in colder areas to prevent the ground freezing, making them difficult to pull. Beetroot freezes well once blanched, and young beetroot can be pickled for winter use.

Good choices Red globes: Boltardy, Red Ace F1, Wodan F1, Crimson Globe, Bull's Blood, Solo F1, Kestrel, Pronto, Pablo F1, Moneta
Other colours: Albina Vereduna (white), Chiogga (pink and white ringo), Burpees Golden (yellow)
Cylindrical shapes: Alto F1, Cylindra, Monorubra

carrots

Freshly pulled and crunchy, there is nothing to match the flavour of home-grown carrots. Carrots come in a wide range of colours, including yellow, white and purple as well as the more common orange. They are also available in round or long, tapering varieties.

	J	F	M	A	M	J	J	A	S	O	N	D
Sow			*	*	*	*	*					
Harvest	*	*				*	*	*	*	*	*	*

From sowing to harvest 12–15 weeks

Site & soil Choose an open, sunny site. Carrots have a preference for light, well-drained soils, but will grow in other soils. Dig the soil deeply and remove as many small stones as possible as they cause the carrots to fork – round carrots are better in stony soil. If you have a heavy clay soil, make a conical hole for each plant, fill with a light compost and sow the seed in the top.

Sowing & planting Carrots will not germinate below 7°C (46°F), so wait for the soil to warm up before sowing. Early crops can be sown under cover or under a cloche.

Sow very thinly in 1 cm (½ in) deep drills in rows at least 15 cm (6 in) apart. Thin the seedlings to about 8 cm (3 in) apart, preferably in the late evening when carrot flies are not around (see page 142). If growing in a block, thin seedlings to 10 cm (4 in) apart.

Sow at two to three week intervals to get a succession of crops throughout the summer and into the winter.

Care Keep the area weeded but be careful not to disturb the roots when they are young. Do not bruise the foliage or you risk attracting carrot flies (see below). Water regularly in dry weather to keep the roots succulent.

Problems The chief problem is carrot fly, the larvae of which bore into the roots. Choose a variety that has some resistance to this pest, and sow thinly so that you don't have to thin the seedlings as the smell of bruised foliage attracts the flies. It is also wise to thin in the late evening when the flies are less active, and to bury the thinnings deep in the compost bin to hide their smell. Slugs can also be troublesome, especially in winter.

Harvesting Carrots can be pulled as soon as they have reached the desired size. Pull the first of the season when they are quite small, though, as they have a very distinctive and wonderful flavour.

Storing Carrots can be left in the ground until you want them. However, they are difficult to dig up during severe frosts, so cover the rows with straw to prevent the ground freezing, or dig them up and store them in a cool shed in boxes of sand. They also freeze well.

Good choices Early crops: Amsterdam Forcing 3-Sprint, Primo F1, Early Nantes 5, Mokum F1, Flyaway F1, Chanteney Red-cored 2
Maincrop: Bangor F1, Autumn King, Carson F1, Infinity F1, Resistafly F1, Siroco F1
Other colours: Honeysnack, Crème de Lite, Purple Haze F1, White Satin, Harlequin F1, Rainbow F1, Yellowstone
Round carrots: Parmex, Ronda, Paris Market 4, Paris Market 5, Early French Frame 4 Lisa

salsify and scorzonera

These unusual root vegetables are not often seen in supermarkets, yet they are delicious and easy to grow. Both have a subtle flavour; that of salsify is faintly reminiscent of oysters, while scorzonera has a delicate, nutty flavour. They are grown in the same way, much in the manner of parsnips.

	J	F	M	A	M	J	J	A	S	O	N	D
Sow			*	*								
Harvest	*	*							*	*	*	

From sowing to harvest 20 weeks

Site & soil These two vegetables need an open, sunny position. In its second year, salsify will produce beautiful purple flowers so it can be grown in the flower beds. Both have long, straight roots and need a deep soil, preferably free draining. Avoid stony ground or the roots become forked. If you have heavy soil, make a conical hole for every plant, fill it with a light compost and sow the seed in the top to give a free root run.

Sowing & planting Do not sow too early as the seed will rot if the ground is too cold. In mid spring, station sow (see page 34) at 20 cm (8 in) intervals in a 1 cm (½ in) deep trench, with rows spaced 30 cm (12 in) apart. Sow two or three seeds at each station and thin to one seedling as soon as possible. If you are planting in blocks (see page 18), station sow at 23 cm (9 in) intervals. Scorzonera can be sown slightly closer together.

Care Keep the area well weeded, but avoid disturbing the plants when they are still at seedling stage – weed by hand rather than using a hoe, as this may damage the maturing roots. Water during prolonged dry periods.

Problems Both are trouble free and easy to grow.

Harvesting Dig the roots when they are big enough to eat, which will not be before the autumn. Dig carefully as they are relatively thin and can easily break. Scorzonera may not get big enough in its first year and can be left in the ground until the second.

   The leaves of both plants can be blanched in spring by covering the plants with a deep mulch. Pick the emerging leaves and use them like chicory.

Storing Both vegetables are usually left in the ground until required. After digging, they will keep for a few days in a cool place or will store for up to two months in a box of just-damp sand.

Good choices Both salsify and scorzonera are usually sold by seed merchants as just that. There are rarely individual varieties available, although salsify is sometimes labelled 'Sandwich Island' and scorzonera may be offered as 'Duplex'.

potatoes

If you have only ever eaten shop-bought potatoes, you won't realize the range of different flavours available. As well as the different varieties, each with its own unique flavour, there is the unbeatable taste of the first potatoes of the season, freshly dug and lightly boiled.

	J	F	M	A	M	J	J	A	S	O	N	D
Plant			*	*	*							
Harvest							*	*	*	*		

From planting to harvest 15–20 weeks

Site & soil Potatoes are easy to grow and not too demanding with regards to conditions: an open site is best, but they will tolerate a little shade. They will grow in most soils, but do better in a light one. The soil should be relatively rich, but not recently manured.

Sowing & planting Potatoes are planted as tubers, or seed potatoes – buy fresh, disease-free stock each year. Allow the tubers to sprout before planting (called chitting) by placing them in egg boxes with most of the eyes uppermost. Keep in a bright place, out of direct sunlight, at about 18°C (64°F), then move them to a cooler place when they shoot. When the shoots are about 2.5 cm (1 in) long, after about six weeks, they are ready to plant.
   Dig a trench 15 cm (6 in) deep and lay the potatoes in it 30 cm (12 in) apart, with 45 cm (18 in) between rows. Cover the potatoes, then draw the soil up over each row to form a ridge.

Care Keep the rows earthed up by covering any shoots that show with more soil. Keep the soil free of weeds and water during periods of drought. If frosts are still likely after the leaves of early potatoes have come up, cover them with fleece, straw or newspaper.

Problems The most serious is blight (see page 42), a fungal disease that also affects tomatoes. Ridge up the rows to help prevent spores getting to the tubers. If blight attacks, remove all infected foliage at once and burn it, then leave the tubers in the ground for at least three weeks.

Slugs may eat holes in the tubers, especially those left too long in the soil. Remove the slugs and lift the tubers as soon as possible to reduce the problem. Reduce the chance of diseases by always buying certified stock and rotating the crop to fresh ground each year (see page 30).

Harvesting Dig the first new potatoes as soon as they are about 2.5 cm (1 in) across, when the plants come into flower. Maincrop potatoes are harvested once the foliage begins to die down. Leave them on the surface of the soil for at least a few hours to dry the skins.

Storing Lift all the potatoes at the onset of autumn and store them in a cool, frost-free place. Store in hessian or paper sacks. It is important that the tubers are protected from light or they will go green and become toxic. Only store disease-free tubers.

Good choices First earlies: Maris Bard, Arran Pilot, Lady Christi, Accent, Swift, Pentland Javelin, Foremost
Second earlies: Maris Peer, Smile, Maxine, Nadine, Kestrel
Maincrop: Cara, King Edward, Maris Piper, Desiree, Santo
Salad potatoes: Anya, Charlotte, Pink Fir Apple, Ratte, Mimi

jerusalem artichokes

With their distinctive nutty flavour and starchy texture, Jerusalem artichokes are perfect for soups, casseroles and purées, or simply sliced and sautéed in butter. Most people are surprised to learn that the Jerusalem artichoke is, in fact, a sunflower.

	J	F	M	A	M	J	J	A	S	O	N	D
Plant		*	*									
Harvest	*	*	*						*	*	*	*

From planting to harvest 16 weeks

Site & soil Grow Jerusalem artichokes in an open, sunny position if possible, although they will tolerate a little shade. Avoid a windy situation as they can grow quite tall. Most garden soils are suitable, but avoid badly drained or poor soils – light soils make harvesting easier.

Sowing & planting Jerusalem artichokes are grown from tubers. Dig a 15 cm (6 in) deep trench and place a tuber every 30 cm (12 in) along it. Remember to plant them with the buds facing upwards. Draw the soil back over the trench and gently firm it down. Set the rows at least 1 m (3 ft) apart as the plants become quite tall. If you are planting in blocks (see page 18), set the tubers about 45 cm (18 in) apart in individual holes.

Care Jerusalem artichokes are very easy to grow. Weeding is the main activity, but be careful not to hoe off the emerging shoots, especially while they are still just below

the surface. Hand weeding is safer. Draw earth some distance up the stems as they grow to help support the plants. In windy areas, support the stalks with strings or wires fixed to a stake at each end of the row. Towards the end of summer, cut off the top half of the stems to reduce wind rock.

Problems Jerusalem artichokes are generally trouble free. Slugs, however, may be a problem, especially as the artichokes are usually left in the ground until required. The only other thing is likely to be subsequent crops, as even the smallest piece of tuber left in the ground will grow again. Be sure to clear them thoroughly at the end of the season, or they may become a nuisance.

Harvesting Dig the tubers as required any time after the leaves have begun to wither. Try to remove every tuber from each plant at a time, even if they are too small for the kitchen, or, as explained above, they will regrow.

Storing Generally there is no question of storage as Jerusalem artichokes can be left in the ground until required. In really cold areas where winter digging is difficult, dig all or some of the tubers and store in a cool place in a box of just-damp sand.

Good choices They are normally simply sold as 'Jerusalem artichokes', although there is one named variety, 'Fuseau', which produces regular-shaped tubers.

celeriac

With its nutty, celery-like flavour, celeriac can be grated raw into salads or served cooked, perhaps sliced and baked with cream and chilli, or boiled and mashed with butter. This delicious vegetable is relatively easy to grow and stores well so it is always on hand when needed.

	J	F	M	A	M	J	J	A	S	O	N	D
Sow		*	*	*								
Plant					*	*						
Harvest	*	*	*						*	*	*	*

From sowing to harvest 26 weeks

Site & soil Celeriac prefers an open, sunny site, but will tolerate shade. Since it remains in the soil all winter, avoid frost pockets. The soil should be fertile and moisture retentive without being waterlogged. Humus-rich soil is ideal – dig plenty of compost into the soil in the autumn.

Sowing & planting It is best to sow celeriac under cover. If you wait until the frosts have finished before sowing outside, the bulbs will not have time to develop before winter sets in.

Sow in modules in heat in late winter or early spring, or in a cool greenhouse in mid spring. When the seedlings are big enough to handle, transfer to individual pots and grow on. Once the threat of frost has passed, harden them off (see page 34) and plant outside at 30 cm (12 in) intervals in rows about 38 cm (15 in) apart. Use the same distances if planting in blocks (see page 18).

156

Care Weed carefully around them, preferably by hand. Keep watered if the weather turns dry as celeriac dislikes dry conditions. As the celeriac begins to mature, remove the lower leaves so that the bulb is exposed.

Problems In the early stages after planting out, watch out for slug damage. Celeriac rarely suffers from any other pests and diseases, but it may catch the same diseases that affect celery (see page 162). If you are worried about celery leaf miner (see page 162), keep the plants covered with fleece or mesh.

Harvesting Lift the bulbs once they have swollen to a decent size, any time from late summer onwards. The longer they are in the ground, the more flavour they have so don't start harvesting too soon.

Storing Celeriac can be left in the ground until it is required. In colder areas where winter digging is difficult, cover the rows with straw or, if necessary, lift the bulbs and store in a cool place in a box of just-damp sand.

Good choices Brilliant, Monarch F1

celery

Celery is invaluable in the kitchen, served raw in salads and with cheese, or cooked in soups, casseroles and sauces. It can even be braised as a vegetable in its own right. The 'trench' varieties have the best flavour, but newer self-blanching and green varieties are quicker and easier to grow.

	J	F	M	A	M	J	J	A	S	O	N	D
Sow			*	*								
Plant					*	*						
Harvest								*	*	*	*	

From sowing to harvest 15–20 weeks

Site & soil Choose an open, sunny site if possible, although celery will tolerate a little shade. Celery prefers a light, moisture-retentive soil – a plot manured the previous autumn is ideal. Avoid waterlogged conditions.

Sowing & planting Sow the seed under cover in modules in early to mid spring, then transfer to individual pots when the seedlings are big enough to handle. Harden off (see page 34) and plant out the young plants after the threat of frosts is over.

Plant self-blanching and green varieties in blocks, with plants spaced 25 cm (10 in) apart, so that the plants blanch each other, that is exclude light to make the stems white.

As the name suggests, trench varieties used to be planted in a shallow trench, then the soil was drawn up around the stems to blanch them as they grew. Nowadays it is more usual to plant trench celery on flat soil, but use

cardboard sleeves covered with black plastic and tied with string to exclude light from the stems. Plant them 35 cm (14 in) apart with 75 cm (30 in) between rows.

Care Watering must be consistent or celery will become stringy, so be sure to water regularly in dry periods and never let the soil dry out.

As already described, tie cardboard and plastic sleeves around trench varieties to keep the stems white as they grow. Tuck some straw around self-blanching varieties when they are about 20 cm (8 in) high to help exclude light.

Problems Slugs are the biggest threat, both at planting out and harvest time. Celery leaf miners can also be troublesome, but these are rare. They tunnel into the leaves and stems, causing a tracery of brown. Remove and destroy affected foliage. Celery will become stringy and tough if deprived of nutrients or moisture, so keep well watered and apply regular high-nitrogen feeds.

Harvesting Harvest before frosts strike, simply digging up the clumps. Trench varieties can stay in the soil a bit longer.

Storing Celery is usually pulled as it is needed, although it will keep for a few days in a refrigerator. If you have to harvest a lot at once, store in a cool place, preferably in a box of just-damp sand. You can also move plants to a greenhouse and roughly replant them until required.

Good choices Green and self-blanching varieties:
Octavius F1, Victoria F1, Loretta F1, Granada F1, Greensleeve, Golden Self blanching 0, Galaxy, Tango F1
Trench varieties: Hopkins Fenlander, Mammoth White, Martine, Mammoth Pink

florence fennel

Fennel is useful not only for its aniseed-flavoured bulb, which can be sliced raw in salads or cooked in pasta dishes, risotto, stews and bakes, but also for its feathery foliage, which makes an excellent herb to accompany fish and chicken dishes.

	J	F	M	A	M	J	J	A	S	O	N	D
Sow				*	*	*						
Harvest							*	*	*	*		

From sowing to harvest 12 weeks

Site & soil Fennel needs a warm and sunny position sheltered from the wind. The soil should be moisture-retentive as fennel does not like to dry out, but avoid waterlogged conditions. A humus-rich soil is ideal, but it shouldn't be too rich – a site manured for a previous crop would be perfect.

Sowing & planting Sow under cover in mid spring in modules, and plant out as soon as the threat of frost is over, causing as little root disturbance as possible. Space plants at 30 cm (12 in) intervals, in rows 30 cm (12 in) apart.

Alternatively, sow directly into the open soil in late spring or early summer, sowing a batch every three weeks to get a succession of crops. Make 1 cm (½ in) deep drills and station sow several seeds at 30 cm (12 in) intervals (see page 32–34). Leave at least 30 cm (12 in) between rows. If planting in blocks (see page 18), space plants 30 cm (12 in) apart.

Care Keep fennel well watered – it resents drying out and will quickly bolt (come into flower) if it does. As the bulbs begin to develop, earth them up by drawing soil up round the bulbs to roughly half their height, to prevent them getting too tough.

Problems Slugs can be a threat, especially to seedlings and young plants. The other major problem is lack of water, which will cause them to bolt and produce flowers at the expense of the growing bulb. Make certain there is plenty of humus in the soil to retain moisture, and water regularly if there is no rain.

Harvesting When the bulbs are about the size of a tennis ball, cut them off just above the base. The roots usually resprout to produce new foliage, which can be used in a variety of dishes and salads.

Storing Florence fennel is usually harvested as it is required as it will not keep long after cutting. It will tolerate a little frost, but by the onset of winter it is usually past its best. Once fennel is cut, it can be kept for a few days in the refrigerator.

Good choices Pronto F1, Amigo, Fennel di Firenze, Orion, Victoria F1

lettuce

With the wide range of flavours, colours and textures available to the lettuce-grower, salads will never be the same again. Choose from lettuces that form tight heads, to loose-leaf lettuces that can be cut whole or harvested a few leaves at a time as you need them.

	J	F	M	A	M	J	J	A	S	O	N	D
Sow		*	*	*	*	*	*	*	*	*		
Harvest	*	*	*	*	*	*	*	*	*	*	*	*

From sowing to harvest 6–15 weeks

Site & soil Lettuces prefer an open, sunny position, but they will tolerate light shade, and indeed benefit from it in warm weather. They grow in most garden soils as long as they are not waterlogged. Moisture-retentive soils are best, so choose a plot manured for a previous crop. They grow well under cover and in containers.

Sowing & planting If you have a greenhouse, cold frame or cloche, it is possible to sow and harvest lettuce in virtually any month of the year, although winter crops are the most difficult. Sow under cover in trays in late winter, then harden off (see page 34) the young lettuces before planting out.

Sow in the open ground from spring onwards, sowing a few seeds every two weeks to maintain a regular supply of fresh lettuce. Sow in 1 cm (½ in) deep drills with 30 cm (12 in) between rows. Thin the seedlings to 15–30 cm (6–12 in) apart, depending on variety. If growing in blocks, space plants 15–35 cm (6–14 in) apart.

Care Water lettuces well during periods of dry weather, so that their growth is not checked and they maintain their succulence. Weed regularly by hand or with a hoe, taking care not to dislodge or injure the plants.

Problems Check regularly for slugs and snails, which pose the biggest threat. In the unlikely event of any diseases striking, destroy the plants and start again elsewhere – it's not worth the effort to treat it.

Harvesting Pull or cut crisphead, butterhead and Cos lettuces as soon as they are big enough to harvest. If you have planned your sowing there should be a constant supply. Cut loose-leaf varieties as whole heads, or simply remove as many leaves as you need at a time. The same plants will go on producing replacement leaves for some time, providing an economic use of space.

Storing Use lettuces as soon as they are harvested. They will last a short while in the salad compartment of the refrigerator but will soon lose their crisp freshness.

Good choices Crispheads (Icebergs): Lakeland, Webbs Wonderful, Triumph, Balmoral, Saladin, Sonette
Butterheads: All Year Round, Sangria, Winter Density, Estelle, Tom Thumb
Cos: Claremont, Little Gem, Counter, Lobjoits Green, Corsair, Chatsworth
Loose-leaf varieties: Frillice, Bijou, Salad Bowl, Lollo Rossa, Pandero, Lollo Bionda, Catalogna Cerbiatta

salad leaves

From land cress to purslane, rocket to sorrel, salad leaves add a touch of the exotic to the salad bowl and a mix of flavours from mild to peppery. They are expensive to buy but ridiculously easy to grow, and you'll have the convenience of garden-fresh leaves to hand whenever you want them.

	J	F	M	A	M	J	J	A	S	O	N	D
Sow	*	*	*	*	*	*	*	*	*	*	*	*
Harvest	*	*	*	*	*	*	*	*	*	*	*	*

From sowing to harvest 3–10 weeks

Site & soil Most salad leaves prefer a sunny, open position, but many will also tolerate light shade. They will grow in any reasonable garden soil. They also do well under cover, or even on a kitchen windowsill – most potting composts are suitable if growing in containers.

Sowing & planting Sow just one type, or look out for seed mixtures that contain a selection of different plants. Salad leaves can be sown at any time of year. For winter and early crops they are best grown under cover (even a cloche will do), but for the rest of the year they can be sown outside.

Sow thinly in 1 cm (½ in) deep drills with rows set 15–20 cm (6–8 in) apart. There is usually no need to thin them. If growing in blocks, broadcast the seed thinly then rake it in, or sow in close drills.

Care Since most are small plants, it is important not to let them get swamped by weeds. Hand weed to avoid

accidentally hoeing up the salad leaves. Keep watered during dry weather, even during winter as the sun can dry compost rapidly under glass.

Problems The most serious threat is likely to be from slugs. Flea beetles (see page 44) can be a problem with some of the crops, especially rocket: cover with fleece or apply a little derris if they have already arrived. Keep a watch for pigeons and other birds – netting is the best way to keep them out. Generally, though, salad leaves are fast growing and trouble free.

Harvesting Harvesting could not be simpler: just pick them as you need them. Choose a few leaves from each type you grow to make a varied salad bowl.

Storing It is best to pick them as you need them – they do not store well. If necessary, they will keep for a day in the salad compartment of the refrigerator.

Good choices Land cress, mustard salad, rocket, winter purslane, corn salad, summer purslane, sorrel, watercress, mitzuba, cress

endives

Endives are lettuce-like plants that come in curly frisée varieties, or broad-leaved escaroles. They can be left with a slightly bitter twang or they can be sweetened by blanching as they grow. These plants make a decorative and flavoursome addition to the salad bowl.

	J	F	M	A	M	J	J	A	S	O	N	D
Sow				*	*	*	*					
Harvest					*	*	*	*	*	*		

From sowing to harvest 7–12 weeks

Site & soil Choose an open, sunny site if possible, although they will tolerate light shade. Endives will grow in most soils, but a lighter soil is better for winter crops and waterlogged conditions should be avoided.

If growing under cover, plant in soil beds or containers filled with a good-quality potting compost.

Sowing & planting For early crops, sow in mid spring under cover and grow the plants on in a greenhouse or under cloches. Alternatively, sow in modules under cover in late spring and transplant the young plants to the open garden when conditions are warm enough, hardening them off before planting out (see page 34).

Wait until conditions are warm enough to sow in the open ground, usually by early summer. Sow in 1 cm (½ in) deep drills with rows set 35 cm (14 in) apart. When big enough, thin to about 30 cm (12 in) intervals. If planting in blocks, set the plants 30 cm (12 in) apart.

Care Keep well weeded, preferably by hand, and water regularly in dry weather. When the endives have reached maturity they can be blanched to make them less bitter, by covering the leaves for about ten days to exclude light. Wait until the leaves are dry, then cover the plant with a bucket for complete blanching or just cover the centre of the plant with a plate.

Problems Slugs and snails can be a real nuisance. If you use slug pellets, make certain they do not lodge in the leaves of the plant. Greenfly can be troublesome, especially to plants growing under cover. If an infestation occurs, remove by hand if you can.

Harvesting Harvest at any time when they have reached maturity. If you blanch them, harvest soon after the ten days as they will begin to deteriorate. Cut the head off rather than pulling out the whole plant, as you may get a second crop of leaves. If you don't need a whole head, simply remove a few of the leaves and leave the rest of the plant for cutting later.

Storing Use endives as soon as possible after cutting. They do not store well and can rarely be kept longer than a day with any degree of freshness.

Good choices Frisée Glory, Frenzy, Wallonne, Glory, Pancaliere

chicory

Chicory produces tasty bitter leaves to perk up salads, or it can be braised and served hot. There are three types: red radicchio for autumn crops, witloof or Belgian chicory, which is forced for winter eating, and sugarloaf chicories like large Cos lettuces with a milder flavour.

	J	F	M	A	M	J	J	A	S	O	N	D
Sow	*	*	*	*	*	*	*	*	*			
Harvest	*	*	*	*	*	*	*	*	*	*	*	*

From sowing to harvest **8** weeks or more

Site & soil Chicories will grow in full sun or light shade. The witloof types need a deep soil; the others will grow in most garden soils as long as they are not too wet. The colourful red radicchio can be grown in the flower borders as they are quite decorative. Avoid very rich soil – a plot manured for a previous crop is ideal.

Sowing & planting Witloof types are grown for forcing. Sow outside in mid summer in 1 cm (½ in) drills. Thin plants to 20 cm (8 in) apart, in rows 30 cm (12 in) apart.

Sow radicchio outside in early summer, or in late summer for overwintering. Space as for witloof chicories.

Sugarloaf types can be sown at any time of year under cover, or outside during the summer months. Space plants at 25 cm (10 in) intervals.

Care Keep all chicories watered in dry weather. Witloof chicories need to be forced. Lift the roots in late autumn

and reduce them to 20 cm (8 in); cut back the leaves to 5 cm (2 in). Replant in large pots of moist potting compost with the crowns just above the surface. Cover with a bucket to exclude all light and keep at about 13°C (55°F).

Problems Slugs are the most likely threat. Other than that, chicories are generally trouble free.

Harvesting Harvest sugarloaf and radicchio chicories as soon as they are big enough. Cut off the head rather than pulling up the whole plant as the remaining stalk may sprout again. If you don't need a whole head, harvest just a few leaves and leave the rest for later.

Cut the blanched 'chicons' of witloof chicory after three to four weeks of forcing. Again, leave the stalk to resprout for a second crop.

Storing Chicories are best eaten as soon as they are harvested. They may last a day or so in a refrigerator but will lose their crispness.

Good choices Witloof: Witloof Zoom, Normato, Apollo
Radicchio: Cesare, Treviso Precoce Mesola, Rossano
Sugarloaf: Pain de Sucre, Snowflake

radishes

Radishes are quick and simple to grow just about anywhere, including in containers. Pull a few as a crunchy and nutritious nibble, or use to pep up your salads. They come in a wide range of colours, shapes and flavours, and all taste better home-grown than shop-bought.

	J	F	M	A	M	J	J	A	S	O	N	D
Sow		*	*	*	*	*	*	*	*	*		
Harvest			*	*	*	*	*	*	*	*	*	*

From sowing to harvest 4 weeks

Site & soil Sow in an open, sunny position, or in light shade if the weather is warm. Radishes will grow in virtually any soil, but a light, moisture-retentive soil is ideal. If possible, choose a plot manured for a previous crop.

Sowing & planting Sow early crops under cover in autumn or late winter in their permanent positions – they cannot be transplanted. Otherwise, sow outside from early spring onwards. Sow just a few seeds at once: short rows at two-week intervals are better than infrequent, long rows. Save space by growing them between other slower-growing crops, such as parsnips or brassicas.

Sow the seed thinly in 1 cm (½ in) deep drills with 15 cm (6 in) between rows. Thin seedlings to 2.5 cm (1 in) apart. If growing in blocks (see page 18), sprinkle the seed over the soil surface and lightly rake to cover it; thin the seedlings to about 7 cm (3 in) apart. The large winter varieties need a little more space.

Care Do not allow the soil to dry out or the radishes quickly become woody and very hot tasting. Keep the area weeded but be careful not to disturb the roots.

Problems Flea beetles (see page 44) may attack: cover the seed bed with fleece or micromesh to prevent it, or dust with derris if the beetles are already there. Slugs may also be a problem, especially with emerging seedlings.

Harvesting Harvest the radishes as soon as they are big enough. Be careful not to loosen adjacent plants as you pull them. Discard any that are obviously old or running to seed as these will be woody and tough, and the flavour will be very hot.

Storing It is not possible to store radishes, so eat them as soon as they are harvested. They will keep a day or so in the refrigerator, but will lose their crunchiness. Winter radishes can be left in the ground for longer, and should be covered with straw in frosty areas.

Good choices Globe varieties: Cherry Belle, Rudi, Prinz Rotin, Pink Beauty, Rougette, Amethyst
Cylindrical varieties: Flamboyant Sabrina, French Breakfast, Fluo F1, Patricia
Winter varieties: Black Spanish Round, Wintella
Chinese mooli radishes: China Rose, Mantanghong, Tsukushi Spring Cross, Mid Spring Cross, Mino Early

tomatoes

Home-grown tomatoes, eaten while still warm from the
sun, taste so much better than anything you can buy.
Whether they are cherry, plum or beefsteak tomatoes,
red, yellow, green or purple, choose varieties for their
superior flavour and prepare to be amazed.

	J	F	M	A	M	J	J	A	S	O	N	D
Sow	*	*	*	*								
Planting				*	*							
Harvest							*	*	*	*		

From sowing to harvest 8 weeks or more

Site & soil Tomatoes need sunshine, so choose a warm,
open site. They do well in greenhouses or in containers
where they will thrive against a warm wall. Tomatoes
tolerate most soils, but prefer a well-drained, fertile soil
that doesn't dry out too rapidly. If planting in containers,
use a good-quality potting compost or buy specially
formulated growing bags. Avoid composts that dry out
rapidly, especially if you are growing your tomatoes in
hanging baskets.

Sowing & planting If growing in a greenhouse, sow seeds
one to a pot under heat in mid to late winter. For outdoor
plants, sow under cover in mid spring so the young plants
are of a decent size for planting out as soon as the threat
of frost is past outside. A wide range of young tomato
plants is available from garden centres and nurseries if you
don't have anywhere warm and bright to raise the seedlings.

Care Cordon tomatoes need to be supported by stakes or canes. Cut out any side shoots as they appear to keep just one central stem. Bush varieties do not need supporting and the side shoots are retained.

Water regularly and consistently once the fruit begins to swell. Feed plants with a liquid tomato fertilizer – this is particularly important with container-grown plants as the regular watering leaches nutrients from the compost.

Problems One of the worst problems is blight (see page 42). If you spot it, dig up and burn the plants to prevent it spreading. Intermittent watering can cause the fruit to split, so try to establish a routine and keep the soil just moist at all times.

Harvesting Pick the fruit as soon as it ripens. If frost threatens at the end of the season, pick the remaining green tomatoes and let them ripen indoors, or use them as green tomatoes in chutneys and other dishes.

Storing Tomatoes are always best when freshly picked, but they will keep in a bowl for a few days inside. If you have a glut, cook and purée the excess and freeze for later use. At the end of the season, hang the plants upside down in a greenhouse and pick the fruit as it ripens, or ripen them on a windowsill in the kitchen.

Good choices Outside tomatoes: Marmande, Red Alert Roma, Tornado, San Mazano, Tumbler, Tigrella, Red Alert Greenhouse tomatoes: Big Boy, Shirley, Golden Cherry, Vanessa, Sparta, Brandy Wine, Santa, Black Prince Greenhouse or outside: Ailsa Craig, Alicanto, Gardonor's Delight, Sweet Million, Golden Sunshine, Moneymaker, Sakura, Plumito

aubergines

Aubergines are exciting vegetables with which to cook, being mainstays in Mediterranean, Middle Eastern and Asian cuisines. Roast and purée them for patés and dips, bake in tomato sauce or use in Indian curries. There is a wide range of colours and sizes from which to choose.

	J	F	M	A	M	J	J	A	S	O	N	D
Sow		*	*									
Harvest							*	*	*			

From sowing to harvest 16 weeks

Site & soil Aubergines can be grown outside in warm areas, but they are better grown under cover in a greenhouse or cloche. Alternatively, start them inside in containers, then move them outside to a warm, sunny position, preferably against a warm wall, when the temperature is above 20°C (68°F). Use a good-quality, rich potting compost or choose a plot outside with deep, relatively rich soil with plenty of well-rotted organic matter.

Sowing & planting Whether kept in containers or planted in the open ground, aubergines are usually started under cover. Soak the seed in warm water for a day before sowing. Sow seeds in modules or individual pots in late winter or early spring, preferably with gentle heat from an electric propagator. When large enough to handle, transfer the seedlings to growing bags or 20 cm (8 in) pots. In warmer areas, plant out into the open ground once the threat of frost has passed.

Care While tending them, watch out for the rather nasty spines, which can be painful. Keep the plants well watered and warm. Some varieties grow tall, so provide stakes for support if necessary. If you want larger fruit, restrict the plants to six fruit each. Feed with a high-potash fertilizer, such as a liquid tomato feed, once the fruit starts to swell.

Problems Aubergines grown under cover are likely to suffer the usual greenhouse pests of whitefly, red spider mite and aphids (see pages 42–44). Take any appropriate action if deemed necessary. Fungal diseases such as mildew may be a problem if there is not enough air circulating, so maintain good ventilation.

Harvesting Pick once the fruits are large enough. If they lose their shine or brown areas begin to form, they are past their best and should be discarded. Harvest by cutting the stalk where it joins the main stem, minding the prickles.

Storing Aubergines do not store very well but will keep for about a week in a cool place or in the refrigerator. If you have a glut, cut them up, fry in olive oil and freeze for later use.

Good choices Black Beauty, Moneymaker F1, Ophelia F1, Kermit F1, Fairy Tale F1, Early Long Purple, Black Enorma F1, Calliope, Mohican F1

peppers and chillies

Easy, fun and prolific, peppers and chillies are decorative plants for the patio and garden. Choose from red, orange, yellow, green and purple varieties in a whole range of shapes, sizes and flavours, and use them in everything from Mediterranean to Oriental dishes.

	J	F	M	A	M	J	J	A	S	O	N	D
Sow			*	*								
Harvest							*	*	*			

From sowing to harvest 20 weeks

Site & soil Peppers and chillies do best under cover of a greenhouse or cloche, but will grow happily outside in good weather in a warm, sunny spot – against a warm wall is ideal. Use a good general compost in containers, or choose a site with fertile, well-drained soil in the open garden.

Sowing & planting There is a huge range of seed on offer for both chillies and peppers, and a good range of young plants in garden centres in late spring.

Sow the seed under cover in individual pots or modules in mid to late spring. Avoid sowing earlier unless you have a heated greenhouse. When large enough, transfer the young plants to larger pots or growing bags, or into a border in the greenhouse. Space the plants at 30–45 cm (12–18 in) intervals if growing in a bed.

If you are planting them outside, wait until all risk of frost is over and the temperature is above 15°C (59°F).

Care The temperature must not drop below 15°C (59°F), although 21–30°C (70–86°F) is best. The soil will dry out rapidly at these temperatures, so keep a eye on them as they may need watering several times a day. As fruit begins to develop, feed with a high-potash fertilizer, such as a liquid tomato feed.

Problems If they are growing in a greenhouse, whitefly, red spider mite and aphids can be troublesome (see pages 42–44). Take action only if they become a serious problem. Keep the plants well ventilated to prevent fungal diseases such as mildew.

Harvesting Harvest as soon as the fruit is big enough. Chillies get hotter the longer they are grown, so harvest as you like them. Peppers change colour as they age: green, red, yellow and they also become sweeter. Again, harvest as you like them.

Storing Peppers are best eaten soon after picking, although they will keep for a few days in a cool place. If you have a glut, they freeze well. At the end of the season, hang the plants upside down in a frost-free but cool and pick as required. Chillies can be dried and stored in an airtight jar.

Best choices Peppers: Lany, Ace F1, Minimax, Gypsy F1, Redskin, Gourmet, California Wonder, Mini-Sweet
Long-fruited peppers: Corno di Torro, Romano Mixed, Marooni Rosso, Bullhorn Mix, Big Banana
Chillies: Hot Mexican, Big Sun, Demon Red, Jalapeño, Fuego, Apache F1, Heatwave, Cayenne, Etna, Hungarian Hot Wax

cucumber

Home-grown cucumbers are far superior in both taste and texture to watery supermarket fare. Cucumbers used to be divided into long, smooth indoor-grown varieties, and rougher, ridged outdoor varieties, but modern breeding has now made it possible to grow smooth cucumbers outdoors.

	J	F	M	A	M	J	J	A	S	O	N	D
Sow				*	*	*						
Harvest						*	*	*	*			

From sowing to harvest 12 weeks

Site & soil Grow indoor varieties under glass or polythene, in containers, growing bags or a greenhouse border. Any good-quality container compost will do.

Short ridge cucumbers, the newly bred, long outdoor varieties and gherkins all need an open, sunny site outside, but will tolerate a little shade especially during a hot summer. They need a fertile, friable, free-draining soil.

Sowing & planting Don't start cucumbers too early unless you are going to grow them in a heated greenhouse. The best time for sowing is mid to late spring – both indoor and outdoor varieties are treated in the same way.

Sow seeds in modules or individual pots. Put two seeds in each pot, placing the seeds on their sides so they rest in the soil on one edge. If both germinate, remove one seedling as soon as possible. As soon as they are big enough, transfer to their permanent positions. This must be after all risk of frost has passed for outdoor varieties.

Care Trailing varieties, whether grown inside or out, need a support over which to grow – canes, strings or netting are the most usual. Ridge varieties do not require this. Pinch out the growing tip when the plant reaches the top of the support or has covered enough ground. Keep well watered and throw water on the floor of the greenhouse in hot weather to keep the atmosphere humid. Remove any male flowers that appear on indoor varieties to prevent the cucumbers from tasting bitter – the male flowers are those with a long, straight stem behind them.

Problems Red spider mite, whitefly and aphids can attack those grown indoors (see pages 42–44), while slugs can be a nuisance outdoors.

Harvesting Cut the cucumbers when they are big enough, removing them with a small length of stalk still attached. Once fully grown, do not leave on the plant too long or they will turn yellow.

Storing Cucumbers are best eaten straight from the plant. They will keep for a few days in a cool place but not much longer. Gherkins can be eaten fresh or pickled.

Good choices Indoor varieties: Carmen F1, Futura F1, Birgit F1, Galileo F1, Landora F1, Saladin F1, Zerina F1
Outdoor varieties: Burpless Tasty Green, Bush Champion F1, Marketmore F1, Long White, Swing F1, Masterpiece, Crystal Apple, Sindy F1
Gherkins: Bimbostar F1, Diamant, Venlo

courgettes and marrows

Courgettes are a summer staple and hugely versatile in the kitchen. Even one plant will produce a good crop of delicious green or yellow fruits. If you want marrows, simply let a few courgettes get large, or grow a specific variety. Both courgettes and marrows are easy and prolific plants.

	J	F	M	A	M	J	J	A	S	O	N	D
Sow				*	*	*						
Plant				*	*							
Harvest							*	*	*			

From sowing to harvest 8 weeks

Site & soil Choose an open, sunny position sheltered from strong winds or the large leaves will get torn. Courgettes will grow in any good garden soil, preferably one rich in humus (see page 12), so add plenty of well-rotted manure or garden compost. Some gardeners grow them in a pocket of soil on the compost heap.

Sowing & planting Either sow seed under cover in early spring, or outside in late spring. Don't sow too early; plant out young plants grown under cover, or germinate seed in the garden, just after the last threat of frost.

If raising young plants under cover, sow two seeds in each module or individual pot with the seeds lying on their edges. Remove the weaker seedling if they both germinate. Harden off plants (see page 31) before planting outside.

To sow outside, sow two seeds 1 m (3 ft) apart for bush varieties and up to 2 m (6 ft) apart for trailing marrows.

Care Keep plants well watered, especially when they are establishing themselves. Train trailing varieties up strong supports or spread the foliage out evenly over the ground. Anchor long stems in more windy sites.

Problems Slugs are among the worst enemies of courgettes and marrows, which are most vulnerable when the plants have just germinated or been planted out. Various viruses (see page 44) can also strike – dig up and burn badly affected plants.

Harvesting Pick the courgettes as they become big enough. The smaller they are, the better flavour and texture they have, but if the crop is limited allow them to grow slightly bigger. Keep a keen eye as they soon grow into whopping marrows. Remove any that become too large to encourage more smaller fruits to grow.

Storing Courgettes will keep for a few days in the refrigerator, but are best eaten as soon as possible after picking. If you have a glut, slice and fry them in a little oil and freeze them for soups, sauces and casseroles. Marrows can be stored for some months in a cool, dark place with good ventilation – but first let the skins harden in the sun after picking.

Good choices Courgettes: Parador F1, El Greco F1, All Green Bush, Defender F1, Sylvaner F1, Venus F1, Gold Rush F1, Zucchini F1
Marrows: Badger Cross F1, Long Green Bush, Tiger Cross F1, Bush Baby

pumpkins and squashes

Well known for their associations with Halloween, pumpkins also make a delicious ingredient in the kitchen. Winter squashes are very similar to pumpkins and can be treated the same. Summer squashes are cultivated in the same way as courgettes (see pages 204–207).

	J	F	M	A	M	J	J	A	S	O	N	D
Sow				*	*	*						
Plant					*	*	*					
Harvest								*	*	*		

From sowing to harvest 12 weeks

Site & soil Pumpkins and winter squashes prefer an open, sunny site, although they will tolerate some shade. They like a deep soil, rich in organic matter (see page 12) so add plenty of well-rotted compost or manure. For the biggest pumpkins, grow the plants in a pocket of soil on a manure heap or compost heap.

Sowing & planting If you are growing them to eat, rather than making lanterns or entering giant pumpkin competitions, it is best to choose a small pumpkin variety, or grow winter squashes instead. Young plants are available from garden centres, but these are likely to be the large-fruiting varieties.

Sow the seed under cover in late spring so the young plants will be ready to plant out in the garden as soon as the risk of frost is over. Set the seeds on their sides in individual pots and cover with a layer of compost. Grow

on under cover, then harden off (see page 34), before planting outside. Planting distances vary so check on the packet for the correct distance for your variety. Bush varieties need 60–100 cm (2–3 ft), while trailing ones need up to twice that.

Care Keep the area well weeded, but avoid loosening the plant while doing so. Water well while the plants are becoming established. Trailing varieties can be trained up supports or left to trail along the ground; peg stems down in windy areas if necessary.

Problems Slugs are a nuisance, especially when the plants are first set out or first emerge if sown in situ. Later they will also eat into the fruits. Mildew (see pages 42–44) can also be a problem – ensure there is plenty of air circulating and ignore all but very serious cases.

Harvesting Pick as soon as the fruits become large enough. Cut the fruits from the main stem, leaving a piece of stalk on each pumpkin or squash. If you intend to store the fruits, leave them on the plants as long as possible.

Storing Pumpkins and winter squashes will keep for several months, depending on the variety. Leave on the plants until just before the first predicted frost, then cut and store in a dry, cool, airy place which is free from frost.

Good choices Pumpkins: Dill's Atlantic Giant, Aladdin F1, Baby Bear, Spellbound F1, Maro F1
Winter squashes: Crown Prince, Blue Hubbard, Festival F1, Hunter, Sweet Dumpling, Orange Dawn, Turk's Turban
Summer squashes: Sunburst F1, Zephyr F1, Green Buttons F1, Scallopini Mix, Early Golden Crookneck

spinach

Spinach is packed with vitamins A and C, and is perfect for stir-fries, casseroles, soups and raw in delicious salads. Pick the leaves while young and tender if you are eating them raw, or allow them to mature for cooked dishes. Spinach is easy to grow, as long as the weather is not too hot.

	J	F	M	A	M	J	J	A	S	O	N	D
Sow			*	*	*				*			
Harvest				*	*	*					*	*

From sowing to harvest 5 weeks

Site & soil Spinach is one of the few crops that grows happily in light shade, indeed in hot summer weather this is the best place for it, as it has a tendency to bolt if too hot. Choose an open, airy position or grow autumn sowings under cover. Spinach will tolerate most soils, but does best on a plot manured for a previous crop.

Sowing & planting Sow directly into greenhouse beds or containers, or under cloches for early and late crops. Otherwise, sow in the open garden from early spring. Sow a few seeds at two-week intervals to get a continuous crop.

Sow the seed in 1 cm (½ in) drills with 30 cm (12 in) between rows. Thin the seedlings when big enough to about 15 cm (6 in) apart. Small-leaf varieties can be thinned to about 10 cm (4 in). To reduce the amount of thinning, you can station sow (see page 34). If you are growing in blocks (see page 18), space plants about 15 cm (6 in) apart.

Care Spinach is easy to care for, particularly as it is a fast-growing crop. Keep the area well weeded, particularly in the early stages of its growth. Water if necessary to keep it growing steadily. This is important in warm weather.

Problems Spinach does not suffer from many pests and diseases. Occasionally it may suffer from mildew (see pages 42–44) in a confined area, but good ventilation will help prevent this. The only other problem is bolting (see page 212) about which little can be done once it happens. To prevent it, keep plants growing steadily by watering well and plant later crops in light shade.

Harvesting Start to pick the leaves as soon as they are large enough, taking just a few leaves from each plant. If you need the whole plant, cut above the main stalk and it may reshoot with more leaves. Keep picking until the plants begin to bolt. If you have sown at fortnightly intervals there should be a steady supply.

Storing Spinach does not store when fresh and should be used as soon as it is picked. It will, however, freeze well if you wilt the leaves first.

Good choices Trianthlon, Bordeaux F1, Palco F1, Campania F1, Barbados F1, Galaxy F1, Mediana, Tetona F1, Oriento F1, Samish F1

leaf beet and new zealand spinach

These two easy-going leaf vegetables are great substitutes for spinach in the kitchen and are much simpler to grow as they have no tendency to bolt (see page 212). They also have long seasons of production, so you could be picking fresh and nutritious leaves all year round.

	J	F	M	A	M	J	J	A	S	O	N	D
Sow			*	*	*			*				
Harvest	*	*	*	*	*	*	*	*	*	*	*	*

From sowing to harvest leaf beet 8 weeks, New Zealand spinach
6 weeks

Site & soil Both plants tolerate a wide range of conditions and soils, making them very easy to accommodate. Leaf beet is good for windy and exposed positions, while New Zealand spinach will tolerate hot, dry conditions. Leaf beet can be grown under cover as a winter crop.

Sowing & planting Both types can be either sown under cover or outdoors in situ. Sow under cover in modules in early spring. When the plants are large enough, harden off carefully (see page 34) and plant out in their final positions, either in containers or in the open soil.

Sow outside in mid to late spring in 2 cm (¾ in) deep drills with rows set about 40 cm (16 in) apart. Thin leaf beet seedlings to about 23 cm (9 in) apart, New Zealand spinach seedlings to 45 cm (18 in) apart. Station sow (see page 34) if preferred to avoid a lot of thinning. If planting in blocks (see page 18), plant at the same distances.

Care Keep the area well weeded, especially around New Zealand spinach, which tends to ramble across the soil and could become entangled in weeds, making harvesting difficult. Water leaf beet regularly in dry weather; New Zealand spinach will tolerate drought.

Problems Apart from the usual nuisance of slugs attacking young or emerging plants, both are trouble free. Leaf beet can suffer from beet leaf spot, a mild fungal disease that shows as round spots on the leaves, with a pale centre and purple edge. This problem is not worth worrying about as the damage is usually insignificant.

Harvesting Start to pick individual leaves as soon as the first leaves are big enough. They will go on producing for a long period. If the plants begin to look tired, cut off all the leaves and let a new crop grow. You can pick and eat the shoot tips of New Zealand spinach as well as the leaves. Leaf beet crops sown in late summer can be harvested throughout the winter if grown under cover.

Storing The leaves wilt soon after picking, so use as fresh as possible. Both will freeze quite well.

Good choices These plants are rarely sold as anything other than their names. Leaf beet is sometimes also called Perpetual Spinach.

swiss chard

Whether it is smooth or crinkly, white, pink, yellow, purple or rainbow colours, swiss chard is a feast for the eyes as well as the stomach. The freshly picked leaves of this highly decorative plant have a crispness and flavour that tired leaves from the shops can never achieve.

	J	F	M	A	M	J	J	A	S	O	N	D
Sow			*	*			*	*				
Harvest	*	*					*	*	*	*	*	*

From sowing to harvest 8 weeks

Site & soil Swiss chard is a tolerant plant that grows in sun or shade, and will happily survive in windy positions. It will grow in most garden soils and in deep containers. If you are growing it in the flower beds, position it so the evening sun illuminates the colours in the leaves.

Sowing & planting Sow either in modules or individual pots under cover, or direct in the open soil. It is important to sow thinly as each 'seed' is in fact a cluster of several seeds. Late-summer sowings will provide winter crops, which can be grown either inside or outside, although the former will produce better leaves.

In the open ground, sow in 2 cm (¾ in) deep drills with rows set 15 cm (10 in) apart. You need to thin the emerging seedlings to about 23 cm (9 in) apart, so it is best to station sow (see page 34) at roughly these intervals. If you are planting in blocks (see page 18), space plants 30 cm (12 in) apart.

Care Swiss chard needs very little maintenance considering the length of its season. Water in dry weather to keep it growing well. For outside winter crops the quality of the leaves can be improved by covering with cloches.

Problems This is a trouble-free crop that rarely needs any attention. It can suffer from beet leaf spot (see page 218), but rarely to the extent that it affects the quality of the vegetable so no remedy is usually required. Beet leaf miners can also be a minor irritant. The white larvae make large brown patches on the leaves. If you come across any, just squeeze the larvae between your fingers.

Harvesting You can start cutting the leaves as soon as they are big enough, but allow the plant to retain some so that it has the energy to grow to full size. If, as the season progresses, the leaves become large and rather coarse, cut all the foliage off and allow the plant to regenerate.

Storing The leaves soon begin to wilt after picking, so they are best used straight from the plant. However, they can be frozen successfully.

Good choices Charlotte, Bright Lights, Bright Yellow, Fordhook Giant, Lucullus, Rhubarb Chard

seakale

Seakale is a culinary treat. The stems are steamed like asparagus, while the leaves are used as spring greens. The plant crops well for about six years, and it is a valuable addition to potagers (see page 24) for its silvery-grey foliage and masses of white flowers.

	J	F	M	A	M	J	J	A	S	O	N	D
Sow			*									
Planting			*	*								
Harvest			*	*	*							

From sowing to harvest 2 years; from thongs to harvest 1 year

Site & soil In the wild, seakale grows on the beach, so it likes a sunny, open position. The soil should be sandy and free-draining, but add a certain amount of well-rotted organic material (see page 12). Prepare the site well as the plant will be there for a number of years.

Sowing & planting Seakale can be sown from seed or planted as 'thongs' (pieces of root). The seed has a very hard case, so scratch the surface with sandpaper before sowing. Sow in pots or in the open ground in spring, and move to their final positions when they are big enough.

You can either buy thongs or take them as root cuttings from a three-year-old plant in early winter. Stand the pieces of root upright in damp sand in a cool place. Plant out in mid spring once buds have formed on the top of each, spacing the plants 60 cm (24 in) apart.

Care Not a great deal of attention is required, but keep the area weeded as the plants do not like to be overgrown. Feed plants every year after harvesting (see page 36) by mulching the soil with well-rotten compost and forking in a little bonemeal or seaweed meal.

Problems Seakale is generally trouble free. Slugs can be a nuisance and eat enough of the emerging foliage to kill the plant; reduce their numbers using which ever method of control you prefer.

Harvesting In late winter or early spring, cover the plants with a bucket to exclude all light, then cover with straw or bubblewrap to keep the plants a little warmer. The resulting blanched stems can be cut once they are big enough. Continue cutting off the stems until late spring, then leave the plant to recover.

Storing Seakale does not keep well, so it should be used as soon as it is harvested.

Good choices Angers, Ivory White, Lily White

rhubarb

The first delicate pink rhubarb stems of the season are a long-awaited luxury for vegetable gardeners everywhere. Rhubarb is an easy and prolific plant that goes on producing for many years. The distinctive flavour of its handsome red stems complements both sweet and savoury dishes.

	J	F	M	A	M	J	J	A	S	O	N	D
Plant		*	*							*	*	
Harvest		*	*	*	*	*						

From planting to harvest 12 months

Site & soil Rhubarb will grow in sun or light shade. It will tolerate a windy position, but benefits from some protection. It will happily grow on most soils, except waterlogged ones, but does best in a deep, fertile soil. Prepare the bed well before planting by digging in plenty of well-rotted organic material (see page 12).

Sowing & planting It is possible to grow rhubarb from seed but the results are variable so it is better to grow from root cuttings, called 'sets'. Plant into ground that was prepared six months before so all perennial weeds have been removed. Plant out in mid to late autumn, or in late winter to early spring, whenever the weather and soil are suitable. The latter period is better for cold or wet areas. Plant with the crown just below the soil surface. One clump is often enough, but if you are planting more, space them 1 m (3 ft) apart.

Care Keep the area free from perennial weeds as, once established, they will be difficult to eradicate. Remove the flower stalks as soon as they appear on the plant. Mulch each autumn with well-rotted organic material (see page 38) and cut away the dead leaves to let the frost get to the crown.

Problems Rhubarb should give years of trouble-free service. On rare occasions, it may get a viral infection (see page 44). If this happens, dig up the plant and burn it. Don't replant on the same site – choose a new position some distance away.

Harvesting In its second year, start to pull the stems, not cut them, as they appear in spring, leaving about half of them on the plant. Stop harvesting in mid summer to give time for the plant to regenerate. Some varieties can be forced after the first few frosts to encourage them to produce tender early stems. Do this by covering the plant with a deep bucket or dustbin to exclude all light, then cover the bucket with straw to keep the plant a little warmer. You should get a crop around three weeks early.

Storing Rhubarb does not store well fresh, but it can be frozen once cooked.

Good choices Timperley Early, Red Champagne, Stockbridge Arrow, Albert, Victoria

sweetcorn

Home-grown sweetcorn is far superior to anything you can buy – the sugars start to convert to starch after picking, so the fresher it is, the sweeter it is. Barbecue the cobs whole straight after picking. Choose 'supersweet' cultivars for flavour, or quick-maturing varieties for cooler climates.

	J	F	M	A	M	J	J	A	S	O	N	D
Sow				*	*	*						
Planting					*	*						
Harvest							*	*	*			

From sowing to harvest 12 weeks

Site & soil Sweetcorn likes a sunny, open site. Avoid very windy positions, although sweetcorn en masse does not generally suffer wind damage. It will grow on most soils as long as they are not too dry nor too wet. A free-draining, moderately fertile soil is best. Sweetcorn can be grown under cover, useful in areas where the soil takes a long time to warm up in the spring.

Sowing & planting Sweetcorn can be sown under cover in modules or individual pots in mid spring, or outside in the open garden in early summer. Don't sow either too early – all risk of frost must be over before plants are set outside, and the soil should be at 16°C (61°F) for outdoor sowing or planting. Cover the soil with polythene to warm it up.

To aid pollination, it is important to grow sweetcorn in blocks rather than rows. If sowing outside, station sow (see page 34) at 30–35 cm (12–14 in) intervals.

Care Keep well weeded, preferably by hand as sweetcorn plants resent root disturbance. In windy areas it may be necessary to protect against the wind or support the plants – some gardeners earth up the stems slightly as the plant grows to develop more supporting roots. Water well as the cobs begin to fill out.

Problems Generally sweetcorn is trouble free. Slugs can attack young plants, so keep them at bay. Mice, birds and pheasants in particular can steal the sown seed or the ripening cobs. Netting is about the only way to prevent this. Small areas of plants will suffer more than large ones.

Harvesting When the silk tassels turn brown, the corn is ripe and can be cut from the plant just below the cob.

Storing There is no doubt that sweetcorn tastes best when cooked straight after picking, but it will keep a few days in the refrigerator. It also freezes well.

Good choices Butterscotch F1, Lark F1, Sweet Sensation, Swift F1, Ovation F1, Sunrise, Extra Tender & Sweet F1, Northern Extra Sweet F1, Indian Summer F1

index

238

acknowledgements

Publisher: Jane Birch
Editor: Kerenza Swift
Executive Art Editor: Penny Stock
Designer: Cobalt
Production Controller: Carolin Stransky

Picture Acknowledgements:

Alamy John Glover 225; Alison Thompson 113; Arco Images GmbH 167; Bon Appetit 177; Dave Bevan133; Holmes Garden Photos 155; INTERFOTO Pressebildagentur 125; Nigel Cattlin 43, 126, 161; Organics image library 227; The National Trust Photolibrary 147;

Clive Nichols 143, 171, 205, 207;

FLPA Duncan Smith 63; Nigel Cattlin 57, 233;

Fotolia Natalyaivania 203; tomcat2170 109;

Gap Photos Clive Nichols 15, 123; Elke Borkowsk 193; Elke Borkowski 9, 25, 31, 47; FhF Greenmedia 21, 37, 129; Friedrich Strauss 185; Geoff du Feu 89; Geoff Kidd 45; Graham Strong 27; Howard Rice 219; J S Sira 93; Jonathan Buckley 71, 99, 103, 183; Maddie Thornhill 35; Marcus Harpur 235, Mark Bolton 59, 61, 69, 97; Maxine Adcock 75; Neil Holmes 119; Nicola Browne 111, 153; Paul Debois 137, Rice/Buckland 13, 39; Richard Bloom 73; S & O 8, 29, 67; Sarah Cuttle 49; Victoria Firmston 81; Visions 33, 197, 201; **Garden Picture Library** Michael Howes 53;

Garden World Images 121, 139; Dave Bevan 43, 50, 87, 91, 145, 165, 187, 223; FhF GreenMedia/Richard Loader 95; Glenn Harper 163; Jacqui Dracup 45; Liz Cole 55; Martin Hughes-Jones 181; Mein Schoener Garten 17, 85, 191; Nicholas Appleby 19; R Loader 159; Rita Coates 83; Sarah Lee 199; Sharon Pearson 217; Trevor Sims 131, 157;

istockphoto.com Blue Sunflower images 115; Magdalena Rittenhouse 213; Robert Simon 215;

Octopus Publishing Group Limited Juliet Greene 179; Freia Turland 41, 43, 45, 105, 189, 221; Howard Rice 77, 169; Laura Forrester 23, 195; Michael Boys 149, 229;

Photolibrary Alec Scaresbrook 175; Botanica 211; Duisterhof Miki 151; Francois De Heel 65; Howard Rice 79, 107; Jacqui Hurst 209, 231; Mayer/Le Scanff 135, Michael Howes 141; Ottmar Diez 101, Paul Franklin 173;

Shutterstock Cameron Cross 117,

'Who are you?' she said, looking up at him. 'I don't even know your name.'

Of course she didn't know. She wouldn't be looking up at him so trustingly if she knew who he was. Some women attempted to court him for his reputation. Madeline Langley would not. He knew that instinctively. She would shun the wicked man Earl Tregellas was reputed to be.

A shy amusement lit the amber eyes. 'Will you not tell me, sir?' She smiled.

Lucien traced the outline of it with his eyes. He doubted that he would see her smile again once he told her his name.

The band played on. Their feet moved in time across the floor. Silence stretched between them.

'I am Tregellas.' There was nothing else he could say.

'Tregellas?' she said softly.

Shock widened the tawny glow of her eyes. The smile fled her sweet pink lips. Uncertainty stood in its stead.

'Earl Tregellas? The Wick—' She stopped herself just in time.

'At your service, Miss Langley,' he said smoothly, as if he were just any other polite gentleman of the *ton*.

Margaret McPhee loves to use her imagination—an essential requirement for a trained scientist. However, when she realised that her imagination was inspired more by the historical romances she loves to read rather than by her experiments, she decided to put the ideas down on paper. She has since left her scientific life behind, retaining only the romance—her husband, whom she met in a laboratory. In summer, Margaret enjoys cycling along the coastline overlooking the Firth of Clyde in Scotland, where she lives. In winter, tea, cakes and a good book suffice.

Recent novels by the same author:

THE CAPTAIN'S LADY
MISTAKEN MISTRESS

THE
WICKED EARL

Margaret McPhee

MILLS & BOON®

MILLS & BOON and MILLS & BOON with the Rose Device
are registered trademarks of the publisher.

First published in Great Britain 2007
Harlequin Mills & Boon Limited,
Eton House, 18-24 Paradise Road, Richmond, Surrey TW9 1SR

© Margaret McPhee 2007

ISBN-13: 978 0 263 85172 4
ISBN-10:   0 263 85172 9

Set in Times Roman 10½ on 12½ pt.
04-0507-86386

Printed and bound in Spain
by Litografia Rosés S.A., Barcelona

THE
WICKED EARL

Chapter One

London—February 1814

'Sit up straight, Madeline. And can you not at least attempt to look as if you're enjoying the play?'

'Yes, Mama.' Madeline Langley straightened her back. 'The actors are very good, and the play is indeed interesting. It's just Lord Farquharson...' She dropped her voice to an even lower whisper. 'He keeps leaning too close and—'

'The noise in here is fit to raise the roof. It's little wonder that Lord Farquharson is having trouble hearing what you have to say,' said Mrs Langley.

'But, Mama, it is not his hearing that is at fault.' Madeline looked at her mama. 'He makes me feel uncomfortable.'

Mrs Langley wrinkled her nose. 'Do not be so tiresome, child. Lord Farquharson is expressing an interest in you and we must encourage him as best we can. He will never offer for you if you keep casting him such black looks. Look at Angelina—can you not try to be a little more like her? No scowls mar her face.' Mrs Langley bestowed upon her younger, and by far prettier, daughter, a radiant smile.

Angelina threw her sister a long-suffering expression.

'That is because Angelina does not have to sit beside Lord Farquharson,' muttered Madeline beneath her breath.

Angelina gave a giggle.

Fortunately Mrs Langley did not hear Madeline's comment. 'Shh, girls, he's coming back,' she whispered excitedly. Amelia Langley straightened and smiled most encouragingly at the gentleman who was entering the theatre box with a tray containing three drinks glasses balanced between his hands.

'Oh, Lord Farquharson, how very kind you are to think of my girls.' She fluttered her eyelashes unbecomingly.

'And of you too, of course, my dear Mrs Langley.' He passed her a glass of lemonade. 'I wouldn't want you, or your lovely daughters, becoming thirsty, and it is so very hot in here.'

Mrs Langley tittered. 'La, Lord Farquharson. It could never be too hot in such a superior and well-positioned theatre box. How thoughtful of you to invite us here. My girls do so love the theatre. They have such an appreciation of the arts, you know, just like their mama.'

Lord Farquharson revealed his teeth to Miss Angelina Langley in the vestige of a smile. 'I'm sure that's not the only attribute that they share with their mama.' The smile intensified as he pressed the glass into Angelina's hand.

'So good of you, my lord, to fight your way through the crowd to fetch us our lemonades,' Mrs Langley cooed.

'For such fair damsels I would face much worse,' said Lord Farquharson in a heroic tone.

Mrs Langley simpered at his words.

Madeline and Angelina exchanged a look.

Lord Farquharson's fingers stumbled over Madeline's in the act of transferring the lemonade. The glass was smooth and cool beneath her touch. Lord Farquharson's skin was warm and moist. 'Last, but certainly not least,' he said and gazed meaningfully into Madeline's eyes.

Madeline suppressed a shudder. 'Thank you, my lord,' she said and practically wrenched her hand free from his.

Lord Farquharson smiled at her response and sat down.

Madeline turned to face the stage again and tried to ignore Cyril Farquharson's presence by her side. It was not an easy matter, especially as he leaned in close to enquire, 'Is the lemonade to your taste, Miss Langley?'

'It is delicious, thank you, my lord.' The brandy on his breath vied with the strange, heavy, spicy smell that hung about him. He was so close that she could feel heat emanating from his lithe frame.

'Delicious,' he said, and it seemed to Madeline that a slight hiss hung about the word as he touched her hand again in an overly familiar manner.

Madeline suddenly discovered that drinking lemonade was a rather tricky task and required both of her hands to be engaged in the process.

Thankfully the lights dimmed and the music set up again to announce the resumption of *Coriolanus*. Mr Kemble returned to the stage to uproarious applause and shouts from the pit.

'He's a splendid actor, is he not?' said Lord Farquharson in a silky tone to Mrs Langley. 'They say that Friday is to see his last performance.'

'Oh, indeed, Lord Farquharson. It will be such a loss. I've always been a staunch admirer of Mr Kemble's work.'

Madeline slid a glance in her mother's direction. Only that afternoon Mrs Langley had made her feelings regarding John Philip Kemble known, and admiration was not the underlying sentiment.

* * *

The second half of the play had not long started when Lord Farquharson proclaimed he was suffering with a cramp in his left leg and proceeded to manoeuvre his chair. 'It's a souvenir from Salamanca. I took a blade in the leg,' he said to Mrs Langley. 'I'm afraid it plays up a bit from time to time.' He grimaced, and then stretched out his leg so that it brushed against Madeline's skirts.

Quite how her mother failed to notice Lord Farquharson's blatant action, especially given that she was seated on her elder daughter's left-hand side, while his lordship was situated a few feet away on Madeline's right, Madeline did not know. She threw her mother a look of desperation.

Mrs Langley affected not to notice. 'Such bravery, Lord Farquharson.'

Lord Farquharson smiled and touched his foot against Madeline's slipper.

'Mama.' Madeline sought to catch her mother's eye.

'Yes, dear?' said Mrs Langley, never taking her eyes from the stage.

'Mama,' said Madeline a little more forcefully.

Lord Farquharson leered down at her, a knowing look upon his face. 'Is something wrong, Miss Langley?'

'I'm feeling a little unwell. It is, as you have already observed, a trifle hot in here.' She fanned herself with increasing vigour.

'My dear Miss Langley,' said Lord Farquharson, mock-concern dripping from every word as he attempted to squeeze her hand.

Madeline pulled back. 'A little air and I shall be fine.' She rose and made for the back of the box.

Mrs Langley could scarcely keep the look of utter exasperation from her face. 'Can you not wait a little? Angelina and I are enjoying the play. Oh dear, it really is too bad.'

Lord Farquharson saw opportunity loom before his eyes. 'It seems such a shame for all three of you charming ladies to miss the play, and just when Coriolanus is about to deliver his soliloquy.'

Mrs Langley made a show of sighing and shaking her head.

'I do not mind,' said Angelina. But no one heeded her words.

'What if…?' Lord Farquharson looked at Mrs Langley hopefully, and then tapped his fingers across his mouth. 'Perhaps it is an impertinence to even suggest.'

'No, no, my lord. You impertinent? Never. A more trustworthy, considerate gentleman I've yet to meet.'

Madeline's shoulders drooped. She had an awful suspicion of just what Lord Farquharson was about to suggest. 'Mama—'

'Madeline,' said Mrs Langley, 'it is rude to interrupt when his lordship is about to speak.'

'But, Mama—'

'Madeline!' her mother said a trifle too loudly, then had the audacity to peer accusingly at Madeline when a sea of nearby faces turned with curiosity.

So Madeline gave up trying and let Lord Farquharson ask what she knew he would.

'Dear Mrs Langley,' said his lordship, 'if I were to accompany Miss Langley out into the lobby, then both your good self and Miss Angelina could continue to watch the play uninterrupted. I give you my word that I shall guard Miss Langley with my very life.' He placed a hand dramatically over his heart, the diamond rings adorning his fingers glinting even in the little light that reached up from the stage. 'You know, of course, that I hold your daughter in great affection.' A slit of a smile stretched across his face.

'I would be happy to accompany Madeline,' said Angelina, and received a glare from her mother for her pains.

'And miss Mr Kemble's performance when it is unnecessary for you to do so?' said Lord Farquharson. 'For have I not already said that I will take care of Miss Langley?'

Mrs Langley clutched her gloved fingers together in maternal concern. 'I'm not sure… She is very precious to me,' said Mrs Langley.

'And rightly so,' said Lord Farquharson. 'She would make a man a worthy wife.'

Mrs Langley could not disguise the hope that blossomed on her face. 'Oh, indeed she would,' she agreed.

'Then I have your permission?' he coaxed, knowing full well what the answer would be.

'Very well,' said Mrs Langley.

Madeline looked from her mother to Lord Farquharson and back again. 'I would not wish to spoil his lordship's evening. Indeed, it would be most selfish of me to do so. I must insist that he stay to enjoy the rest of the play. I shall visit the retiring room for a little while and then return when I feel better.'

'Miss Langley, I cannot allow a young lady such as yourself to wander about the Theatre Royal unguarded. It is more than my honour will permit.' Lord Farquharson was at Madeline's side in an instant, his fingers pressed firm upon her arm.

She could feel the imprint of his hand through her sleeve. 'There really is no need,' she insisted and made to pull away.

'Madeline!' Her mother turned a steely eye upon her. 'I will *not* have you wandering about this theatre on your own. Whatever would your papa say? You will accept Lord Farquharson's polite offer to accompany you with gratitude.'

Mother and daughter locked gazes. It did not take long for Madeline to capitulate. She knew full well what would await her at home if she did not. She lowered her eyes and said in Lord Farquharson's direction, 'Thank you, my lord. You are most kind.'

'Come along, my dear.' Lord Farquharson steered her out of the theatre box and across the landing to the staircase, and all the while Madeline could feel his tight possessive grip around her arm.

Earl Tregellas's gaze drifted between Mr Kemble's dramatic delivery upon the stage and the goings-on in Lord Farquharson's box. He watched Farquharson with an attention that belied his relaxed manner and apparent interest in the progression of *Coriolanus,* just as he had watched and waited for the past years. Sooner or later Farquharson would slip, and when he did Lucien Tregellas would be waiting, ready to strike.

It was not the first time that Mrs Langley and her daughters had accompanied Lord Farquharson. He had taken them up in his carriage around Hyde Park, and also to the Frost Fair with its merry-go-rounds, swings, dancing and stalls. On the last occasion, at least Mr Langley had been present. Indeed, Mrs Langley seemed to be positively encouraging the scoundrel's interest in her daughters; more accurately, in one daughter, if Lucien was being honest. And not the pretty little miss with the golden ringlets framing her peaches-and-cream complexion, as might be expected. No. *She* had been seated safely away from Farquharson. It was the elder and plainer of the sisters that seemed to be dangled before him. Lord Tregellas momentarily pondered as to the reason behind Farquharson's interest. Surely the younger Miss Langley was more to his taste?

Tregellas restrained the urge to curl his upper lip with disgust. Who more than he knew exactly what Farquharson's taste stretched to? He saw Farquharson move his chair closer to the Langley chit. Too close. He watched the brief touch of his hand to her arm, her hand, even her shoulder. Miss Langley, the elder, sat rigidly in position, but he could tell by the slight aversion of her face from Farquharson that she did not welcome the man's attention. Mrs Langley's headpiece was a huge feathered concoction, and obviously hid Lord Farquharson's transgressions from the lady's sight, for she raised no comment upon the gentleman's behaviour.

Miss Langley's attention was focused in a most deliberate manner upon the stage. Tregellas's gaze dropped to take in the pale plain shawl wound around her shoulders that all but hid her dress, and the fact that she seemed not to wear the trinkets of jewellery favoured by other young women. She did not have her sister's dancing curls of gold. Indeed, her hair was scraped back harshly and hidden in a tightly pinned bun at the nape of her neck. Her head was naked, unadorned by ribbons or feathers or prettily arranged flowers. It struck Lucien that, unlike most women, Miss Langley preferred the safety of blending with the background in an unnoticeable sort of way.

Lord Tregellas watched as Miss Langley rose suddenly from her seat and edged away towards the back of the box. He was still watching when Lord Farquharson moved to accompany the girl. He saw Mrs Langley's feathers nod their encouragement. Farquharson and the girl disappeared. Silently Lucien Tregellas slipped from his seat and exited his own theatre box.

'Lord Farquharson, I feel so much better now. We should rejoin Mama and Angelina. I wouldn't want you to miss any more of the play.' Madeline could see that he was leading her in a direction far from the auditorium. A tremor of fear rippled down her spine.

Lord Farquharson's grip tightened until she could feel the press of his fingers hard against her forearm. 'How considerate you are of my feelings, Miss Langley,' he said, drawing his face into a smile. 'But there's no need. I know the play well. I'll relay the ending if you would like. Following his exile, Coriolanus offers his services to Aufidius, who then gives him command of half the Volscian army. Together they march against Rome, but Coriolanus is persuaded by his family to spare the city. Aufidius accuses him of treachery and the Volscian general's men murder Coriolanus. Aufidius is overcome with sorrow and determines that Coriolanus shall have a "noble memory". So, Miss Langley, now that you know the ending, there is nothing for which to rush back.'

Madeline felt a glimmer of panic as he steered her around a corner. A narrow corridor stretched ahead. 'Lord Farquharson.' She stopped dead in her tracks, or at least attempted to. 'I thank you for your synopsis, but I would rather see the play for myself. Please return me to my mother immediately, my lord.'

Lord Farquharson's smile stretched. 'Tut, tut, Miss Langley…' he bent his head to her ear '…or may I call you Madeline?'

'No, you may not,' snapped Madeline, pulling away from him with every ounce of her strength.

But for all that Lord Farquharson was a slimly built man, he was surprisingly strong and showed no sign of releasing her. Indeed, there seemed to be an excitement about him that had not been there before. He stretched an arm around her back and, when she was fully within his grasp, marched her along the length of the passageway. Not even his slight limp deterred their progress.

Madeline's heart had kicked to a frenzied thudding. Blood pounded at her temples. Her throat constricted, tight and dry. But still she resisted each dragging step. 'What are you doing? This is madness!'

His fingers bit harder. 'Have a care what you are saying, Madeline. And stop causing such a fuss. I only wish to speak to you in some privacy, that is all.'

'Come to Climington Street tomorrow. We can speak privately then.' If only she could buy some time, some space in which to evade him. Thoughts rushed through her head. Surely Mama would notice that they were gone too long and come to seek her? Wouldn't she? But Madeline knew deep in the pit of her stomach that her mother would do no such thing. The chance of marrying her offspring to an aristocrat, and a rich one at that, had driven the last vestige of common sense from her mother's head.

'Please, Lord Farquharson, release me, you're hurting me!' She saw him smile at her words and felt the bump of his hip against her as he dragged her onwards.

And then suddenly they stopped and he steered her into a small dimly lit alcove at the side.

'This shall do nicely,' he announced and pulled her round to face him, his fingers biting hard against her shoulders.

Madeline's breaths were short and fast. She struggled to control the panic that threatened to erupt. Sweat trickled down her back, dampening her shift, and her heart skittered fast and furious. She forced herself to some semblance of calm, and looked up at him. 'What do you want?'

'Why, you, of course, my dear.' Excitement had caused the hint of a flush in his cheeks that contrasted starkly with the smooth pale skin of the rest of his face. The suggestion of sweat beaded his brow and upper lip. His dark red hair had been swept dramatically back to best show the bones of his cheeks. It was a face that some thought handsome. Madeline did not. The skin around his eyes seemed tight and fragile, tinged with a shadow of the palest blue. It served only to emphasise the hard glitter of his smoky grey eyes. His gaze fixed firmly on her.

Madeline gritted her teeth hard to stop the tremble in her lips. 'You are a gentleman and a man of honour, Lord Farquharson.' His actions rendered this description far from the truth, but she hoped that the reminder would prompt him to abandon his scheme, whatever it may be. 'Surely you do not mean to compromise me?'

Farquharson's mouth twisted. His hands were rough against her shoulders. Nothing sounded. Not a hint of music or laughter or applause. No footsteps. No voices. Not even the closing of a door. He looked at her a moment longer, and she had the sensation that not only did he know precisely the extent of her fear, but that it pleased him.

Madeline's teeth clenched harder.

'As if I would do such a thing,' he said and lowered his face to scarcely an inch above hers.

Alcoholic breath enveloped her. Icy fingers of fear clawed at her until her limbs felt numb and useless. She looked up into his eyes, his hard, cold, glassy eyes, and saw in them her doom.

'Just one kiss, that's all I ask. One little kiss.' His gaze dropped to caress her lips.

Madeline struggled, thrusting all of her weight against him in an attempt to overbalance him.

'You cannot escape me, Madeline,' he said softly and lowered his lips slowly towards hers…

'Ah, there you are, Miss Langley,' a deep voice drawled.

Lord Farquharson practically catapulted her against the wall in his hurry to remove his hands from her. He spun to face the intruder with fists curled ready by his side. 'You!' he growled.

Madeline's eyes widened at the sight of her timely saviour. He was a tall gentleman with a smart appearance, long of limb and muscular of build. His hair was slightly dishevelled and black as a raven's wing, and he was dressed in black breeches with a neatly fitted and exquisitely cut tail-coat to match. The man was certainly no one of her acquaintance, although he seemed to be of a somewhat different opinion.

'I wondered where you had got to,' he said in the same lazy drawl and stepped closer to where Madeline and Lord Farquharson stood.

Madeline stared at him, unable to believe quite what was happening.

'I trust that Lord Farquharson has been behaving with the utmost decorum?'

His was a harsh face, angular and stark, a bold nose and square-edged jaw, and clear pale blue eyes that brushed over hers.

'He…' Madeline faltered. If she told this stranger the truth, her reputation would be well and truly ruined. No one would believe that he had dragged her down here against her will, in the middle of a performance of one of the season's most successful plays. Lord Farquharson was a rich man, an aristocrat. Madeline Langley was a nobody. Willing or not, she knew what people would say. She bit at her lip and dropped her gaze. 'I must return to my family. They'll be worried about me.' She hoped.

The stranger smiled, but the smile did not touch his eyes.

Casually he turned his face to Lord Farquharson. The Baron blanched. 'Lord Farquharson—' a chill entered his voice as he uttered the name '—will escort you back to your mother. Immediately.'

Lord Farquharson stared in sullen resentment, but said not one word.

'And I need not mention that he will, of course, be the perfect gentleman in doing so.'

It seemed to Madeline that there was some kind of unspoken battle of wills between the two men. Lord Farquharson was looking at the stranger as if he would gladly run him through with the sharpest of swords. The stranger, on the other hand, was smiling at Lord Farquharson, but it was a smile that would have cleaved a lesser man in two.

Lord Farquharson grudgingly took her arm. This time he seemed most disinclined to make contact with her sleeve, touching her as if she were a fragile piece of porcelain. 'Miss Langley,' he ground out from between gritted teeth, 'this way, if you please.' He then proceeded to lead her briskly back down the corridor, retracing the path along which he had dragged her not so many minutes before.

Although Madeline could not see him, she knew that the dark-haired stranger stalked their every step. His presence was her only protection from the fiend by her side. She wanted to shout her thanks to him. But she could not. She did not even dare to turn her head back. They moved in silence, their progress accompanied only by the muffled steps of their shoes upon the carpet. It was not until they reached the landing leading to Lord Farquharson's box that the man spoke again.

'I trust you'll enjoy what is left of the play, Miss Langley.' He executed a small bow in her direction before turning his attention once more to Farquharson. 'Lord Farquharson,' he said, 'perhaps you have not noticed quite how clear and un-impeded the view is from these boxes.' He looked meaning-fully at Lord Farquharson and waited for them to step through the curtain that led into the Baron's box.

'There the two of you are,' said her mother. 'I hope that a little turn with Lord Farquharson has you feeling better, my dear.' Mrs Langley did not notice that her daughter failed to answer.

Angelina eyed her sister with concern.

Madeline sat down in the chair, taking care to make herself as narrow as possible lest Lord Farquharson's hands or feet should happen to stray in her direction. But he made no move to speak to her, let alone touch her. The air was still ripe with the spicy smell of him. She stared down at the stage, seeing nothing of Mr Kemble's performance, hearing nothing of that actor's fine and resonant voice. Her mind was filled with the image of a dark-haired man and how he had arrived from nowhere at the very hour of her most desperate need: a tall, dark defender.

She could not allow herself to think of what would have happened had the stranger not appeared. Whatever her mother thought, Lord Farquharson was no gentleman, and Madeline meant to speak the truth of him in full as soon as they were home. But who was he, the dark-haired stranger? Certainly his was a face she would not forget. Classically handsome. Striking. Forged in her mind for ever. A shiver rippled down her spine. Something, she would never know what, made her glance across to the boxes on the opposite side of the theatre. There, in one of the best boxes in the house, was her dark defender, looking right back at her. He inclined his head by the smallest degree in acknowledgement. Madeline's breath caught in her throat and a tingling crept up her neck to spread across her scalp. Before anyone could notice, she averted her gaze. But, try as she might, she could not rid herself of the foolish notion that her life had just changed for ever.

'What on earth did you think you were doing?' said Mrs Langley to her elder daughter. 'Trying your hardest to undo all of my good work!'

'Mama, he is not the man you think,' replied Madeline with asperity.

'Never was a mother so tried and tested by a daughter.'

Madeline controlled her temper and spoke as quietly and as calmly as she could manage. 'I'm trying to tell you that Lord Farquharson came close to compromising me at the theatre tonight. He is no gentleman, no matter what he would have you believe.'

'What on earth do you mean, child?' Mrs Langley clutched dramatically at her chest.

'He tried to kiss me tonight, Mama.'

'Kiss you? Kiss you?' Mrs Langley almost choked. 'Lord Farquharson tried to kiss you?' Her cheeks grew suddenly flushed.

'Yes, indeed, Mama,' replied Madeline with a sense of relief that her mother would at last understand the truth about Lord Farquharson.

'Lord, oh Lord!' exclaimed her mother. 'Are you certain, Madeline?'

'Yes, Mama.'

Mrs Langley stood closer to Madeline. 'Why did you not speak of this before?'

'He frightens me. I tried to tell you that I disliked him.'

Her mother stared at her. 'Dislike? What has "dislike" to do with it? Now, my dear…' she took Madeline's hand in her own '…you must tell me the whole of it.'

Madeline detected excitement in her mother's voice. 'I've told you what happened. He tried to kiss me.'

'Yes, yes, Madeline, so you say,' said Mrs Langley with undisguised impatience. 'But did he do so? Did Lord Farquharson kiss you?'

Madeline bit at her lip. 'Well, not exactly.'

'Not exactly!' echoed her mother. 'Either he kissed you or he did not. Now, what is it to be?'

'He did not.'

Mrs Langley pursed her lips and squeezed Madeline's hand. 'Think very carefully, Madeline. Are you sure?'

'Yes.'

Mrs Langley gave what could almost have been a sigh of disappointment. 'Then, what stopped him?'

Madeline found herself strangely reticent to reveal the dark-haired stranger's part in the affair. It seemed somehow traitorous to speak of him. And her mother was sure to misunderstand the whole episode. Surely there was nothing so very wrong with a little white lie? 'He…he changed his mind.'

'Gentlemen do not just change their minds over such matters, Madeline. If he did not kiss you, it's likely that he never intended to do so.'

'Mama, he most certainly meant to kiss me,' insisted Madeline.

A speculative gleam returned to Mrs Langley's eye. 'Did he, indeed?' she said. 'You do understand, of course, that were his lordship to compromise you in any such way then, as a man of honour, he would be obliged to offer for you.'

'Mama! How could you even think such a thing?'

'Come now, Madeline,' her mother cajoled. 'He is a baron and worth ten thousand a year.'

'I would not care if he were the King himself!' Madeline drew herself up, anger and outrage welling in her breast.

Mrs Langley sucked in her cheeks and affected an expression of mortification. 'Please afford me some little measure of respect. I'm only your mother, after all, trying my best to catch a good husband for a troublesome daughter who refuses the best of her mother's advice.'

Madeline knew what was coming next. She had heard its like a thousand times. It was pointless to interrupt. She allowed her mother to continue her diatribe.

'You care nothing for your poor mama's nerves or the shame of her having a stubborn plain daughter upon her hands for evermore.' Fortunately a sofa was close enough for Mrs Langley to collapse on to. 'Whatever will your papa say when we are left with you as an old spinster?' She dabbed a tiny piece of lacy material to the corner of her eye. 'I've tried so hard, but it seems that my best just is not good enough.' Her voice cracked with heavy emotion.

'Mama…' Madeline moved to kneel at her mother's side. 'You know that isn't true.'

'And now she has taken against Lord Farquharson, with whom I have tried so hard to secure her interest.' Her mother gave a sob.

'Forgive me,' said Madeline almost wearily. 'I do not mean to disappoint you. I know you wish to make a good match for me.'

Mrs Langley sniffed into her handkerchief before stroking a hand over Madeline's head. 'Not only a good match, but the best. Can't you see, Madeline, that I only want what's best for you, so that I can rest easy in my old age, knowing that you're happy.'

'I know, Mama. I'm sorry.'

Her mother's hand moved in soothing reassuring strokes. 'It is not your fault that you have the looks of the Langleys and are not half so handsome as Angelina.' The stroking intensified.

Madeline knew full well what a disappointment she was to her mother. She also knew that it was unlikely she would ever fulfil her mother's ambition of making a favourable marriage match.

'That is why I have sought to encourage Lord Farquharson.'

Madeline stiffened.

Mrs Langley felt the subtle change beneath her fingers. 'Oh, don't be like that, Madeline.' She removed her hand from Madeline's hair. 'He's a baron. He has a fine house here in London and a country seat in Kent. Were you to marry him, you would want for nothing. He would take care of your every need.'

Madeline looked with growing disbelief at her mother.

'My daughter would be Lady Farquharson. *Lady* Farquharson! Imagine the faces of my sewing group's ladies if I could tell them that. No more embarrassment. No more making excuses for you.'

'Mama,' said Madeline, 'it is not marriage that Lord Farquharson has in mind for me.'

Mrs Langley laughed. 'Tush! Don't be so silly, girl. If we but handle him properly, I'm sure that we can catch him for you.'

Madeline placed her hands over her mother's. 'Mama, I do not wish to catch him,' she said as gently as she could.

Amelia Langley's eyes widened in exasperation. She

snatched her hands from beneath her daughter's and narrowed her lips. 'But you'll have him all the same. Such stuff and nonsense as I've ever heard. Madeline Langley turning her nose up at a baron! I'll bring Lord Farquharson to make you an offer if it's the last thing I do, so help me God. And you, miss, will do as you are told for once in your life!'

Chapter Two

The ballroom was ablaze with candlelight from three massive crystal-dropped chandeliers and innumerable wall sconces. The wooden floorboards had been scraped and polished until they gleamed, and the tables and chairs set around the periphery of the room were in the austere neo-classical style of Mr Sheraton. The hostess, Lady Gilmour, was holding court in a corner close to the band and its delightful music. Despite the heat, the French doors and windows that lined the south side of the room remained closed. It was, after all, still only February and the year had been uncommonly cold. Indeed, frost was thick upon the ground and the night air held an icy chill. With the Season not yet started, London was still quiet, but Lady Gilmour had managed to gather the best of London's present high society into her townhouse. Everybody who was anybody was there, squashed into the noisy bustle of the ballroom, and spilling out into the hallway and up the sweep of the staircase.

Mrs Langley was in her element as Lord Farquharson had managed to obtain an invitation for her entire family. She was making the most of the evening and taking every opportunity to inveigle as many introductions as possible. Mr Langley, having found an old friend, had slipped discreetly away, leaving his wife to her best devices.

'Lady Gilmour,' gushed Mrs Langley, 'how delightful to meet you. May I introduce my younger daughter, Angelina? This is her first Season and we have such high hopes for her. And this is my elder daughter, Madeline. She is such a dear girl,' said Mrs Langley. 'She has engaged the interest of a certain highly regarded gentleman. I cannot say more at the minute other than…' Mrs Langley leaned towards Lady Gilmour in a conspiratorial fashion and lowered her voice to a stage whisper '…we are expectant of receiving an offer in the very near future.'

Madeline, who had been smiling politely at Lady Gilmour, cringed and turned a fiery shade of red. 'Mama—'

'Tush, child. I'm sure that Lady Gilmour can be trusted with our little secret.' Mrs Langley trod indelicately on Madeline's slipper. Her smile could not have grown any larger when Lady Gilmour offered to introduce Angelina to a small group of other débutantes. Looking fresh and pretty in a ribboned white creation that had cost her poor papa a considerable sum he could not afford, Angelina followed in Lady Gilmour's wake.

'Keep up, Madeline,' whispered Mrs Langley as Madeline trailed at the rear. 'What a perfect opportunity for Angelina.'

Less than fifteen minutes later, Angelina's dance card for the evening was filled. A crowd of eager gentlemen stood ready to sweep the divine Miss Angelina off her feet. Mrs Langley's head swam dizzy with excitement, so much so that she clear forgot all about her plans for Madeline and Lord Farquharson. 'Oh, I do wish your father was here to see this. Where is Mr Langley?'

'He's talking to Mr Scott,' answered Madeline, happy that her father had managed to escape.

'Typical!' snorted Mrs Langley. 'Angelina is proving to be a success beyond our wildest dreams and her father's too busy with his own interests to even notice.' Mrs Langley shook her head sadly, but her spirits could not remain depressed for long, especially when Angelina took to the floor with Lord Richardson, who was the second son of an earl. 'La, is she not the most beautiful child on the floor?' demanded Mrs Langley, clutching at Madeline's hand.

'Yes, Mama,' agreed Madeline with a soft smile. 'She is indeed beautiful.'

'And elegant,' added Mrs Langley.

'Elegant, too,' said Madeline.

'And graceful.'

'Yes.'

Mrs Langley looked fit to burst with pride. 'That's my baby out there, my beautiful baby. Oh, how it brings it all back. I was just the same when I was eighteen.'

Mrs Langley and Madeline were so taken up with Angelina's progress around the dance floor that they did not notice the arrival of Lord Farquharson.

'Mrs Langley, Miss Langley,' he said, lingering a little too long over Madeline's hand. 'I hope I'm not too late to claim a few dances from the delightful Miss Langley.'

Madeline's lips tightened. 'I'm afraid I'm not dancing tonight, my lord. I twisted my ankle earlier in the day.'

Mrs Langley drew her a scowl before announcing, 'I'm sure that your ankle is much repaired, Madeline. And a dance with Lord Farquharson shall not tax you too much.'

'But—' started Madeline.

'Madeline.' Her mother threw her the 'wait until I get you home' look.

Grudgingly Madeline held the card out to Lord Farquharson, who smiled and tutted and lingered over the empty spaces beside each dance name.

'Can it be that Miss Langley has kept her dance card free for my sake? Is it too much for my heart to hope?'

Mrs Langley cooed her appreciation of the sugary compliment.

Madeline examined a scuff on the floor and waited until he pressed the card back into her hand. It was now warm and slightly damp to the touch. She held it gingerly by the edge and scanned to see which dances he had selected. A lively Scotch reel and, heaven help her, the waltz!

Lord Farquharson's slim white fingers took hold of one of her hands. 'Just in the nick of time,' he said as the band struck up. 'I believe this is my dance, Miss Langley.' And with that he whisked her out to join the lines of bodies upon the floor.

The dance had a nightmarish quality about it. Not only was Madeline thrust into the limelight, a place in which she was never happy, but she had Lord Farquharson squeezing her hand, whispering in her ear and peering down the bodice of her dress for the entirety of the time. She was perforce obliged to smile politely and skip daintily about, as if she were enjoying the occasion immensely. It seemed to Madeline that a piece of music had never lasted so long. She progressed down the set, birling in the arms of every man in turn, each one granting her but a brief respite from Farquharson's company, for no sooner had she thought it than the dance had led her to meet in the middle of the set with Lord Farquharson once more. At long last the music ceased, and Lord Farquharson returned her to her mother. His eyes glittered with something that Madeline did not understand.

'She has the grace of a swan,' he said to Mrs Langley.

Mrs Langley, who had seen Madeline tread on Lord Farquharson's toes no less than four times, miss several steps, and drop her handkerchief halfway through, marvelled that a gentleman could be so forgiving of her elder daughter's failings. 'Dear Lord Farquharson, you are so kind to Madeline.'

They smiled at one another.

Madeline looked away and counted to ten—slowly.

Mrs Langley raved about Angelina's growing posse of admirers. Was the young man with blond hair merely a baronet? Angelina could do so much better. Let them move here to better see Angelina's progress around the floor. And they simply must gain an introduction to a patroness of Almack's. Mrs Langley could not survive without securing tickets for one of the assembly room's famous balls. It would be quite the best place to catch a husband for Angelina. And so the time passed. Madeline did not mind. She preferred her place in the background, quietly observing what was going on around her. Nodding her head and smiling politely, but never really engaging. At least there was no Lord Farquharson forcing his attention upon her. Even so, he managed to catch her eye across the room on several occasions as if to remind her of what lay ahead: the waltz. Madeline's throat grew dry and tight at the very thought. She could see him watching her through the crowd, licking his lips, smiling that smile that made her blood run cold.

Quite suddenly Madeline knew that she could not do it; she could not let him rest his hands upon her and draw her close, pretending to be the perfect gentleman when all along he was just biding his time, waiting for an opportunity to strike. And strike he would, like the snake in the grass that he was. She shuddered. No matter what Mama thought, Lord Farquharson was not honourable. He would ruin her and there would be no offer of marriage. He did not want her as a wife any more than Madeline wanted him as a husband. What his lordship wanted was something quite different. Madeline drew a deep breath and determined that, come hell or high water, she would keep herself safe from Lord Farquharson's attentions. Mrs Langley scarcely noticed when Madeline whispered that she was going to find her papa.

Mr Langley was not anywhere in the grand ballroom. Nor could he be found in the magnificence of Lady Gilmour's entrance hall. Madeline followed the stairs up, searching through the crowd for a sight of her father. It seemed he was not there either. She spent a little time within the ladies' retiring room, just because she was passing that way, and enquired of several ladies within if they had seen a gentleman by the name of Mr Langley. But the ladies looked at her as if she had just come up from the country and said that they knew no Mr Langley. So that was that.

She left and was about to make her way back downstairs when a hand closed tight around her wrist and pulled her to the side.

'Miss Langley, what a pleasant surprise to find you up here.' Lord Farquharson pressed his mouth to the back of her hand. 'But then perhaps you were looking for me.' He stepped closer and did not release his grip on her wrist.

Madeline knew that the people surrounding them afforded her protection from the worst of Lord Farquharson's intent. But she also knew that she could not risk drawing attention to herself or her situation lest they think the worst. 'No,' she said, and tried surreptitiously to disengage herself.

But Lord Farquharson had a grip like an iron vice, and tightened it accordingly. 'Tut, tut, why don't I believe you?' he laughed.

'I'm looking for my papa. Have you seen him?' Madeline hoped that Lord Farquharson did not know just how much he frightened her.

The sly grey eyes watched her. 'I do believe that I saw him not two minutes since, Miss Langley. But it was in the strangest of places.' Lord Farquharson's face frowned with perplexity.

In the strangest of places. Yes, that sounded most like where Madeline's papa would be found. Papa hated large social occasions and would frequently wander off to hide in the most obscure of locations. 'Where did you see him, my lord?'

Lord Farquharson's grip loosened a little. 'On the servants' stairwell at the other side of that door.' He gestured to an unobtrusive doorway at the other end of the landing. 'He seemed to be wandering upstairs, although I cannot imagine why he should be heading in such a direction.'

Madeline could. Anywhere away from the hubbub of activity. Papa would not notice more than that. 'Thank you, Lord Farquharson.' She looked pointedly at where he still held her.

'You've not forgotten my waltz?'

How could she? 'No, my lord, I've not forgotten.'

'Good,' he said, and released her.

Lord Farquharson fluttered a few fingers in her direction, then turned and walked briskly down the main staircase.

Madeline waited until she could see that he had gone before heading towards the servants' stairwell.

'Papa?' she called softly as she wound her way up the narrow staircase. The stone stairs felt cold through her slippers. 'Papa?' she said again, but only silence sounded. The walls on either side had not been whitewashed in some time and, as there was no banister, bore the marks of numerous hands throughout the years. A draught wafted around her ankles and the band's music dimmed to a faint lilt in the background.

The stairwell delivered her to the rear of the upper floor. She stepped out, scanning the empty landing. Several portraits of Lord Gilmour's horses peered down at her from the walls. Where could Papa be? A number of doors opened off the landing, to bedchambers, or so Madeline supposed. She stopped outside the first, listening for any noise that might indicate her father's presence. Nothing. Her knuckles raised and knocked softly against the oaken structure.

'Papa,' she whispered, 'are you in there?'

Madeline waited. No reply came. The handle turned easily beneath her fingers. Slowly she pushed the door open and peeked inside. It was a bedchamber, decorated almost exclusively in blue and white. A large four-poster bed stood immediately opposite the door. Mr Langley was clearly not there. Madeline silently retreated, pulling the door to close behind her. Quite suddenly the door was wrenched from her grasp, and Madeline found herself pulled unceremoniously back into the bedchamber. The door clicked shut behind her. Madeline looked up into the eyes of Lord Farquharson.

'My dear Madeline, we meet again,' he said.

Madeline kicked out at him and grabbed for the door handle. But Lord Farquharson was too quick. He embraced her in a bear hug, lifting her clear of the door.

'Now, now, Madeline, why are you always in such a hurry to get away?'

'You tricked me!' she exclaimed. 'You never even saw my father, did you?' How could she have been so stupid?

Lord Farquharson's shoulders shrugged beneath the

chocolate brown superfine of his coat. 'You've found me out,' he said and pulled her closer.

She could feel the hardness of his stomach, and something else, too, pressing against her. 'Release me!'

'The Earl won't save you this time, my dear. He's not even here. I checked.'

Madeline refused to be bated. Speaking to him, pleading with him, would be useless. Cyril Farquharson would not listen to reason. She willed herself to stay calm, forced herself to look up into his eyes, to relax into his arms.

Lord Farquharson's eyes widened momentarily, and then he stretched a grin across his face. 'I think we begin to understand one another at last.'

Madeline sincerely doubted that.

Lord Farquharson's grip lessened. 'Madeline,' he breathed, 'you are such a fearful little thing.' The intent in his gaze was so transparent that even Madeline, innocent as she was, could not mistake it. 'I will not hurt you.' His fingers scraped hard down the length of her arm.

Apprehension tightened in her belly. 'But you are doing so already, my lord,' she said, drawing back her leg and delivering her knee to Lord Farquharson's groin with as much force as she could muster. She did not wait to see the effect upon Lord Farquharson, just spun on her foot and ran as fast as she could, banging the door shut behind her. Across the landing, down the stairwell, running and running like she had never run before. The breath tore at her throat and rasped in her ears. Her feet touched only briefly against each stair. And still she ran on, pulling her skirts higher to prevent them catching around her legs. Anything to flee that monster. She rounded the corner, dared a glance back, and then slammed hard into something large and firm. A gasp escaped her. She stumbled forward, her feet teetering on the edge of the stair, arms flailing, reaching for some anchor to save her fall.

A pair of strong arms enveloped her, catching her up, pulling her to safety. Please God, no. How could Lord Farquharson be here so quickly? She had been so sure that he was behind her; even thought she'd heard the pounding of his feet upon the stairs. But it was only the sound of her own blood pounding in her ears. 'No!' She struggled within his arms, reaching to find some purchase against the smooth surface of the walls.

'Miss Langley?' The deep voice resonated with concern.

Madeline ceased her fight. She recognised that voice. Indeed, she would have known it anywhere. She looked up into a pair of pale blue eyes. It seemed that her heart skidded to a stop, before thundering off again at full tilt. For the arms wrapped around her belonged to none other than her dark defender. She glanced nervously behind, fearful that Lord Farquharson would creep upon them.

Her defender raised one dark eyebrow. 'I take it Farquharson is behind this—again?'

Madeline nodded nervously. 'He…' Her voice was hoarse and low. She cleared her throat and tried again. 'He's upstairs in one of the bedchambers.' Only when she said it did she realise exactly how that must sound.

His eyes narrowed and darkened. She felt the press of his hands against her skin. 'Farquharson.' The word slipped from his throat, guttural and harsh in the silence surrounding them. He set her back upon the stair and brushed past her. Anger radiated from his every pore. He began to climb quickly and quietly up the narrow stairwell.

'No!' shouted Madeline, twisting to follow him. Her feet thudded after his. 'No,' she shouted again. 'It's not what you think. He didn't—' She reached ahead, grabbed for the tails of his coat disappearing round the next bend and tugged. 'Wait!'

The man stopped suddenly and looked back down at her.

She released her grip on his coat and leaned back, panting against the wall.

'What do you mean, Miss Langley?'

'He tried to kiss me,' she said, still catching her breath. 'But I managed to get away before he could succeed.'

She could see the tension in the muscles of his neck and around the stiff set of his jaw. His eyes were sheer ice. 'Did you learn nothing from the last time? What the hell were you doing alone in a bedchamber with Farquharson?'

Madeline's mouth gaped in shock. 'He tricked me. I didn't know he would be there. I was looking for my father.'

'And your father is likely to be hiding in one of Lady Gilmour's guest bedchambers?' He raised a cynical eyebrow.

'It is not unlikely,' she said quietly.

Long fingers raked his hair, ruffling it worse than ever. 'Miss Langley, if you are too foolish to know it already, I will tell you in no uncertain terms. Lord Farquharson is a dangerous man. You would be wise to steer well clear of him.'

'That's what I'm trying to do, but my mother wishes to promote a match between Lord Farquharson and myself. She's determined to encourage his interest.'

'Is your mother insane?'

Madeline's lip began to tremble. She clamped it down with a firm nip of her teeth. It was one thing to know she would be left upon the shelf, and quite another to have so handsome a gentleman imply the same bluntly to her face.

'I mean no insult, but believe me, Miss Langley, when I say that Lord Farquharson has no interest in marriage.'

Lord, he thought she was hopeful of such a thing! 'And I

have no interest in Lord Farquharson,' she said curtly. She
turned away and started to retrace her steps back down the
stairwell, then hesitated and faced him once more. 'Thank you,
Mr....'

He made no effort to introduce himself.

'Both for tonight and last week. I'm indebted to you for
your intervention.'

Those pale eyes watched her a moment longer before he
said, 'Don't thank me, Miss Langley, just stay away from Farquharson.'

She chewed at her bottom lip, wondering whether to tell
him. He would think the worst of her if she did not, and
somehow the stranger's opinion mattered very much to
Madeline. 'Sir,' she said shyly.

'Miss Langley,' he replied and crooked his eyebrow.

The lip received several nasty nips from her teeth. She
looked at him, and then looked at him some more.

'Was there something you wished to tell me, Miss Langley?'

Madeline twisted her hands together. 'It's…just that Lord
Farquharson has claimed me for the waltz. Perhaps he will
not recover in time, but—'

'Recover?' her defender enquired. 'What in Hades did you
do to him?'

'My father showed me how to disable a man by using my
knee, should the occasion ever arise.'

His mouth gave only the smallest suggestion of a smile.
'And the occasion arose.'

'Yes,' she said simply.

They looked at one another.

'Find whatever excuse you must, Miss Langley, but do not
waltz with Farquharson.'

Madeline seriously doubted that the Prince Regent himself

could come up with an excuse acceptable to her mother. But there was always the chance, after the incident in the bedchamber, that Lord Farquharson would have changed his mind over dancing with her. 'I'll try,' she said. And she was gone, her feet padding softly down the cold stone stairs that would lead her back to the ballroom.

'There you are, Madeline. Where is your papa? Did you not tell him of Angelina's success?' Mrs Langley was all of a flutter.

Madeline opened her mouth to reply.

'Never mind that now. You've missed so much. You will not believe what has just happened.' She clapped her hands together in glee. 'Mr Lawrence was taken quite ill, something to do with what he ate at his club earlier in the day.'

'Poor Mr Lawrence,' said Madeline, wondering why Mr Lawrence's malady so pleased her mother.

'Yes, yes,' said Mrs Langley. 'It meant that he could not dance with Angelina as he promised.' Her excitement bubbled over in a giggle.

'Mama, are you feeling quite well?'

Mrs Langley touched a hand to her daughter's arm. 'You'll never guess what happened.'

Madeline waited expectantly.

'The Duke of Devonshire stepped in to take his place and danced with Angelina!' She clasped her hand to her mouth. 'Isn't it just too, too good?'

Madeline glanced across the dance floor to see a rather dashing-looking young man with twinkling blue eyes and warm sand-coloured hair twirl her sister through the steps of a country dance. Angelina was glancing up at the man through long lashes, her golden curls bouncing against the pretty flush of her cheeks. 'Yes, it is wonderful.'

'Wonderful indeed!' Mrs Langley breathed.

Madeline cleared her throat. 'Mama, my head hurts quite dreadfully.'

'Mmm,' mused Mrs Langley, barely taking her eyes from Angelina's dancing form. 'You do look rather pale.'

'I wondered whether Papa might take me home in the carriage. I'm sure that he wouldn't mind.'

'I tell you of Angelina's success and in the next breath you're asking to go home.'

'Mama, it isn't like that. Lord Farquharson—'

'Lord Farquharson!' interrupted her mother. 'I begin to see how this is going. Your papa may not realise what you're up to, but I most certainly do!' Mrs Langley turned on Madeline, her mouth stretched to a false smile in case anyone should think that Mrs Langley and her daughter were having anything but the most pleasant of chats. 'You are so determined to refuse a dance with Lord Farquharson that you will destroy the evening for us all. You think to thumb your nose at a baron and care not a jot if you ruin your sister's chances.'

'No, Mama, you and Angelina will stay here, nothing would be ruined for her.'

'Are you so wrapped up in your own interest that you cannot see Angelina has the chance to catch a duke? That child out there,' said her mother, 'has only kindness in her heart.' Mrs Langley glanced fleetingly at her younger daughter upon the dance floor. 'Not one word has she uttered about Lord Farquharson's preference for you. Not one!'

'Little wonder! She is relieved that she does not have him clutching for her hand.' As soon as the words were out Madeline knew she should not have said them. Oh, Lord. She shut her eyes and readied herself for her mother's response.

Mrs Langley's eyes widened. The false smile could no longer be sustained and slipped from her face. 'Madeline Langley, you go too far. Your papa shall hear of this, indeed he shall. All these years I've slaved to make a lady of you, so that you might make a decent marriage. And now, when I'm on the brink of bringing all my hard work to success, you threaten to ruin all, and not only for yourself.'

Madeline counted to ten.

'Pray do not look at me in that superior way as if I know not of what I speak!' Mrs Langley's small lace handkerchief appeared.

Madeline continued to fifteen.

'You have not the slightest compassion for your poor mama's nerves. And all the while Mr Langley makes your excuses. Well, not any more.'

And twenty.

'You are not going home,' Mrs Langley announced. 'You will sit there and look as if you are having a nice time, headache or not. When the time comes, you will dance with Lord Farquharson and you will smile at him, and answer him politely. Do I make myself clear?'

'Mama, there's something I must tell you of Lord Farquharson,' said Madeline.

Her mother adopted her most stubborn expression. 'I know all I need to know of that gentleman, Madeline. You will waltz with him just the same.'

Madeline looked at her mother in silence.

'Mama. Madeline.' Angelina appeared at her mother's shoulder. As if sensing the atmosphere, she glanced from her mother's flushed face to her sister's pale one. 'Is something wrong?'

'No, nothing is wrong, my angel,' replied Mrs Langley

with a forced smile. 'Madeline was just saying how much she was looking forward to dancing this evening.'

Angelina coiled an errant curl around her ear. 'Oh,' she said, 'I came to war— I came to tell Madeline that Lord Farquharson is over there looking for her.'

'How fortuitous,' said Mrs Langley.

Fortuitous was not the word Madeline would have chosen. She turned her head in the direction Angelina had indicated.

Lord Farquharson raised his glass to her in salutation. Even across the distance Madeline could see the promise upon his face.

'What is it, Lucien? First you insist on uprooting me from a very cosy hand of cards at White's, then you trail me here after Farquharson, and now you've got a face like thunder on you.' Guy, Viscount Varington, regarded his brother across a glass of champagne.

'Farquharson's up to his old tricks again.' Lucien rotated the elegant glass stem between his fingers. The champagne inside remained untouched.

'You cannot forever be dogging his steps. Five years is a long time. Perhaps it's time to leave the past behind and move forward.'

Lucien Tregellas's fingers tightened against the delicate stem. 'Move on and forget what he did?' he said bitterly. 'Surely you jest?'

Guy looked into his brother's eyes, eyes that were a mirror image of his own. He smiled a small, rueful smile.

'Farquharson has not changed. He's been a regular visitor to a certain establishment in Berwick Street these years past, slaking his needs, and you know for what manner of taste Madame Fouet's house caters. I could do nothing about that.

Even so, I always knew that it would not be enough for him. He wants another woman of gentle breeding, another innocent. And I'll kill Farquharson rather than let that happen.' There was a stillness about Lucien's face, a quietness in his voice, that lent his words a chilling certainty.

'You think he will try again, even with you waiting in the wings?'

'I know he will,' came the grim reply. 'He's planning it even as we speak, and that foolish chit over there is practically falling over herself to be his next victim.'

Guy followed his brother's gaze across the room to the slender figure of the girl seated by the side of an older woman.

'Miss Langley thinks to catch herself a baron. Or, more precisely, her mama does. Miss Langley herself appears to be strangely resistant to any advice to the contrary that I might offer.' A scowl twitched between his brows.

'Then leave her to it,' said Guy with a shrug of his shoulders. 'If the girl refuses to be warned off, then perhaps she deserves Farquharson.'

Lucien's gaze still had not shifted from Miss Langley, his eyes taking in her downcast face, her rigid posture. 'No woman deserves that fate.'

A wry little laugh sounded, and Guy drained the remainder of the champagne from his glass. 'What would London say if they knew that the notorious Earl Tregellas, the man of whom they are all so very afraid, is on a mission to safeguard every virgin in this city from Farquharson's roving eye? There's a certain irony in that, wouldn't you say?'

'There's no comparison between me and Farquharson,' Lucien said. The fragile glass snapped between his fingers. He set the broken pieces down on the tray of a passing footman.

'Calm down, big brother. I loath what Farquharson is as much as you.'

'No. I assure you, you do not.'

'Your feelings are understandable, given what happened,' said Guy quietly.

A muscle twitched in Lucien's jaw.

'What about the girl? Is she really in danger?' Guy glanced again at Miss Langley.

'She's in much more danger than she could ever realise,' replied his brother, looking him directly in the eye.

Earl Tregellas and Viscount Varington, two of society's most infamous bachelors, albeit for vastly differing reasons, turned their gaze upon the slight and unassuming figure of Miss Madeline Langley.

Chapter Three

Madeline glanced uneasily around. It was almost time. She knew he would come for her; her actions of earlier that evening would not stop him. The stranger had been right to tell her to make her excuses, but he had never dealt with her mother. It was bad enough having to suffer Lord Farquharson's assaults without having her own mother encourage the situation in the hope of forcing him to a wedding. Madeline shuddered at the thought.

She sneaked a glance at her mother. Mrs Langley was engrossed in chattering to Mrs Wilson. Madeline's eyes raked the ballroom. Still no sign of Papa. Over at the far side, partly hidden by some Grecian-styled columns and lounging beside another man, was her dark defender, Their gazes locked. Her heart kicked to a canter. She felt the blush rise in her cheeks and looked hastily away. What would he think of her sitting waiting for Lord Farquharson to come and claim her for the waltz? And he was right! But what else could she do with Mama guarding her so well? A visit to the retiring room had been refused. And at the suggestion that she go home with

Miss Ridgely her mama had warranted a warning glare. Even now Mama's hand rested lightly against her arm. Madeline dared not look at the stranger again, even when she saw Lord Farquharson begin to make his way slowly, steadily, towards her. Every step brought him closer.

Madeline felt the coldness spreading throughout. Her mouth grew suddenly dry and her palms somewhat clammy. She bowed her head, coaxing her courage. *I can do this. I can do this,* she inwardly chanted the mantra again and again. *It is in full view of everyone. What can he do to me here, save dance?* But just the anticipation of being held in his grip, within his power, brought a nausea to her throat. She steeled herself against it. Willed herself to defy him. *Don't let him see that you're afraid.* She steadied her breath, curled her fingers to fists. The spot on the floor disappeared, replaced instead by a pair of large, black-leather buckle slippers. Madeline swallowed once. The shoes were connected to a pair of stockinged shins. The shins led up to a pair of fine black knee breeches. The breeches stretched tight to reveal every detail of well-muscled and long thighs. Madeline's eyes leapt up to his face.

'I believe this is my dance, Miss Langley,' her dark defender said smoothly and, without waiting, plucked Madeline straight from her chair on to the floor.

Lord Farquharson came to an abrupt halt halfway across the ballroom, and stared in disbelief.

Mrs Langley's mouth opened to squawk her protest, and then shut again. She could only sit and stare while her eldest daughter was whisked into the middle of the dance floor.

'Well, really!' exclaimed Mrs Wilson by her side. 'You do know who that is?'

'Indeed,' replied Mrs Langley weakly. 'That is Earl Tregellas.'

'The Wicked Earl,' said her friend with a disapproving frown. 'What an earth is he doing, dancing with Madeline?'

For once in her life Mrs Langley appeared to be lost for words.

The dark-haired stranger held her with a firm gentleness. The light pressure of his hand upon her waist seemed to burn straight through the material of her dress and undergarments, to sear against her skin. The fingers of his other hand enclosed around hers in warm protection. Beneath the superfine material of his coat she could feel the strength of his muscles across the breadth of his shoulders. The square-cut double-breasted tail-coat was of the finest midnight black to match the ruffled feathers of his hair. He looked as if he had just stepped out of the most elegant tailor's establishment in all England. A white-worked waistcoat adorned a pristine white shirt, the collar of which stood high. The white neckcloth looked to be a work of art. Madeline felt suddenly conscious of her cheap dress with its plain cream-coloured material and short puffed sleeves. As usual she had declined to wear the wealth of ribbons and bows set out by Mama. Neither a string of beads nor even a simple ribbon sat around her neck. The square-shaped neckline of her dress was not low; even so, in contrast with the other ladies, she had insisted upon wearing a pale pink fichu lest any skin might be exposed.

'Miss Langley, you seem disinclined to follow my advice.'

The richness of his voice drifted down to her. She kept her focus fixed firmly on the lapel of his coat. What else was he to think? Hadn't she known that it would be so? 'I could not leave,' she said. It sounded pathetic even to her own ears.

'Could not, or would not? Perhaps you are in concordance with your mother's plans to catch yourself a baron after all.'

'No!' Her gaze snapped up to his. His eyes were watching with a dispassion that piqued her. 'No,' she said again. 'It isn't like that at all.'

He raised a dark eyebrow as if in contradiction. 'Perhaps you even welcome Lord Farquharson's attentions.' His gaze meandered down over her body, lingered momentarily upon her well-covered bosom, and dawdled back up to see the blush flood her normally pale cheeks.

She gripped at her lower lip with her teeth, as if to hold back the answer that would have spilled too readily forth. 'If you really think that, then you may as well pass me to him this very moment.' Her body tensed as she waited to see what he would do.

His steps were perfection, smooth and flowing, guiding her first here, then there, progressing with grace around the floor. For such a big man he was certainly light on his feet. As they turned to change direction, the irate face of Lord Farquharson swam into view. He was standing ready to catch her by the edge of the dance floor. Madeline's eyes widened. The stranger swung her closer towards Lord Farquharson. Her heart was thumping fit to leap free from her chest. A tremble set up in her fingers. The stranger was going to abandon her into Lord Farquharson's arms! Madeline's eyelids flickered shut in anticipation. She readied herself for the sound of Lord Farquharson's voice, prepared herself to feel the grasp of his hands.

'You can open your eyes now,' the stranger said. 'I haven't the least intention of releasing you to Farquharson.'

Madeline opened her eyes tentatively to find that they had progressed further around the ballroom, leaving Lord Farquharson well behind. She allowed herself to relax a little.

He felt the tension ease from her body and knew then that she hadn't lied about her feelings for Farquharson. And although it shouldn't have made the blindest bit of a difference, the knowledge pleased him. He wouldn't have abandoned her to Farquharson even if she'd been screaming to get there. She seemed so small and slender in his arms, much smaller than he had realised. He looked into her eyes and saw with a jolt that they were the clear golden hue of amber. Strange that he had not noticed that during either of their previous meetings. He had never met a woman with quite that colouring before. They were beautiful eyes, eyes a man might lose himself in. The sound of Miss Langley's voice dragged him back from his contemplation and he chided himself for staring at the chit.

She was looking at him expectantly, as if waiting for some kind of response.

'I beg your pardon,' he said. 'My attention was elsewhere.' The shadow of something flitted across her face, then was gone.

'Lord Farquharson does not look happy. You have stolen his dance,' she said.

'He has no damn right to dance with any woman,' he said harshly, then, remembering the woman in his arms, said, 'Forgive my language, Miss Langley. I did not mean to offend you.'

She smiled then, and it was a smile that lit up her face. Lucien wondered how he could ever have thought her plain. 'Rest assured, sir, whatever else you have done, you have not offended me.'

Lucien studied her closely.

'Indeed, you have nothing but my gratitude,' she continued 'I dread to think of my circumstance now had you not intervened on my behalf.' He could feel the warmth of her beneath his fingers; he could see it in her face. No, Madeline Langley had not encouraged Farquharson. There was an honesty about her, a quiet reserve, and a quickness of mind that was so lacking in most of the young women he had encountered.

She smiled again and he barely heard the notes of the band, concentrating as he was on the girl before him. The prim plain clothing could not completely disguise what lay beneath. The narrowness of her waist beneath his palm, the subtle rise of her breasts, those slender arms. Lucien could see very well what had attracted Farquharson. Innocence and fear and something else, something he could not quite define.

'Who are you?' she said, looking up at him. 'I don't even know your name.'

Of course she didn't know. She wouldn't be looking up at him so trustingly if she had known who he was. Some women attempted to court him for his reputation. Madeline Langley would not. He knew that instinctively. She would shun the wicked man Earl Tregellas was reputed to be.

A shy amusement lit the amber eyes. 'Will you not tell me, sir?'

He hesitated a moment longer, enjoying the innocent radiance in her face. No woman looked at him like that any more. Artful coquetry, pouting petulance, flagrant fear, and, of course, downright disapproval—he had known them all. Miss Langley's expression fell into none of those categories.

She smiled.

Lucien traced the outline of it with his eyes. He doubted that he would see her smile again once he told her his name.

The band played on. Their feet moved in time across the floor. Silence stretched between them.

'I am Tregellas.' There was nothing else he could say.

'Tregellas?' she said softly.

He watched while she tried to place the name, the slight puzzlement creasing a tiny line between her brows. Perhaps she did not know of him. And then he saw that she did after all. Shock widened the tawny glow of her eyes. The smile fled her sweet pink lips. Uncertainty stood in its stead.

'Earl Tregellas? The Wick—' She stopped herself just in time.

'At your service, Miss Langley,' he said smoothly, as if he were just any other polite gentleman of the *ton*.

Her gaze fluttered across his face, anxiety clouding her beautiful eyes, before she masked them with long black lashes. He thought he felt her body stiffen beneath his fingers.

'I'm not Farquharson,' he growled. 'You need have no fear of me.' Hell, he was trying to save her, not ravish her himself. And anyway, he had no interest in young ladies of Miss Langley's ilk. Indeed, he had not paid attention to any woman in five long years, or so he reminded himself.

She raised her eyes and looked at him, really looked at him, as if she could see the man beneath, the real Lucien Tregellas.

'No, you're not Farquharson.' Her voice was scarcely more than a whisper.

Lucien found that he could not take his eyes from hers. The censure that he expected was not there. There was nothing except an open, honest appraisal.

The music came to a halt.

'Thank you, Miss Langley,' he said, but whether it was for the dance or for her recognition that he and Farquharson were miles apart, he did not know. Her small hand was still enclosed in his. Swiftly he placed it upon his arm and escorted her back to her mother in silence.

And all the while he was conscious that Miss Madeline Langley had seen behind the façade that was the Wicked Earl.

* * *

'Madeline, what on earth do you think you're playing at?' her mother demanded. 'Do you know who that is?' she whispered between clenched teeth.

'Earl Tregellas,' Madeline said slowly, her words slightly stilted.

'Of all the most ill-mannered men. He takes you off without even consulting your mama! Not so much as a by your leave! How could you dance with him when Lord Farquharson's name is written clearly upon your card against the waltz!' Mrs Langley's hand scrabbled for her handkerchief. 'I declare my nerves are in a terrible state. Oh, Madeline, whatever were you thinking of? He has the blackest reputation of any man in London!'

'I could not refuse him without causing a scene.' She omitted to mention that she would rather have danced with the infamous Wicked Earl a thousand times over than let Lord Farquharson lay one finger upon her. 'I did not wish to embarrass you, Mama.'

'Embarrass me? Embarrass me?' The words seemed to be in danger of choking Mrs Langley. 'Never has a mother been more embarrassed by the actions of such a vexing daughter!' She dabbed at her eyes. 'And what will Lord Farquharson think of this?'

Madeline held her tongue.

'How could you do it, Madeline? It was as good as giving him a cut in front of the world.' Mrs Langley's bosom heaved dramatically.

Madeline tried to ignore the numerous stares that were being sent in her direction. She made no sign of having heard the whispers from the ladies in the seats surrounding them. 'No one knew what was on my dance card. Most likely they would have believed it to be empty as is usual.'

The whispers grew louder.

Angelina tugged at her mother's arm. 'Mama,' she said. 'You must not upset yourself. People are staring.'

Mrs Langley surveyed the attention turned upon her family. It was not the interest she had hoped for. She noticed that even Mrs Wilson had distanced herself somewhat and was now conversing with Mrs Hammond, casting the odd look back at the Langleys. Amelia Langley held her head up high and said in a voice intended to carry, 'Unfortunately, girls, your mama has developed one of her headaches. There is nothing else for it but to retire at once. What a shame, when we were having such a nice time. Come along, girls.' And Mrs Langley swept her daughters from the ballroom. 'I shall have a footman find your papa.'

The journey back to Climington Street was not pleasant. Madeline suffered several sympathetic looks from Angelina, a continuous harangue from her mother, and only the mildest expression of reproof from her father.

The harangue from Mrs Langley paused only while the family made their way into their home, and resumed once more when the front door had been firmly closed. Madeline made to follow Angelina upstairs.

'Where do you think you're going?' her mother screeched. 'We shall discuss this evening's nonsense, miss. Through to the parlour with you. Now!'

Madeline started back down the stairs.

'Think I might just have an early night myself,' mumbled her father and tried to slope away.

But Mrs Langley was having none of it. 'Mr Langley,' she cried. 'Will you not take control of *your* daughter?'

It was strange, or so Madeline thought, that she was always

Papa's daughter when she had displeased Mama, which, of course, was most of the time.

The long-suffering Mr Langley gave a weary sigh and led the way through to the parlour.

'She has made a spectacle of us this evening,' ranted Mrs Langley. 'And most certainly destroyed any chance of an alliance with Lord Farquharson!'

'Calm yourself, Mrs Langley, I'm sure it cannot be quite that bad,' said Mr Langley.

Mrs Langley's face turned a mottled puce. Her mouth opened and closed convulsively. Madeline had never seen her look so distressed. 'If you had not been hiding in Lady Gilmour's conservatory all evening, then you would realise that it is worse than bad!' she shouted.

'Perhaps Lord Farquharson can be persuaded otherwise,' said Mr Langley in an attempt to pacify his wife.

'Madeline snubbed him to dance with Earl Tregellas, for pity's sake!'

'Really?' mumbled Mr Langley, 'I'm sure he'll get over it.'

'Get over it! Get over it!' huffed Mrs Langley. 'How can you say such a thing? Lord Farquharson is unlikely to look in her direction, let alone offer her marriage! She has ruined her chances. We will never be invited anywhere ever again!' wailed Mrs Langley. Tears squeezed from her eyes and began to roll down her cheeks.

'Now, Mrs Langley,' Mr Langley cajoled, 'please don't take on so. I will sort it all out. Come along, my dearest.' He pressed a soothing arm around his wife's quivering shoulders.

But Mrs Langley steadfastly refused to budge. 'What are we to do? Lord Farquharson will never have her now.' The trickle of tears was in danger of becoming a deluge.

Madeline watched the unfolding scene, never uttering a word.

'Speak to her, Arthur,' Mrs Langley pleaded.

Mr Langley patted his wife, straightened, and cleared his throat. 'So, Madeline.' He cleared his throat again. 'What's all this about? How came you to dance with Lord Tregellas over Lord Farquharson?'

Madeline found that she could not tell even her dear papa what Lord Tregellas had done for her; how he had saved her from Lord Farquharson on, not one, but two separate occasions. 'He asked me and took my arm. There did not seem any polite manner in which to decline his request.' Indeed, there had been no request. Lord Tregellas had plucked her straight from her seat and on to the dance floor as if he had every right to do so.

'Did you know who he was?'

'No,' she answered. That, at least, was true. She had not known that her dark defender was the notorious Wicked Earl, not then.

Furrows of worry ploughed across her father's forehead. 'But how came you to his attention, my dear?'

Somehow it seemed strangely traitorous to reveal the truth about Lord Tregellas. She didn't understand why, just knew that it would not be what he wanted. It made no sense. Surely to tell them that he had stepped in to save her honour would have done him only good? Common sense affirmed that. Instinct fought against it…and won. 'I do not know,' said Madeline. She was not in the habit of lying, especially to her papa. Guilt sat heavily upon her shoulders.

'I understand he does not normally dance. Why should he then suddenly take it into his head to dance with a quiet, unassuming and gently bred girl like you?' Mr Langley pondered his own question.

Madeline understood exactly why Lord Tregellas had waltzed with her. She was not foolish enough to think that he actually *liked* her. There was nothing to recommend Madeline Langley to him, indeed to any man, when it came to that. It was simply a matter of saving her from enduring the dance within Lord Farquharson's arms. What she did not understand was why Lord Tregellas should care. She kept her thoughts to herself and shook her head at her father's question.

Mrs Langley snorted in the background. 'Quiet and unassuming?' she echoed. 'It is clear you have spent little time of late in your daughter's company!'

Mr Langley chose to ignore this comment. 'Madeline,' he said as carefully as he could, 'Lord Tregellas is a gentleman of some renown. He may be an earl and in receipt of a large fortune, but…' He hesitated, unsure how best to phrase the next words. 'He has a rather dubious reputation, my dear—'

'Everyone knows what he is reputed to have done,' cut in her mother.

'What did he do?' asked Madeline.

Mrs Langley's mouth opened. 'He is a murderer of the very worst kind. Why do you think he's called the Wicked Earl? He killed the—'

'We shall not lower ourselves to become gossip-mongers, Mrs Langley,' said her father reprovingly.

Madeline looked from one parent to the other. Even she, prim and proper Miss Madeline Langley, had heard talk of Lord Tregellas. He was said to have committed some heinous crime in the past. That fact alone made him strangely fascinating to half the women across London, although he was reputed to treat them all with a cold contempt. Madeline knew that, and still it did not matter. The man that had forced

Lord Farquharson to leave her safe in the Theatre Royal, who had warned her against that fiend, and had saved her again at this evening's ball, was not someone she could fear. He had, after all, given her every reason to trust him. 'It was only one dance,' she said in defence of Lord Tregellas and herself.

'It was the *waltz!*' sobbed her mother. 'Madeline is quite ruined after this evening's fiasco.'

Mr Langley said patiently, 'Come now, my dear, she's hardly ruined. It was, as she said, only a dance.'

The sobbing burst forth into a wail. 'Oh, you understand nothing, Mr Langley!'

Mr Langley wore the weary air of a man who knew exactly what the forthcoming weeks would hold if he did nothing to resolve the situation. 'Perhaps I could have a word with Farquharson.'

'He'll have nothing to do with Madeline now. All my plans lie in ruins.'

'He's a stout fellow. He'll listen to reason,' said Mr Langley.

Her mother stopped wailing and dabbed at her eyes. 'Do you really think so?' she hiccupped.

'Of course,' her father replied. 'I'll go round there tomorrow and explain that Madeline had no notion to dance with Tregellas, that she was taken unawares, and, as a young and inexperienced lady, had no say in the matter. Perhaps I could invite him to dinner.'

Madeline could not believe what she was hearing. Her father thought Farquharson a stout fellow? 'Papa,' she said. 'Please do not. If you knew Lord Farquharson's true nature, you would not suggest such a thing. He is not an honourable man.'

'Mr Langley,' said her mother, 'pray do not heed her. She's taken a set against Lord Farquharson and is determined to thwart my plans. He's a wealthy and respected member of the aristocracy, a war hero and more. And he's worth ten thousand a year. Does that sound like a dishonourable man?'

'Papa, if you knew what he had done—'

'Then tell me, child,' encouraged her father.

'Arthur!' her mother whined.

But Mr Langley made no sign of having heard his wife's complaint. 'Madeline, what has happened?'

Madeline sighed. Papa would listen. He would not make excuses for Lord Farquharson or, worse still, encourage the man's attentions. Once Papa knew the truth, she would be free of Lord Farquharson for ever. It did not matter that she would never marry. Rather that, than wedded to Lord Farquharson. No man other than that villain had ever expressed so much as an interest in her. She was four-and-twenty years old, with a string of failed Seasons behind her. She did not blame her mother and father for not sending her out on to the circuit last year. In fact, it was a blessed relief, and they did, after all, have Angelina to think about. Surely Angelina would more than compensate them for Madeline's failings?

'Madeline?' her father prompted.

Madeline shook the fluttering thoughts from her head. The truth must be told—just without any mention of Lord Tregellas. Taking a deep breath, she relayed what Lord Farquharson had been about, both in the Theatre Royal and at Lady Gilmour's ball. There was no embellishment, no dramatics, just plain facts, minus a certain earl's involvement.

By the end of it Mr Langley was no longer looking his usual mild-mannered self. He fixed a stern eye upon his wife. 'You knew of this, Amelia?' Incredulity edged his voice.

'Only about the theatre. But he did *not* kiss her, Arthur.' Mrs Langley cast imploring eyes up to her husband. 'I knew nothing of this evening. She said not one word of being alone in a bedchamber with Lord Farquharson. Had I but known…' Mrs Langley pressed her tiny lace handkerchief to her mouth and fell silent.

A small cynical part of Madeline wondered as to her mother's claim. Would she still have had her daughter dance with Lord Farquharson, knowing all that he had done? Mama had been unwilling to hear Madeline speak against the Baron. And social standing and money were so very important to Mrs Langley. It was a pointless question.

'We shall discuss this further, Mrs Langley, once the matter has been satisfactorily resolved.'

Madeline had never seen her father like this before. There was a determined glare in his normally kind brown eyes, a tension in his usually relaxed stance. He rang the bell and requested that the carriage be brought back round. 'Papa?' said Madeline. 'Where are you going?'

'To see Lord Farquharson.'

Madeline felt the blood drain from her face. Visions of duelling pistols and her father lying wounded, or worse, swam in her head. She prayed that he would not do anything so foolish as call out Lord Farquharson. Not her papa, not her mild-mannered, gentle papa. 'Please, Papa, do not go.'

'I must, my dear,' he said. 'It's a matter of honour.'

'Arthur?' Mrs Langley raised a trembling voice.

'Do not wait up, I may be some time,' said Mr Langley and walked from the parlour.

The clock on the mantel struck midnight as the front door slammed behind him.

* * *

'So you waltzed with Miss Langley just to prevent Far-quharson from doing so?' Guy, Viscount Varington, raised a cynical brow.

The library was quiet; only the slow rhythmic ticking of the clock and the occasional spit from the fire punctuated the silence.

'Why else?' Lucien Tregellas didn't even glance round at his brother, just stood by the carved marble fireplace looking into the dancing yellow flames. They glowed golden in the darkness of the library, reminding him of the lights in Madeline Langley's eyes. Such warmth and honesty as he had not seen in any other woman's eyes. Long dark lashes and that straight little nose…and a clean pleasant smell that reminded him of… It came to him then exactly what Miss Langley smelled of—oranges!

'You've done far more damage to her reputation just by dancing with her than Farquharson ever could.' Guy leaned across the small drum table and captured the decanter.

'Hell's teeth, Guy! I only danced with the girl. Farquharson would have done a damned sight worse. It wasn't as if I ravished her.'

'Might as well have, old chap,' said his brother. 'You haven't danced in the last five years. And when you decide to take again to the dance floor, after such a long absence, you don't choose just any old dance, but the waltz.'

'So?'

'So, all of London's eyes will be upon you now to see what Tregellas meant by waltzing with the very proper Miss Langley.' Guy filled two balloon glasses with the rich amber liquid from the decanter.

'Then London will have a long wait.'

Guy pressed a glass into his brother's hand. 'Really?'

Lucien arched an eyebrow and ignored the comment.

Guy continued on, knowing full well his brother's irritation. 'You know, of course, that the chit will now be thrust under your nose at every opportunity. Why should Miss Langley's mama settle for a mere baron when an earl has just *waltzed* right into her sight?'

'Your puns get worse, Guy.' Lucien's fingers rubbed against the Tregellas coat of arms artfully engraved upon the side of his glass. 'Mrs Langley may do her worst. I had no interest in Madeline Langley other than to stop Farquharson getting his hands on her.'

'Had?' queried Guy with an expression that bellied innocence.

'Had, have, what's the difference?'

'You tell me,' came Guy's rejoinder.

Lucien took a large swig of brandy. The liquid burned a satisfying trail down to his stomach. 'I made my meaning clear enough to Farquharson.'

'And what of Miss Langley? Did you make your meaning clear to her, too? Perhaps she has expectations following her waltz this evening. A girl like that can't have too many men hanging after her.'

Lucien took another gulp of brandy. 'Miss Langley has no expectations of me.' He thought momentarily of Madeline Langley's clear non-judgemental gaze, and a touch of tenderness twitched at his lips. The girl didn't have a conniving bone in her body.

'News of your waltz with Miss Langley will be all over town by tomorrow afternoon, and you know what people will think.' Guy paused to take a delicate sip from his glass. 'Dallying with a respectable girl can only mean one thing in their tawdry little minds—that you have finally decided to take a wife and beget an heir.'

'Let them think what they will,' Lucien shrugged. 'We both know that I have no intention of marrying, and as for the Tregellas heir…' Lucien raised his glass in the direction of his brother '…I'm looking at him. Hell will freeze over before I find myself in parson's trap.'

A peculiar smile hovered around Guy's mouth. 'We'll see,' he said softly. 'Only the devil or a fool tempts fate.'

Not so very far away in Brooks's Club on St James's Street, Cyril Farquharson was also sipping brandy. His attention was not on the small circle of fashionable gentlemen with whom he was sitting. Indeed, Lord Farquharson's thoughts were concerned with someone else entirely; and that someone was Miss Madeline Langley. The whores at Madame Fouet's had been meagre rations to feed his appetite. Five years was a long time to starve. He had grown tired of them. They were too willing, too coarse and worldly wise, and, even though they role-played otherwise, that fact detracted something from the experience for Farquharson. And he was tired too of Tregellas's constant watching, his constant waiting. Damn the man for curtailing the best of his pleasures. But Farquharson would be held in check no longer. He hungered for a gentlewoman, someone young and innocent and fearful, someone with that unique *je ne sais quoi;* in short, someone like Madeline Langley.

She had taken years in the finding, but Farquharson had known that Madeline was the one from the moment he had seen her. She was quiet and reserved and afraid of him, all the things he liked in a woman. He played with her, like a cat played with a mouse. He liked to see her discomfort when he stepped too close or lingered too long over her hand. He liked the way she tried to hide her fear and her futile efforts to avoid him. Dear, sweet, fearful Madeline. He meant to take his pleasure of her…in the worst possible way. If the empty-headed Mrs Langley was determined to dangle her delicious daughter before him in the hope of trapping him in marriage, who was he to refuse the bait? Cyril Farquharson was far too cunning to be caught. So he had enjoyed his game with Madeline Langley until Tregellas had entered the scene.

The interruption in the Theatre Royal during the play had been an irritation. Tregellas's dance with the girl at Lady Gilmour's ball went beyond that. It smacked of more than a desire to thwart Farquharson. Tregellas had not looked at a female in years, and now he had waltzed with the very woman that Farquharson held within his sights. Perhaps Tregellas had an interest in Miss Langley. There was an irony in that thought. Lord Farquharson mulled the matter over. By the time that he finished his brandy and headed for home, he knew just what he was going to do. In one fell swoop, not only would he secure Miss Langley to do with whatsoever he might please, but he would also effectively thwart any move that Tregellas might mean to make. And that idea appealed very much to Cyril Farquharson. He smiled at his own ingenuity and looked forward to Madeline Langley's reaction when she learned what he meant to do.

Chapter Four

Madeline did not see her father again until the next morning. All the night through she had lain awake, unable to find sleep; tossing and turning beneath the bedcovers, until her cheeks burned red with the worry of it all. Papa was well meaning, but he had no real appreciation of the malice contained in a man like Lord Farquharson. It seemed that Madeline could see the cruel grey eyes and the sneer stretched across Lord Farquharson's lips. Dear Lord in heaven, Papa didn't stand a chance! Lord Farquharson would dispense with her gentle father before Mr Langley had so much as taken his second breath. What good did Papa think that complaining would do? None, as far as Madeline could see. And God forbid that he took it into his head to challenge Lord Farquharson! She did not even know if her father owned a pair of duelling pistols. Papa was far too sensible to call Lord Farquharson out. Wasn't he?

The bed linen was very crumpled and Madeline very tired by the time morning came. The foggy dullness of her brain contrasted with the tense agitation of her body. She rose early, washed, dressed, took only the smallest cup of coffee and

waited in the quiet little dining room, ignoring the heated
salvers of ham and eggs. Her stomach was squeezed so tight
by anxiety that even the smell of the food stirred a wave of
nausea. It was not until after nine o'clock that her father
finally appeared, with her mother in tow.

Mrs Langley was surprisingly calm in the light of what had
yesterday been cited as the biggest catastrophe of the century.
In fact, Madeline might even have gone so far as to say that
her mother was looking rather pleased. At least Papa did not
seem to have taken any hurts. His arm was not in a sling nor
did he limp. His eyes were bagged with tiredness, but were
not blackened from bruising. Indeed, he had not one visible
scratch upon him. Madeline breathed a sigh of relief.
Tension's hold slackened a little. 'Papa!' she breathed. 'Thank
goodness you're safe.' She ran to him and placed her arms
around him in a grateful embrace. 'I was so worried.'

Mr Langley did not return Madeline's tremulous smile.
Rather, he reached out a tired old hand and pulled her gently
to him. 'Madeline,' he said, and there was sadness in his
voice.

Something was wrong. Madeline felt it immediately. She
started back and stared up into his eyes. 'What is it, Papa?
What has happened?' It did not make sense. He was home,
returned safely, hurt, it seemed, by nothing more than Farquharson's words. The first hint of apprehension wriggled
down Madeline's spine. What had Lord Farquharson said?
And then a worse thought made itself known. 'You have
not…killed him, have you?' she asked.

'No, child.' Mr Langley shook his grizzled head.
'Although, I begin to think that I would be better placed if I
had.'

'Then what…?'

Mrs Langley touched a hand to her husband's arm; she could no longer hide her smile. 'Pray tell Madeline the good news, Mr Langley,' she said.

Madeline looked up into her father's face and waited for the words to fall.

'Lord Farquharson apologised for his lapse of control. He said that his normal behaviour was overcome by the magnitude of his feelings for you.'

The first tentacles of dread enclosed around Madeline's heart. 'And?' Her voice was nothing more than a cracked whisper.

'He has offered to do the decent thing. Lord Farquharson wishes to marry you, Madeline.'

His words clattered harsh against the ensuing silence.

She stared at her father, resisting the enormity of what he had just said.

Mr Langley's palm dabbed against Madeline's back as if to salve the hurt he had just dealt her. 'As a gentleman he should never have tried to compromise you. But the deed is done and he would redeem himself by making you his wife. He said it was ever his wish since first he saw you. I believe he does care for you, my dear. Perhaps in time you will come to be happy together.'

'No.' Madeline shook her head. 'No!' The word reverberated around the room. 'I cannot marry him, Papa. I will not!'

Mrs Langley came forward then. 'Your father has already agreed it. Lord Farquharson is already organising a party at which your betrothal will be announced. The invitations are to be written and sent today.'

'The party can be cancelled.'

The smile wiped from Mrs Langley's face. 'You see how she tortures me, Mr Langley!' she cried. 'She would rather make fools of us before all of London than do as she is bid.'

None of it seemed real. They were but players upon a stage, mouthing lines that would wreck her life for ever. Madeline struggled to shake the thick fleece that clouded her thoughts. 'Papa, please, I cannot do this.'

'Madeline,' he said gently, and it seemed as if his heart were breaking. 'If you really cannot bear to marry Lord Farquharson, then I am obliged to take other steps. He has impugned your honour. As your father, I cannot just sit back and let that happen. If word were to get out of your meeting with Farquharson in Lady Gilmour's bedchamber, then your reputation would be utterly tarnished, and even Angelina would not remain unharmed.' His eyes shuttered in anguish, and prised open again. 'Either he marries you or I must call him out. The guilt is Farquharson's, not yours, never doubt that, my dear, but we both know that society will not view it that way, and I cannot let you suffer their persecution should the matter come to light.' His fingers fluttered against her hair, drawing her face up to look at him. 'I will not force you to this marriage, Madeline. The choice is yours to make. If you truly cannot bear to have Farquharson as your husband, then so be it.'

Mrs Langley gripped at her husband's arm, pulling it away from Madeline. 'Oh, Mr Langley, you cannot seriously mean to challenge his lordship?' Her voice rose in a panic. 'Duelling is illegal…and dangerous. You might be killed!' She clung to him, tears springing to her eyes. 'And what good would it do? Madeline's reputation will be ruined if she does not marry him, regardless of the outcome of any duel. I beg of you, Mr Langley, do not give her the choice. Madeline must wed him and be done with it.'

'It is a matter of honour, Mrs Langley, and I shall not force her to wed against her will,' said Mr Langley.

Madeline's teeth clung to her lower lip. Her throat constricted ready to choke her. She would not cry. She would not.

'You may have some little time to think on your decision, but if you decide against the marriage, Madeline, speed might yet prevent the sending of the invitations.'

Mrs Langley was tugging at her husband's hand. 'No, Arthur, no, please!'

For Madeline there was, of course, no decision to be made. Marry Lord Farquharson, or have her father risk his life. The choice was not a difficult one, and in its making, a cold calm settled upon her. Tears and fear and anger would come later. For now, Madeline moved like an automaton.

Mr Langley turned to go.

'Wait, Papa…' Madeline stayed him with a hand '…I've made my choice.'

Her father's kindly brown eyes looked down into hers.

'I will marry Lord Farquharson.'

Mrs Langley's face uncrinkled.

'Are you certain, my dear?' he asked.

'Yes.' Such a little word to tilt the axis of the world.

An uncertain smile blossomed on Mrs Langley's face. 'It will not be so bad, Madeline. You'll see. His lordship will make up for his mistakes, I'm sure he will.' She patted at her daughter's arm. 'And he *is* a baron.'

Madeline barely felt her touch. Yes, Lord Farquharson would more than make up for his mistakes, just not in the way her mother thought. There had been nothing of care or affection in his eyes. Whatever he meant to do, Madeline knew that it would not be with her welfare or her wishes in mind. Neither would matter once she was his wife. He could do what he pleased with her then, and no one would mind in the slightest. Farquharson's wife. The ball of nausea within her stomach started to grow. 'Please excuse me, Mama, Papa. I feel suddenly rather…tired.'

'Of course, my dearest,' said Mrs Langley.

Her father looked drained, wrung out. 'It's for the best,' he said.

Madeline tried to smile, tried to give him some small measure of false assurance, but her lips would do nothing but waver. 'Yes,' she said again, and slipped quietly from the room.

'Hell!' Earl Tregellas's curse drew the attention of several of the surrounding gentlemen dotted around the room.

'Lucien?' Guy watched the rigidity grip Lucien's jaw and saw the telltale tightening of his lips. He leaned forward from his chair, all previous lounging forgotten, keen to know exactly what was printed in today's copy of *The Morning Post* that had wrought such a reaction from his brother. Lucien normally preferred to keep his emotions tightly in check in public.

Lucien Tregellas threw an insolent stare at those gentlemen in White's lounge area who were fool enough to be still expressing an interest. The grandfather clock over by the door ticked its languorous pace. A few newspapers rustled. The chink of porcelain and glass sounded. And the normal quiet drone of conversation resumed. 'Come, Guy, I've a mind to get out of here.' He folded the newspaper in half and threw it nonchalantly on to the small occasional table by his elbow.

Both men rose, and, with their coffee still unfinished on the table, left the premises of White's gentlemen's club without so much as a backward glance.

Lucien's curricle was waiting outside, the horses impatiently striking up dust from the street. 'Do you mind if we walk?'

Guy shook his head. Things must be bad.

A brief word to his tiger and Lucien's curricle was gone, leaving the brothers alone in the late winter's pale sunlight.

They walked off down St James's Street. 'Well?' said Guy.

Lucien made no reply, just clenched his jaw tighter to check the unleashing of the rage that threatened to explode. To any that passed it would seem that Earl Tregellas was just out for a casual morning stroll with his brother. There was nothing in his demeanour to suggest that anything might be awry in his usual lifestyle. Lucien might disguise it well, but Guy was not indifferent to the tension simmering below the surface of his brother's relaxed exterior. That Lucien had failed to prevent his outburst in White's was not a good sign.

'Are you going to tell me just what has you biting down on your jaw as if you were having a bullet extracted?'

Lucien's long stride faltered momentarily and then recovered. 'Lord Farquharson entertained a small party last evening in Bloomsbury Square to announce his betrothal to Miss Madeline Langley, elder daughter of Mr Arthur Langley and Mrs Amelia Langley of Climington Street.'

Guy stopped dead on the spot. 'He means to *marry* her?'

'It would appear so.' There was a harshness in Lucien's features, an anger that would not be suppressed for long.

'But why?' Guy turned a baffled expression upon Lucien.

'Keep walking, Guy.' Lucien touched a hand briefly to his brother's arm.

'Why not just turn his attention to another, easier target? By Hades, I would not have thought him to be so desperate for Miss Langley above all others. The girl has nothing particular to recommend her. She doesn't even look like—' Guy caught himself just in time. 'Sorry, Lucien, didn't mean to…'

'I warned him if he ever tried to strike again that I would

be waiting. Perhaps he thought that I was bluffing, that I would just sit back and let him take Madeline Langley. I did not think he would resort to marriage to get his hands on her.'

They walked in silence for a few minutes before Guy slowly said, 'Or he may have misinterpreted your defence of Miss Langley.'

'Don't be ridiculous,' snapped Lucien. 'Why on earth would he think that I have any interest in the girl?'

Guy raised a wry eyebrow. 'For the same reason that half of London did only yesterday.'

'What else was I supposed to do? Watch him run his lecherous hands all over her? Let him force her to a dance she did not want…and more?'

'It seems that Miss Langley has changed her opinion of Farquharson. She might not have wanted to dance then, but she wants to marry him now.'

Lucien thought of the fear and revulsion on Miss Langley's face as that brute had tried to force himself upon her; of her terror when she'd quite literally run straight into him on that servants' stairwell; and her loathing at the prospect of waltzing with Farquharson. 'I cannot believe that it is so.'

'There's nothing so fickle as women. You should know that, Lucien. Saying one thing, then changing their minds at the drop of a hat. It's amazing what the odd bauble or two can buy these days.'

'Madeline Langley isn't like that. You've seen her, Guy. She isn't that sort of woman.'

'Plain and puritanical maybe, Lucien, but still as likely to yield to temptation as any other. The Langleys are not wealthy. The pretty golden looks of the younger Langley chit are bound to catch her a husband. Not so with the elder

Miss Langley. Perhaps she decided Farquharson was preferable to life as an old maid.'

Lucien shook his head. 'No.' He could not imagine Miss Langley agreeing to touch Farquharson, let alone marry him.

'Let it rest, Lucien,' his brother advised. 'You've done all you can to save the girl. If she's foolish enough to become his wife, then there's nothing more you can do. Your conscience, at least, is clear.'

'My conscience is anything but clear. My actions have brought about this situation.'

'You don't know that,' countered Guy.

'I threw down the gauntlet and Farquharson took it up.'

'Perhaps he planned to marry her all along.'

'Perhaps. Whatever the reasoning, I cannot let Miss Langley become his wife.'

'Oh, and just how do you propose to stop the wedding? Stand up and announce the truth of what Farquharson did? Stirring up the past will release Miss Langley from the betrothal, but at what cost? It's too high a price, Lucien.'

'I'll find another way.'

Guy sighed. 'What is Miss Langley to you? Nothing. She's not worth it.'

'Whatever Madeline Langley may or may not be worth, I'll be damned if I just abandon her to Farquharson. You know what he'll do.'

'He might have changed, learned his lesson over the years.'

Lucien drew his brother a look of withering incredulity. 'Men like Farquharson never change. Why else has he been visiting Madame Fouet's all these years?'

'Face it, Lucien. Short of marrying Miss Langley yourself, there's not a cursed thing you can do to stop him.'

A silence hiccupped between them.

A crooked smile eased the hardness of Lucien's lips. 'You might just have an idea there, little brother.'

Guy laughed at the jest. 'Now that really would be beyond belief, the Wicked Earl and Miss Langley!' Still laughing, he grabbed his brother's arm. 'What you need is a good stiff drink.'

'Amen to that,' said Lucien.

The more that Lucien thought on it, the more sense it seemed to make. He knew what would happen if Farquharson married Miss Langley, knew that he could not stand by and let another woman walk to her death, willing or not. For all that his brother said, Lucien still could not bring himself to believe in Miss Langley's sudden capitulation. Could she really want Farquharson as a husband? Lucien drank deeper and stared unseeing into the dying embers of the fire. Did the answer to that question even make any difference? Farquharson was Farquharson. No woman, knowing the truth about him, would willingly agree to so much as look at the man. Lucien remembered too well that of which Farquharson was capable. Mercifully the brandy anaesthetised the worst of the pain that the memories triggered. He emptied the contents down his throat and reached for the decanter again.

Farquharson. Farquharson. Farquharson. For five long years Lucien had thought of little else. Nothing but that and his own vow to ensure that Farquharson never struck again. Then Miss Madeline Langley had entered the picture and history was suddenly in danger of repeating itself, while all he could do was watch it happen. Lucien's lip curled at the very thought. His eyes closed tight against the spiralling anger. When they opened again, he was perfectly calm, his thinking never clearer. Lucien Tregellas knew exactly what he was going to do. Raising the stakes was a risky move but, if played well, would resolve the situation admirably. Guilt prickled at his conscience. He quashed it. Even if he was using her for revenge, Miss Langley would also benefit from the arrangement. And besides, being with him would be infinitely safer for the girl than being with Farquharson.

Madeline sat demurely on the gilt-legged chair, her mother positioned on one side, Angelina on the other. Since the announcement of her betrothal to Lord Farquharson, Madeline had been elevated in her mother's order of things. There had been trips to cloth warehouses, milliners, drapers and Burlington Arcade. Shopping, shopping and more shopping. Life had taken on a frenzied whirl of dances and parties and balls. The little house in Climington Street looked more like a florist's shop following the daily arrival of Lord Farquharson's bouquets. And now, Mrs Langley had managed to obtain the ultimate in social acceptance—vouchers for Almack's Assembly Rooms. Amelia Langley had finally arrived, and the look on her face told the world that she knew it was so.

Through it all Madeline appeared as the ghost of the person she had been. She moved mechanically, her emotions disengaged by necessity. It was the only way to get through this, the only way to survive Lord Farquharson's little visits to take afternoon tea with the Langley household, to bear his hand upon her arm, the touch of his lips to her fingers. It was the shell of Madeline Langley who allowed Lord Farquharson to lead her out on to dance floor after dance floor, to whisper promises of love into her ear, to take her up in his chaise around Hyde Park at the most fashionable of hours for all the world to see. The real Madeline Langley was curled up tight in a ball somewhere in the deep, dark recesses of that protection. So it was Madeline's shell, and not Madeline herself, who sat that night in Almack's.

It did not matter that they were in the famous assembly rooms. It did not matter that the night was chilled, or that the air within the dance rooms was stuffy and hot. It did not even matter when one of the ladies patronesses gave permission for Madeline to waltz with Lord Farquharson, or when his fingers lingered about her waist, or when he gazed with such promise into her face. Madeline saw nothing, heard nothing, felt nothing. And by being so, Madeline's shell could do what it had to do.

'Madeline, Mrs Barrington has promised me the recipe for a wonderful lotion that clarifies the skin and removes any blemish or shadow. It will do wonders for your complexion, my dear.'

Madeline sat, like she had done on every other occasion since learning of her betrothal to Lord Farquharson, and said nothing.

Colonel Barclay materialised as if from nowhere. 'My dear Mrs Langley, may I introduce a good friend of mine, Viscount Varington. He has been admiring you and your daughters from across the room for some time now. I have taken pity on the poor man and decided to put him out of his misery by bringing him here for a word from your sweet lips.'

The tall, dark and extremely handsome Lord Varington swooped down to press a kiss to Angelina's hand. 'Miss Langley,' he uttered in a sensuously deep voice. 'Such a pleasure to make your acquaintance, at last.' And delivered her a look of dangerous appreciation.

Angelina smiled and glanced up at him through down-cast lashes.

'I can see from where Miss Langley gets her golden beauty.' He touched his lips to Mrs Langley's hand.

Mrs Langley tittered. 'La, you flatter me too much, sir.'

'Not at all,' said Lord Varington, his pale blue eyes bold and appraising. 'Is it possible that Miss Langley is free for this next dance? A most improbable hope, but…'

Angelina scanned down her dance card, knowing full well that Mr Jamison's name was scrawled against the dance in question, and indeed that every successive dance had been claimed. Her eyes flickered up to the hard, handsome face waiting above them.

Lord Varington smiled in just the way that he knew to be most effective, showing his precisely chiselled features to perfection. He cast a smouldering gaze at Angelina.

Angelina opened her mouth to explain that she could not in truth dance with him.

But Mrs Langley was there first. 'How fortuitous your timing is, my lord. It seems that Mr Jamison is unwell and is unable to stand up with Angelina as he promised. She, therefore, is free to dance with you, my lord.'

'I can breathe again,' murmured Lord Varington dramatically, and took Angelina's hand into his with exaggerated tenderness.

'Oh, my!' exclaimed Mrs Langley and fanned herself vigorously as Angelina disappeared off on to the floor in Lord Varington's strong muscular arms.

It was only then that she noticed that Madeline was missing.

Lucien tucked Madeline's hand into the crook of his arm and continued walking through Almack's marbled vestibule.

'My lord, what is wrong? The note the girl brought said that you needed to speak with me urgently.' Madeline felt his pale blue eyes pierce a crack in the shell that she had so carefully constructed.

'And so I do, Miss Langley, but not here.' He scanned the entrance hall around them, indicating the few bodies passing in chatter. 'It's too dangerous.'

'Dangerous?' Madeline's voice faltered, the crack growing exponentially wider. 'I don't understand—'

Lord Tregellas stopped behind one of the large Ionic pillars and gently pulled her closer. 'Miss Langley,' he interrupted, 'do you trust me?'

'Yes.' The shell shattered to smithereens. 'Of course I do.' Logic deemed that she should not, instinct ensured that she did.

A strange expression flitted across his face and then was gone. 'Then come with me.'

For the first time in two weeks Madeline felt her heart leap free of the ice that encased it. Surely she had misheard him? She looked into his eyes and what she saw there kicked her pulse to a canter.

'Miss Langley.' His voice was rich and mellow. 'We do not have much time. If you wish to escape Farquharson, come with me.'

Come with me. It was the dream that she dare not allow herself to dream. Lord Tregellas had saved her before. Perhaps he could save her now. But even in the thinking Madeline knew it was impossible. No one could save her, not even Tregellas. Foolish hope would only lead to more heartache. Slowly she shook her head. 'I cannot.'

His hands rested on her upper arms. 'Do you desire to marry him?' His voice had a harsh edge to it.

'No!' she whispered. Now that her shell was broken she felt every breath of air, suffered the pain from which she had sought to hide. 'You know that I do not.'

His voice lost something of its harshness. 'Then why have you accepted him?'

She could not tell him. Not here, not like this, not when she knew that in three more weeks she would be Lord Farquharson's wife. 'It's a long story.'

'Too long for here?'

'Yes.' She felt the brush of his thumb against her bare skin between the puff of her sleeve and the start of her long gloves. It was warm and reassuring.

'There are other places,' he said.

Temptation beckoned. Lord Tregellas was more of a man than she ever could have dreamt of. She blushed to think that he could show her any interest…and that she actually welcomed it. Were she to be seen leaving Almack's in the company of the Wicked Earl, she would be ruined. Strangely, the prospect of her own ruination in that manner did not seem such a terrible atrocity. Life with Lord Farquharson seemed far worse. But what Lord Tregellas was suggesting would not only ruin her, but also her family and that was something she could not allow. She shook her head again. 'No.'

'I mean only to help you. You should know something of Lord Farquharson's history before you take your wedding vows. You said that you trusted me. Then give me half an hour of your time, nothing more, to let me tell you of Farquharson's past and of a way you may evade him.'

Madeline bit at her lip and remained unconvinced. It would be wrong of her to go with him. She had her family to think about.

It was as if the Earl read her mind. 'He's a danger not only to you, but to your sister and your parents, too. And you need not be concerned that our departure together shall be noticed. I assure you it will not.'

'My family are truly in danger?' His gaze held her transfixed. He was a stranger, a man reputed by all London to be wicked. She should not believe him. But inexplicably Madeline knew that she did.

'Yes.' He released his hold upon her, stepping back to increase the space between them. 'We're running out of time, Miss Langley. Do you come with me, or not?'

A sliver of tension stretched between them. Pale ice blue merged with warm amber. Madeline looked a moment longer. It seemed so right. Reputations could be wrong. There was nothing of Lord Farquharson in the man that faced her. Lord Tregellas would not hurt her. 'Half an hour?' she said.

'Half an hour,' he affirmed and reached his hand for hers.

The interior of the Tregellas closed carriage was dark, only the occasional street light illuminated the dimness.

Lucien could see the stark whiteness of Madeline Langley's face against the black backdrop. Huge eyes, darkly smudged beneath, and cheeks that were too thin. He doubted that the girl had slept or eaten since the announcement of her betrothal. Guilt stuck in his throat. He swallowed it down. He had done what he could to save Miss Langley. He need have no remorse. Or so he told himself. But telling and believing were two different things. 'It's not much further now.'

'We will be back in time, won't we?' She nibbled at her lip.

The knot of guilt expanded to a large tangle. 'Of course.'

She relaxed a little then, leaning back against the dark drapery in the corner. Her implicit trust stirred his heart.

'Miss Langley.' He ensured that his voice was without emotion. He could not tell her all of it, but he would tell her enough. The girl was not stupid. She would realise that he was right. 'Cyril Farquharson is not to be toyed with. He is evil,

pure and unadulterated. What you have seen of his behaviour is nothing compared to that of which he is capable.'
Lucien paused, tightening the rein on his self-control. 'He is
a man that delights in plucking the most tender of blooms to
crush beneath his heel.'

'What do you mean?' she whispered.

'Exactly that.'

'I don't understand. What did he do?'

Lucien slid another bolt across the barrier to the memories.
'He took a woman, a young and foolish woman, and…'

Madeline waited.

'…killed her.'

Only the sound of their breathing filled the carriage.

'*Killed* her?' He could hear the horror in Miss Langley's
words. 'Who was she? Why did he not stand trial?'

Lucien turned his face to the window. 'It could not be proven.'

'Why not? If he was guilty—'

'He was most definitely guilty, but Farquharson was
careful to destroy the evidence.' Lucien's jaw clamped shut.

There was a moment's silence before Madeline asked,
'And you think he means to…to kill me too?'

He looked back across at the fear-filled little face—fear
that he had put there with his revelation. He hardened his
compassion. She had to know. 'Oh, he will kill you all right,
Miss Langley, and anyone who tries to stop him.'

'I cannot believe it,' she said in a small voice.

'Can't you? What do you feel when you stand close to him,
when he touches you? What do you feel then, Madeline?'

She barely noticed the use of her given name. 'Fear…
loathing… repulsion.'

'Then listen to your instinct, it speaks true.'

'But I am bound to marry him.' She sighed and recounted

what had happened that night after Lord Tregellas had waltzed with her. 'I cannot dishonour my papa and there is Angelina to think of.'

'There is another way,' Lucien said softly, and leaned forward. 'Give me your hand, Miss Langley.'

Every sensible nerve in her body was telling her to resist. Madeline warily reached her hand towards him.

His fingers closed around hers. Her hand was small and slender and chilled. 'You're cold. Here, put this travelling rug around you.' Through the darkness he felt for her, moving across to the other side of the carriage, wrapping the woollen rug across her shoulders, running his hands briskly over the sides of her now-blanketed arms. 'The night air is chilled and you have no cloak.'

'Lord Tregellas.' Madeline's plea brought him up short.

He stopped. Dropped his hands from her arms. Stayed seated by her side. Rumble of carriage wheels. Horses' hooves. Bark of dogs. Men's voices cursing coarse and loud. Bang of doors. Lucien let them all pass, breathing in that small space of time, waiting to utter the words he had never thought would pass his lips. 'Miss Langley,' he said, 'there is one way that would most certainly prevent your marriage to Farquharson.'

'Yes?'

There was such hope in that one little word. The subtle scent of oranges drifted up from Madeline Langley's hair. Anticipation squeezed at Lucien's heart. *Fool!* he chastised himself. *Just ask her the damn question and be done with it.* 'Will you marry me?' He felt the start of the slim body beside him, felt more than saw the shock upon her face.

'You want me to be your wife?' Disbelief raised her voice to a mere squeak.

'Yes. It's by far the best solution to our problem.' He tried to convey that it was the logical answer for them both.

'Lord Farquharson is my problem alone, my lord, not yours. You have no need to marry me. Why should you even care what he does to me, let alone wish to sacrifice yourself on my behalf?'

'I have my reasons, Miss Langley. Suffice to say, it is in both our interests to stop him.' Sacrifice was a very strong word, and the wrong word. It did not describe at all what it was that Lucien Tregellas was doing.

'But marriage?'

Why should she find it so unbelievable? 'Think of it as a marriage of convenience, if you prefer,' he said, trying to make her feel easier.

'I cannot just marry you.'

'Why not?'

'My family, the scandal—'

'Would blow over. Your family will not suffer. I'll ensure that. I'm not without influence, Madeline.'

She seemed embarrassed at the sound of her Christian name upon his lips, and glanced down nervously at her lap. He remembered how innocent she was.

'Lord Farquharson would sue for breach of contract.'

'It's only money, a commodity of which I have plenty.'

A short silence, as if she was digesting his words. He heard her hands move against the blanket.

'Such an act would publicly humiliate Lord Farquharson. He would be obliged to demand satisfaction of his honour.'

'We both know that Farquharson has no honour.'

'Society does not. He would call you out.'

'So much the better.'

'But your life would be in danger. He might injure you, or worse!'

He smiled then, a chilling smile, a smile that held in it five years of waiting, five years of hatred. The light from a street lamp glanced across his stark angular features, casting a sinister darkness to his handsome looks. 'Have no fear of that. I promise you most solemnly that when I meet Farquharson across a field again I will kill him.'

Her breath expelled in one rush.

'Have you any more objections, Miss Langley?'

'It…it does not seem right, my lord.'

'I assure you that it would be the best for everyone, involved.'

'I-I'm a little shocked,' she stuttered.

'That is only to be expected,' he said. 'If you marry me, you would be well provided for, have anything you desire. I have no objection to you seeing your family as and when you please. You would be free to live your own life—within reason, of course. And, most importantly, you would be safe from Farquharson.'

'What do you wish from me in return, my lord?'

He blinked at that. What did he want? All his careful thinking had not made it that far. He had not expected her to ask such a thing. And then he understood what it was she was asking, or at least thought he did. 'Discretion,' he replied, trying to be tactful.

When she still did not understand, he elaborated. 'It would be a marriage in name only, Madeline. We would both go on just as before, nothing need change save your name and our living arrangements for a short while.'

She bowed her head. 'You seem to have considered everything, my lord.'

Another silence.

'Then you must choose, Madeline. Will you be my wife or Farquharson's?'

She touched the fingers of her right hand against her forehead, kneading the spot between her eyes.

He could sense her tension. The small body next to his was strung taut as a bow. 'Madeline,' he said softly, and captured her left hand into his. 'Your half-hour is fast expiring. Will you not give me your answer?'

She shivered. 'Yes, my lord,' she whispered, not daring to look round at his face. 'I will marry you.'

His fingers communicated a brief reassurance to hers and were gone. 'Thank you,' he said, then thumped the roof of the carriage with his cane and thrust his face out of the window, 'Home, please, Jackson.'

'But…but aren't we going back to Almack's? What of my mama—?'

'Speed is of the essence. I'll send a note to your mother explaining our decision.'

'I would prefer to tell her myself, my lord.'

The anxiety in her voice scraped at his conscience. 'I'm afraid that's not possible, Madeline. You'll see her soon enough when we're safely married. I'll explain all once we reach Cavendish Square.'

The carriage drove on in silence.

Chapter Five

Tregellas's townhouse in Cavendish Square was not a house at all, not in the sense that Madeline knew. Mansion was the word she would have used in its stead. It was a large imposing building set back in a fine garden. The hallway alone was bigger than the parlour and dining room put together in the Langleys' home. Floors beautifully laid with Italian marble, walls covered with exquisite neo-classical plasterwork—all nymphs and cherubs, wreaths and festoons—expensive oriental rugs, windows elaborately dressed with rich curtains, huge crystal chandeliers that shimmered in the light of a hundred candles. Madeline stared around her in awe.

'This way, Miss Langley.'

Lord Tregellas steered her down a passageway and into the most palatial, enormous drawing room she had ever seen. But it wasn't the luxurious décor or the expensive furniture that drew Madeline's eye. That was accomplished much more readily by the two gentlemen standing before the fireplace, one of whom she had just seen at Almack's Assembly Rooms, dancing with her sister: Viscount Varington and Colonel

Barclay. Realisation dawned. She peered round at Lord Tregellas with great wide eyes. 'You used your friends to distract Mama and Angelina!'

'I did not think that Mrs Langley would welcome my direct approach.'

That was putting it mildly. Mama would have run squawking to Lord Farquharson as fast as her legs would carry her. Madeline's brow wrinkled. But what, then, were the gentlemen doing here?

The men stepped forward, the taller of the two electing to speak. 'Miss Langley, honoured to make your acquaintance at last.' When he looked into her face she saw that he had the same pale blue eyes as Lord Tregellas. 'I am Varington, and this is our good friend, Barclay.'

'Your servant, Miss Langley,' said the Colonel.

Then Madeline saw who was sitting quietly in the background. And the sight stilled the breath in her throat and brought a tremble to her legs. The elderly clergyman had dozed off in the comfort of the wing chair. The faint catch of a snore resonated in the silence of the room. 'Lord Tregellas!' Madeline swung round to find the Earl directly at her back. 'You cannot…I did not think…Tonight?'

'I took the liberty of procuring a special licence,' Lord Tregellas said.

A snuffling and then a yawn. 'Lord Tregellas, please do forgive me. Must have nodded off. One of the vices of old age, I'm afraid. And this…' he rummaged in his pocket, produced a pair of small round spectacles, and perched them on the end of his nose '…must be the bride.' He peered short-sightedly in Madeline's direction. 'Lovely girl.'

Madeline blinked back at him, wondering if the clergyman could see at all.

'Now…' the clergyman placed an ancient liver-spotted hand on her shoulder '…I should check that this handsome devil hasn't abducted you from beneath your mother's nose.' The clergyman chortled at the hilarity of his joke.

Viscount Varington smothered a cough and grinned at Tregellas.

Lord Tregellas showed not one sign of having heard anything untoward.

'As if Lucien would have any need to do such a thing! Known him since he was a boy, and his brother there, too.' The clergyman glanced across at the Viscount.

Madeline followed his gaze. So Lord Varington and Lord Tregellas were brothers. That explained the similarity in their looks.

'Knew their father, too, God rest his soul.' The clergyman patted her shoulder. 'Sterling fellows, all three. Why, I remember in the old days—'

Lord Tregellas cleared his throat. 'Reverend Dutton, Miss Langley is rather tired after her journey.'

'Of course. Know the feeling myself.' He peered in Lord Tregellas's direction. 'And you, sir, are no doubt impatient to make this lovely lady your wife. Now, where did I put it…?' The clergyman patted at his pockets and gave Madeline a rather confused look. 'Had it a minute ago.'

She felt Lord Tregellas step close against her back, looking over her head, impatience growing sharper by the minute. Her scalp prickled with the proximity of his large and very male body

'Ah, here we are!' A battered old book was waved before them and the clergyman cleared his throat. 'Dearly beloved, ye have brought this child here to be baptised… Oops, wrong one,' mumbled Reverend Dutton. 'Getting ahead of myself there somewhat. You won't need that one for a little while yet.'

Madeline's face flamed.

Lord Tregellas stiffened behind her.

'Dearly beloved, we are gathered together here in the sight of God, and in the face of these witnesses, to join together this man and this woman in holy matrimony.' He stopped and beamed at Madeline. 'Now we're getting somewhere.' Lord Tregellas moved round to stand at her right-hand side and the rest of the old clergyman's words passed as a blur. This was a binding ceremony in the eyes of both God and the law. By the end of it she would be Lord Tregellas's wife; his wife, no less. Not half an hour ago she had been sitting in Almack's, existing minute by minute, doomed by a promise to marry Lord Farquharson, empty save for despair. Now the threat of Cyril Farquharson was gone, removed in one fell swoop by the man standing by her side.

'Madeline.'

His voice invaded her thoughts, pulling her back to the present, to the reality of her situation.

'Madeline,' he said again.

She looked up into those stark eyes. Saw a tiny spark of anxiety in them. Knew he was waiting for her answer. He was a stranger, she had only spoken to him on three evenings, and this was one of them. And he was Earl Tregellas. *Tregellas,* for goodness' sake. The Wicked Earl! How did she even know that what he had told her about Lord Farquharson was true? What she was doing was madness. Absolute insanity. She should have been afraid, but she wasn't. Well, only a little, if truth be told. He had spoken of instincts and trusting them. Every instinct in Madeline's body told her that Lord Tregellas would not hurt her. He had saved her twice from Farquharson. Now he was prepared to give her his name to save her yet again. If she refused him, she knew full well what awaited her—Cyril Farquharson. Just the thought of that man conjured real fear.

His fingers touched to hers as if willing her to speak the words.

And she did.

More voices, more words, warmth of his hand on hers, touch of cold metal upon the third finger of her left hand. Then, with a brush of Lord Tregellas's lips against her cheek, it was done. There would be no going back. She had just become Earl Tregellas's wife, while all the while her mama sat unknowing, waiting for her in Almack's.

'Hell, I thought for a minute that she meant to refuse me in front of Reverend Dutton.' Only Tregellas and his brother remained. Colonel Barclay had volunteered to see the clergyman safely home, and the critical letter had been dispatched to Mrs Langley via Lucien's most trusted footman. Lucien filled two glasses, loosened his neckcloth, and sat down in the buttoned wing chair opposite his brother. Heavy burgundy-coloured curtains hung at the library window, blotting out the night beyond. The room was dark save for a single branch of candles upon the desk by the window and the flames that danced within the fireplace.

Guy helped himself to one of the glasses. 'What would you have done if she had? The best-laid plan would have crumbled beneath a simple refusal.'

Lucien's dark eyebrows angled dangerously. That would have necessitated the introduction of plan B.'

'Plan B?' echoed Guy intrigued.

The firelight exaggerated the clean angles and planes of Lucien's face and darkened his eyes. 'The one in which Miss Langley spends the night unchaperoned in the bachelor residence of Earl Tregellas. Come morning, without so much as touching her, I would have ensured that Miss Langley had no other choice but to marry me.'

'My God, that's wicked. Wicked but effective.'

Lucien shrugged and took a swig of brandy. 'Desperate times call for desperate measures. It would have been in her best interest. And the Wicked Earl is, after all, expected to execute such things.' But the blunt words did not prevent the stab of guilt at the thought of his betraying Miss Langley's trust.

'Then old Dutton's reference to abducting Miss Langley from beneath her mama's nose was even more applicable than we thought,' laughed Guy.

'I did not abduct her,' said Lucien. 'She came most willingly once I had explained the situation.'

'And why not? I do not think there was much chance of her turning down your offer, Lucien. Half the women in London would give their right arm to become Lady Tregellas, no matter what they might say to the contrary. Little Miss Langley has done rather nicely out of your arrangement. Her mama could not have done half so well. Discarded a baron and came up with an earl.'

'Guy,' Lucien argued, 'it isn't like that.'

'Why did you marry her? Like you said, you could have just kept her here for the night. That alone would have been enough to make Farquharson discard her and call you out. Then Farquharson would have been dead, Miss Langley safe, and you in a position to choose a more suitable bride.'

'Miss Langley's reputation would have been ruined. For what that counts for in this town, she might as well be dead, as be carved up by the tabbies. What kind of man do you take me for?'

Guy rolled his eyes and gave a cynical sigh. 'To hear you

speak, one might be pardoned for thinking they were talking to a bloody saint! Have you forgotten what you've spent the last five years doing, big brother? A one-man crusade to deliver vengeance on Farquharson.'

'That's irrelevant. I'm trying to protect her, not ruin her life.'

'Oh, come, Lucien. Face facts. This isn't really about the girl at all. It's about appeasing your conscience and killing Farquharson.'

Lucien refilled their glasses. 'Have a care that you don't go too far, Guy,' he warned.

'Not far enough and not soon enough,' said Guy. 'Hell knows why I agreed to help you in the first place.'

'Then why did you?'

In one swig Guy downed the remainder of his brandy. 'Because you're my brother, and I'm a fool, and…like you, I would not see Farquharson do to Miss Langley what he did to Sarah.' He sighed. 'It's just that marriage seems rather drastic. If you think there's not going to be any repercussions over this, you're sadly mistaken, Lucien. When it comes to an heir, the Langleys aren't exactly the best of breeding stock.'

'You need not worry, Guy. I've told you already, as far as I'm concerned, you're my heir. This marriage doesn't alter that.'

Guy faced his brother with growing exasperation. 'Unless you mean to leave the marriage unconsummated, then I don't see how you can be so…' His eyes narrowed and focused harder on Lucien. 'That's exactly what you're planning, isn't it?'

Lucien tipped some more brandy down his throat. 'As you said, little brother, although I might not have chosen to put it quite so bluntly, this marriage satisfies my need to protect an innocent woman and lure Farquharson to a duel, nothing else. I'll see that Miss Langley is safe and has everything that she wants. But that's as far as it goes. Our lives will resume as normal.' He raked a hand through his ebony ruffle of hair. 'All aspects of it.'

'I think you may have underestimated the effects of married life.' Guy replaced his empty glass upon the drum table.

'And I think we'd better ready ourselves for a visit from Farquharson and Mr Langley.'

Guy waited until his brother reached the door before saying, 'By the way, if Farquharson finds out that you haven't bedded the girl, he'll push to have the marriage annulled.'

'Then we had better convince him otherwise,' came the reply. But as Lucien closed the library door quietly behind him, unease stroked between his shoulder blades and the faint echo of oranges teased beneath his nose.

He took the stairs two at a time and knocked at the door that led to the Countess's rooms. 'Madeline,' he said through the wooden structure, wondering as to the woman whom he had delivered here to this same door not twenty minutes since. He had warned her that Farquharson would come. It was not a matter of if, rather when. He remembered how pale she had looked and the slight tremor in her small cold hand as it lay in his. His grandmother had been a small woman, but her ring had swamped Madeline's slender finger. He reminded himself for the umpteenth time that he had done what he had to to help the girl, to save her from Farquharson, but that didn't stop him from feeling a brute.

She feared Farquharson…and trusted a man who had practically kidnapped her from an evening's dancing. Why else would she have agreed to marry him? Guilt tapped harder at his heart. She trusted him, little knowing that he had sealed her fate from the moment she had climbed into his carriage. 'Hell,' he cursed through gritted teeth. It wasn't supposed to feel like this. The guilt was supposed to get better, not worse. He wondered what would have happened had he been forced to resort to plan B. Thank God it had not come to that. Madeline need never even know of its existence. At least this way she would feel that the choice had been hers. 'Madeline,' he said a bit louder and slowly opened the door that led to his wife's bedchamber.

The room was empty; well lit, warm, luxurious, but empty. The only signs that Madeline had even been there were the slight crinkling of the bedcover as if she'd sat on top of it, and that faint familiar scent. Something rippled down Lucien's spine. 'Madeline,' he said louder still, moving swiftly to the small dressing room and bathroom that led off from the main bedchamber. But Madeline wasn't there either. 'Madeline!' It was almost a shout. Where the hell was she? Didn't she know that Farquharson was out there, coming for them? He felt the pulse throb in his neck.

It was a long time since Lucien had felt fear, but it was fear for Madeline that was now pulsing the blood through his veins with all the force of Thor's hammer. He reacted instantly, backing out of the room, moving smoothly, steadily towards the staircase. Adrenalin flooded through his muscles, lengthening his stride, tightening his jaw. The candle flames in the wall sconces billowed in the draught created by his progress, casting the long dark shadow of a man against the wall. He had almost reached the top of the stairs when he saw her treading up them.

'Madeline.' Her name snapped from his lips. His stride didn't even falter, just continued right on up to her with the same determined speed. His arms closed around her, pulling her up against him, reassuring himself that it was really her, that she was safe. His lips touched to the sleek smoothness of her hair, his cheek grazing against the top of her head that reached just below his chin. The scent of oranges, so light, so clean, engulfed his nostrils. She was soft and malleable beneath his hands, warm and feminine. 'Madeline.' In that word was anger and relief in dual measure. 'Where have you been?' He knew that his voice was unnecessarily harsh. Her face raised to look up into his. Those amber eyes were dark and soulful, as if she was hurt, as if something had been shattered. All the anger drained away, to be replaced with relief. He made no effort to release his hands from her back. 'Where were you?' His eyes scanned her face, taking in the tension around her mouth and the pallor of her cheeks.

'I was looking for you,' she said in a quiet steady voice. 'I wanted to ask you about when Lord Farquharson comes.' Then she turned her gaze away. 'I went to the drawing room, I thought you would be there.'

Lord, he was a fool. The girl had been through the mill. He supposed that this evening had not exactly been the wedding of which most women dreamed of. And Madeline was as likely to have had her dreams as any. It had been a long night and it wasn't over yet. The worst was still to come. Farquharson would come before the night was over. Of that he could be sure. Without thinking he pulled her against him and dropped a kiss to the top of her head. 'I was in the library with Guy, and I was coming to find you to discuss the same thing.' He found he was strangely reluctant to disengage himself from her. He did so anyway, taking her hand in his. 'Come,' he said, leading her slowly back the way he had walked. 'You should rest while you can. And what I have to say is rather delicate and requires some privacy. Your bedchamber is probably the best place.' The irony of his last sentence struck him. She made no resistance, just followed where he would lead, but something had changed, he could see it in her eyes. He just didn't know what.

Madeline perched at the edge of the pretty green striped armchair, beside the fire.

Lucien leaned against the mantelshelf above the fireplace, his foot resting against the white marble slabs.

She watched the warm glow of firelight illuminate his face. Such classically handsome features that could have come straight from one of the statues of Apollo displayed in the antiquities rooms of the British Museum, except she had always envisaged Apollo as golden and this man's colouring was as stark as a raven's wing against snow. Ebony hair, darkly shaped eyebrows and eyes of a blue so pale as to draw the attention of any woman who breathed. She could see why women still cast desirous looks in his direction despite the blackness of his reputation. Just to look at him caused a flutter in her stomach. Madeline stilled the flutter with a heavy hand. She did not know what the emotion was that caused the ache in her breast, just knew that it was there, raw and sore, since she'd overheard his words through the library door, since she knew that he had been untruthful.

Trust. So foolishly given, against all sense of reason, against all that society whispered him to be. She had deemed her own judgement better. And she had been proven wrong. His voice calling her name had been so filled with alarm and anger that she'd been sure that he knew of her eavesdropping. Not that she'd intended to do any such thing. She *had* been looking for him. That much was true. But it hadn't been the drawing room to which she'd been directed by the young footman. Her knuckles had been poised to knock when she'd heard his voice, and that of Lord Varington. Despite knowing that it was against every shred of decency to listen, that was exactly what she had done. Now she would suffer the hurt of learning the truth. She waited for what he had to say.

'Madeline.' He sighed and raked his fingers through the ruffle of his hair, with the merest hint of agitation. 'Farquharson will come tonight, hoping to forestall the marriage ceremony and…and subsequent events.'

She barely heard his words, rerunning the memory of his hands pulling her to him, the feel of his mouth against her hair, almost as if he cared for her. But Madeline knew otherwise. His voice had held relief. Why? The lie had slipped from her tongue; drawing room was so much easier to say than library. Lucien Tregellas did not need to know what she had heard.

'The marriage certificate will prove him too late.'

'Yes, my lord.'

'There is also the matter of the…' He paused and rephrased what he had been about to say. 'It is important that we do not leave him any loopholes to exploit.' He looked at her expectantly.

Madeline felt his gaze upon her. 'No, my lord.'

'You need not call me that, Madeline. You're my wife now. My name is Lucien.'

'Lucien,' she whispered into the silence of the room. The name sounded too intimate upon her lips.

Lucien rubbed his fingers against the strong angles of his jawline. 'As it stands there is such a loophole for Farquharson to find.'

Whatever was he talking of? She was married to him. He had said that would be enough to save her from the fiend. Had he lied about that too? 'What loophole?'

'There are certain expectations following a wedding.'

'My lord?'

'Lucien,' he corrected.

'Lucien, then,' she said. 'I don't understand. You said that marriage to you would protect me from Lord Farquharson. Now you're saying that it does not.'

He pulled the matching chair out from the side of the fire-place and dragged it so that it sat before her. Then he perched his large frame on its dainty green cushion and leaned forward to take both her hands within his. 'No, Madeline. What I'm saying is…' his thumbs caressed her fingers as if seeking to apply a balm to his words '…if it is discovered that the marriage has not been consummated, then it is possible for an annulment to be sought. It is not an easy process, but Farquharson may use anything that is available to him.'

Madeline stiffened and felt the blood warm in her cheeks. 'But you said that you did not wish to…that it was not necessary.' Her pulse picked up its rate. The butterflies stirred again in her stomach.

'No, no,' he said quickly, his thumbs sliding in fast furious strokes. 'You're quite safe.'

Was she? Beneath that sensuous stroking Madeline was starting to feel quite unlike herself. She became acutely aware of just how close his body was to hers, of the warmth that it generated, much hotter than any fire could ever be. The scent of his cologne surrounded her, causing an unexpected tightening in her breasts.

'We need only pretend.' One hand loosed to touch a finger gently to her chin. 'Don't look so afraid. I did not mean to frighten you.'

'I'm not afraid,' she said, and knew that she lied. But it was not Lucien Tregellas that frightened her, but the strength of the feelings that he ignited in her, feelings that the very righteous Madeline Langley had no right to feel. And then she remembered that she wasn't even Madeline Langley any longer, but someone else altogether.

A loud thumping set up below. Someone was at the front door, someone intent on kicking it in by the sound of things.

'Quickly!' Lucien pulled her over to stand by the bed and peeled off his coat with a speed surprising for such a tight-fitting garment. The coat was thrown to the floor, closely followed by his waistcoat and neckcloth. 'Take out your hairpins and remove your dress.'

'My dress?' Madeline gasped.

'Make haste, Madeline,' he said and began to tug his shirt out of his breeches. 'We must make it look as if we have lain together.'

'Oh, my!' Madeline's face blushed scarlet as she swiftly averted her eyes and made to follow his instructions. Pins scattered all over the bedchamber rug beneath their feet and soon her hair was long and flowing. Her heart thumped as loud as the banging at the door. She struggled to loosen the tapes at the back of her dress, but her fingers were shaking so badly that they fumbled uselessly. 'Lucien,' she breathed in panic, 'I cannot—'

In one fluid motion her new husband ripped the dress open; the remainder of the tapes dangled torn and useless. His fingers brushed against her petticoats and shift, burning a path across the skin exposed above them. Madeline almost gasped aloud at the ensuing shimmer, but Lucien gave no sign of having been similarly affected. Together they stripped what remained of the dress from her. She stepped out of it, leaving it in a pile upon the floor.

'Your petticoats and stays, too.' His gaze dropped lower, 'Slippers and stockings as well,' he instructed.

Madeline did as she was bid, until she faced him wearing only her shift. As she clutched her arms across her front in embarrassment, she felt his fingers run through her hair, rubbing and raking, until neat tidiness was no more. She thought she heard him stifle a groan. Maybe he was worried that Farquharson wouldn't be convinced. And then quite suddenly he stopped and stood back, scanning her appearance.

'Very good,' he said rather hoarsely, then touched his hand to her shoulders. 'Rumple the bedcovers as if we have lain there. I'll have Sibton bring you my dressing gown. Put it on over your shift and then wait here until I send for you. All you need do is agree with everything that I say and do not offer any other information. I will deal with all else.'

She nodded her agreement. No matter that he had misled her, she would rather marry Beelzebub himself than Cyril Farquharson.

'All will be well, Madeline.' His fingers slid against her face. 'I'll see Farquharson in hell before I let him touch you.'

Then he was gone, leaving only the trace of his cologne and the scald of his fingerprints against Madeline's cheek.

Madeline sat on the edge of the bed, tense and alone, Lucien's dressing gown wrapped around her. She had rolled the sleeves up as best she could, but still the blue-and-red paisley-patterned silk swamped her, making her feel like a little girl dressing up. She touched the sleeve against her nose, breathed in the clean smell of him, and somehow felt reassured. The strains of Lord Farquharson's voice reached even here. Righteous indignation layered over malice and rage. And still he ranted on. The clock marked the pace of time, second by second, minute by minute. Lucien would send for her soon.

Gingerly she touched her fingers to where his had lingered, wondering that she could react to him in such a way. Her blood surged too strong, too fast. She closed her eyes, letting the sensation flood over her, trying to understand the nature of it. Her body was taut, but not through fear, primed as if readied, waiting, wanting. Wanting!

Madeline's eyes flickered open with a start. Guilt washed a rosy hue across her cheeks. She buried the feelings back down where they belonged, deep in place from where they should never find release. Her heart was beating so loud she barely heard the discreet knock at the door. Thud. Thud. Thud. Her heart galloped. Her cheeks burned hotter.

'My lady.' The hushed voice sounded through the wood.

Madeline jerked back to reality. She rose from the bed, painfully aware of just what it was she was being summoned to do. Persuade Lord Farquharson that she had already lain with her husband, while all the while knowing the irony of the truth. Lucien did not want a wife. Most certainly he did not want to consummate his marriage. A mutually convenient agreement, he had said. Lucien would protect her; she did not doubt that for a minute. He would give her his name, let her live in his house, see that she did not want for money or anything that it might buy. She would be his Countess. She would be safe from Farquharson. It should have been every-thing that Madeline could want. So why did she have this feeling of loss and longing? There was no time to speculate. Drawing deep on her breath and her courage, she opened the bedchamber door and went to face what waited below.

Chapter Six

Anger resonated from Farquharson. His grey eyes darkened and there was a slight snarl about his lips. The waves of his deep red hair had been arranged to perfection. A slight shimmer of perspiration beaded above his lip. 'I tell you, sir, he's lying. Madeline is a gently reared woman. Do you honestly believe that she would abandon her mother and sister midway through an evening at Almack's to elope with this…this scoundrel?'

'I must confess, Lord Farquharson, that such an action seems most out of character for Madeline,' said Mr Langley wringing his hands. He turned to the tall dark-haired man standing by the drawing-room fireplace. 'You have shown us the marriage certificate, my lord, which does indeed appear to prove that you are now legally married to my daughter, but how do we know that Madeline consented to wed you? She is…she was betrothed to Lord Farquharson. To my knowledge she is not even acquainted with you.'

'Then your knowledge is wrong, sir,' said Lucien succinctly. He had no argument with Arthur Langley. The man was only doing what he thought right to protect his daughter. Lucien wondered that Langley ever could have agreed to marry Madeline to that snake in the first place. But then again, Langley wouldn't have stood a chance against Farquharson.

'He bloody well abducted her!' snarled Farquharson. 'Everyone knows of his reputation. He's downright evil.'

'Lord Farquharson,' said Mr Langley, 'I understand your distress, but rest assured that it does not measure in comparison with the extent of mine. We are all gentlemen here, I hope, and as such we should try to keep our language accordingly.'

'Please excuse my slip, Mr Langley,' said Farquharson from between stiffened lips.

Lucien looked at Arthur Langley. 'The matter is easily enough resolved, sir. Call back tomorrow and speak with Madeline yourself. She will soon set your mind at ease.'

'No!' Farquharson moved to stand between the seated figure of Mr Langley and the tall, broad frame of Tregellas. 'He seeks to buy time in which to consummate the marriage. Let him bring her out to face us now, before he has had time to intimidate her. By tomorrow the poor child will be so distraught she won't know what she's saying.'

'Madeline is resting. It would be unfair to subject her to such scrutiny.' Lucien's teeth gritted with the rage that roared within him. That Farquharson had the audacity to accuse anyone else of the heinous crimes for which he himself was responsible!

Farquharson turned to plead his case with Mr Langley, dropping his voice to a more controlled volume. 'Please, Mr Langley, I beg of you,' he wheedled. 'Do not subject Madeline to rape at this man's hands. Look at his state of undress. He was readying himself for the task.' He stared down into the older man's eyes that were heavy with fatigue and worry.

'We've arrived in the nick of time,' he said convincingly. 'There's still time. Demand that he bring her out now. If she was party to this crime, as he claims, then why is he disinclined to do so?'

'Lord Farquharson has a point,' said Arthur Langley slowly. 'I find myself unwilling to accept your word alone, sir. I cannot rest contented without seeing my daughter. Let me hear the words from her own lips and only then will I believe it.' His skin was washed an unhealthy grey and the skin beneath his eyes hung in heavy pouches.

Lucien rang the bell, whispered a word in the suddenly appeared butler's ear, and straightened. 'As you wish, Mr Langley.'

Farquharson glanced at Mr Langley's profile, then glared across the room at Lucien. 'If you've so much as harmed one hair on my betrothed's head…'

Ice-blue eyes locked with smoky grey. 'Madeline's my wife now, Farquharson.'

The tension in the room magnified one hundredfold. The challenge in Lucien's voice was as blatant as a slap on the face.

Arthur Langley stared from one man to the other.

A soft tapping sounded and the door swung open to reveal Madeline.

Lucien's heart turned over at the sight of her: small and slender, his dressing gown covering from her shoulders to her toes and beyond. Eyes the colour of warm aged honey sparkled in the candlelight and lips parted in expectation. Her dark blonde hair was mussed and beddy, its long tresses sweeping sensuously down to her waist. From the hint of a blush that sat across her cheeks to the little bare toes that peeped from beneath the edge of his robe, Madeline had the look of a woman who had just been loved. Lucien found the words emptied from his head, every last rehearsed phrase fled. He stared at her as if seeing her for the first time, wondering that this woman could be his wife.

'Lucien,' she said softly and moved to stand by his side.

'Good God!' Mr Langley uttered weakly.

Farquharson stared, eyes bulging, panting like an enraged bull.

'You see, Lord Farquharson,' said Lucien, 'Madeline is my wife in every sense of the word, and completely by her own volition.'

The drop of a pin would have shattered against the silence that followed his words.

'Madeline?' Mr Langley staggered to his feet. 'Is what he says true? Did you willingly elope with Lord Tregellas?' The brown eyes widened, scanning every inch of his daughter's face.

'Yes, Papa,' she said in a quiet voice. 'I'm sorry. I did not mean to hurt you, or Mama, or Angelina.'

Farquharson's lips curled to reveal his small white teeth. 'He is forcing her to this. The poor child is scared for her life!'

'I assure you that is not the case. Madeline has nothing to fear from *me*.' The emphasis on Lucien's last word did not go unnoticed.

Mr Langley slowly shook his head, his eyes crinkling into closure, his shoulders rounding as if the burden upon them had suddenly become too much to bear. 'Madeline, how could you? I thought that I knew my own daughter, but it seems that I'm wrong.'

'No, Papa…' Madeline made a brief move towards her father, only to find Lucien's hand upon her arm.

Farquharson saw his chance. 'See how he controls her! He's trying to trick us!'

Mr Langley's eyes slowly opened.

'There has been insufficient time for him to have wedded and bedded her!' Farquharson said crudely. 'For all of the rumours, Tregellas is only a man, like any other. He would have to be superhuman to have had her in that time!'

'Lord Farquharson, must you be so blunt?' complained Mr Langley, but there was a light of revived hope in his eyes.

'Madeline, my dove, you must tell us the truth,' said Farquharson, edging closer towards Madeline. 'We will not be angry with you.' His eyes opened wide in an encouraging manner.

Lucien stepped forward, forming a barrier between Madeline and the two men. 'Are you calling me a liar?' he asked in a quiet voice that could not hide the threat beneath.

Farquharson's eyes narrowed, exaggerating the fox-like character of his features. His mouth opened to speak—

'Lucien speaks the truth.' Madeline shifted to stand by her husband's side before Lucien knew what she planned. He felt her small hand slip into his. 'I married him because I love him. And for that same reason I lay with him in the bed upstairs. He is my husband in truth; that fact cannot be undone, for all that both of you would wish it.'

Lucien's heart swelled. He felt the faint tremble of her hand and knew what it cost her to say those words. His fingers squeezed gently against hers, his gaze dropping to the courageous stance of her slight frame.

'I'm sorry, Papa. I hope that you may come to forgive me.'

Farquharson's fury would be leashed no longer. 'And what of me, Madeline? Where are your pretty words of apology for me?' His anger exploded across the room. 'Or don't I count? Doesn't it matter that you have just publicly humiliated me?'

'Lord Farquharson, please!' Mr Langley exclaimed.

'I gave you my heart, Madeline, and this is how you repay me. It would have been kinder to decline me at the start.'

'I tried to tell—'

But Farquharson was in full rant. 'But no. You encouraged me, led me to believe that you would welcome my addresses. And now you run to Tregellas because you think to catch yourself an earl rather than an honest humble baron. There's a name for women like you!'

'Farquharson!' The word was little more than a growl from Lucien's mouth. 'Don't dare speak to my wife in—'

Farquharson continued unabated. 'He only wants you because you were mine. He's an evil, jealous, conniving bastard, and believe me when I say that—'

Lucien struck like a viper, his fist contacting Farquharson square on the chin.

Farquharson staggered back, reeling from the shock, his hand clutching at his jaw.

'Now get the hell out of my house,' said Lucien.

Farquharson drew his hand away and looked at the blood that speckled his fingers. 'Don't think you'll get away with this, Tregellas. You've gone too far this time.'

'Impugned your honour?' suggested Lucien. 'What do you mean to do about it?'

Mr Langley inhaled loudly.

Madeline's face paled.

'You'll find out soon enough, Tregellas,' said Cyril Farquharson, making his way towards the door. 'And as for you, my sweet…' his gaze lingered over Madeline '…you had better start praying. He's not named the Wicked Earl for nothing. You'll rue the day you cast me over for him.' Farquharson peered round at Arthur Langley. 'Come along, Mr Langley,' he instructed. 'There is nothing more than can be done this night.'

Mr Langley cast one last glance at his daughter and then followed. The last Madeline saw of her father was his face, pale and haggard and filled with hurt. The door banged and Mr Langley and Lord Farquharson were gone.

Lucien stood alone at the library window, the heavy burgundy curtains closed around his back. From the room behind came three chimes of the clock. The night sky was a clear inky blue; a waxing moon hung high amidst a smattering of tiny stars. The orangey-yellow glow of the street lamps showed the road to be empty aside from the sparkling coating of frost. Across the square the houses sat serene and dark, not even a chink of light escaping their windows. It seemed that all of London was asleep, all curled in their beds. The hectic humdrum of life had ceased—for now. Somewhere in the distance a dog howled; it was a lonely eerie sound that resonated all the way through to Lucien's bones. It struck a chord. Lucien knew what it was to be lonely.

His thoughts shifted to the woman that lay upstairs: Lady Tregellas, his wife. It had been Madeline who had saved the evening, Madeline who had convinced Farquharson and her father that the marriage was real. He heard again her words, *I married him because I love him.* Such a quiet voice, but so strong in conviction that he had almost believed her himself. God only knew how much he wished it could be true. That any woman could love the man he had become: the man from whom God-fearing women fled, the man whose name was used to frighten naughty children into doing what they were told. It was something he would not ask of Madeline. He had promised her safety and that is exactly what he would give. The bargain they had agreed did not include anything else.

A marriage to ease the terrible guilt that had gnawed day

and night at his soul these past five years. A marriage to bring Farquharson to his knees once and for all. That was all he wanted. The memory of Madeline's small soft hand slipping into his, the sweet smell that surrounded her, the feel of that long silky hair beneath his fingers. Lucien shut his eyes against it. Such thoughts were not allowed. He could not. He would not. She deserved better than that. He parted the curtains to move back into the library, refilled his brandy glass, sat down in his favourite wing chair, and waited for the rest of the night to pass.

Madeline lay in the great four-poster bed in the bedchamber of the wife of Earl Tregellas. She had tossed and turned and sighed, and still sleep would not come. Wife. The word refused to enter her brain. Legally she was Lucien's wife. In the eyes of God and the Church she was his wife. But she didn't feel it. She still felt like plain Miss Madeline Langley, the same as she was yesterday and the day before, and the day before that. It was only the world around her that had changed. The threat of Farquharson had vanished. Mama, Papa and Angelina were fast asleep on the other side of town. Her own bed in the little bedchamber in Climington Street was empty while she lay here alone.

Her eyes travelled again to the mahogany door in the wall that separated her bedchamber from Lucien's. Was he asleep? Did the fact that he was now married mean anything to him? Anything other than a means to bait Farquharson, and protect herself? She wondered why her safety and Farquharson's demise meant so much to him, enough to marry a woman far beneath him, who was so plain as to have been unable to engage a single gentleman's attention, save for Cyril Farquharson. But then again, Lucien barely knew her enough to stand up for a dance, let alone care if she suffered under Farquharson's hands. And she barely knew him.

He had called Farquharson a murderer and said that her own life was at risk, so much so that he had been prepared to hold her hostage overnight to ensure her agreement to a marriage he promised would protect her. He had underestimated her loathing of Lord Farquharson if he thought that necessary. Madeline had the feeling that she had stepped inside something very dark where there were no answers to her questions. Maybe the answers lay with the woman that Farquharson had killed, if, indeed, Lucien had been telling the truth.

Madeline shivered. She thought of those ice-blue eyes and the cold handsome perfection of his looks. Thought, too, of the heat of his touch and the warmth in his voice. And of how his relief had washed over her as he wrapped her in his arms out in the hallway, and the gratitude in his eyes when he faced her after Farquharson and her papa had gone. No, Madeline thought, she had not escaped unchanged at all. Lucien Tregellas had awakened something deep within her. And that something was not part of their arrangement. A marriage of convenience, he had called it. A marriage to suit them both. Better this a thousand times over than facing Farquharson. It was the escape of which she could only have dreamt. She should have been basking in cosy contentment. But she wasn't. When she finally found sleep, it was with the thought of the strong dark man who had made himself her husband.

The following morning Madeline and Lucien sat at opposite sides of the round breakfast table in the morning room. Sunshine flooded in through the windows, lighting the room with a clear pale clarity. The smells of eggs and ham, chops and warm bread rolls pervaded the air. Lucien poured a strong brown liquid into her cup, added a dash of cream, and soon the aroma of coffee was all that filled Madeline's nostrils.

'Did you sleep well?' The answer was plain to see in her wan cheeks and the dark circles below her eyes, but he asked the question anyway.

Madeline nodded politely. 'Yes, thank you. And you?'

'Very well, thank you,' he lied.

An awkward little silence followed.

'Would you care for some eggs, or a chop, perhaps?'

'No, thank you. The coffee will suffice.' She gave a small half-smile and looked around the room, unsure of what to say next.

Lucien helped himself to some ham and rolls. 'I was thinking,' he said.

Madeline's eyes wandered back to him.

'Perhaps it would be better if we went away for a short while. It would let the worst of the gossip die down and allow your parents to grow accustomed to the idea of our marriage.'

'Go away where?' she asked.

Steam rose from Lucien's coffee cup. 'I have an estate in Cornwall. The house is close to Bodmin Moor and not so very far from the coast. There is not much shopping, but you could have a mantua maker take your measurements before we leave and have whatever you wish sent down from London.' Lucien paused, trying to think of something else with which to make Cornwall sound enticing to a woman. 'There is also the latest fashion for sea bathing in which you might care to indulge, and a very pretty beach at Whitesand Bay.' He omitted to mention the positively arctic temperature of the sea at this time of year.

Shopping? Sea bathing? Madeline tried to look pleased. 'It sounds very nice.'

Lucien continued, 'There are frequent house parties in the locality and assembly rooms in the town of Bodmin some few miles away.' Fourteen miles to be precise, but he did not want to put Madeline off.

'For how long would we be away?' She sipped at her coffee, cradling the cup between her hands as if it were some small delicate bird.

Lucien gave a casual shrug of his shoulders. 'A few weeks,' he said nonchalantly.

'Very well.' She smiled nervously. 'I have nothing to take with me save the clothes I am wearing.' She smoothed her hand a little self-consciously over the skirt of the evening dress she had been wearing at Almack's last night; the dress in which he had married her.

Then he remembered what had happened to the tapes in his haste to remove that same dress. Something inside him tightened. Surreptitiously his eyes travelled to her neckline and sleeves. Nothing seemed to be amiss. He wondered if he ought to make an excuse to view the back of her, and thought better of it. 'That can soon be remedied. Buy anything that you like, as much as you want, whatever the cost. Two days should suffice to make your purchases. We'll leave the day after.'

'I was not…I didn't mean that you should…' A delicate pink washed her cheeks.

A slight frown marred Lucien's brow. 'Then you do not wish to go?'

'Yes,' she said looking at him a little embarrassed. 'I want to go to Cornwall. It's just that…my requirements are not what you seem to think. I would like—'

'More days to shop?'

'Oh, no.' Heaven forbid.

'Then what?'

She bit at her bottom lip. 'Nothing.'

Nothing? He looked at her expectantly.

'I had better go and get ready. Such a long day ahead.' She flashed a brief smile and escaped out of the morning room in a flurry of steps.

It was only when she had gone that it dawned on Lucien that Madeline was as ready as she would ever be, for she didn't even have a pelisse or a bonnet in which to dress before facing the world.

Madeline sat across from the maid and the footman in the Tregellas carriage on the way back from a truly horrendous day's shopping. It seemed that either Mama or Lord Farquharson had lost no time in ensuring that all of London had been apprised of the fact that she had eloped with Earl Tregellas. No one else had known and the notice of their marriage would not be published in *The Times* until tomorrow. Not that anyone had actually said anything directly to her face. Indeed, most people did not know who she was. But even so there were several speculative glances, a few hushed whispers and one episode of finger pointing. Mrs Griffiths in Little Ryder Street, studiously polite, gave no hint of knowing that her customer was at the centre of the latest scandal sweeping the city and furnished her with the bulk of her clothing requirements very happily. Brief visits to the perfumery in St James's Street and Mr Fox's in King Street went in much the same way. Only when in Mr Rowtcliff's, the shoemaker, did she actually hear anything that was being said. Two robustly large ladies were deep in conversation as she arrived.

'Abducted a girl clean from beneath her mother's nose,' said the shorter and ruddier of the two.

'And forced her to a wedding,' nodded the other. 'He has a soul as black as Lucifer's, that one.'

The smaller woman screwed up her face. 'Who *is* she? Does anyone know yet?'

'Oh, yes,' replied her friend. 'Plain little thing by the name of Miss Langley. That is, Miss Langley the elder. Got a pretty sister by all accounts. Heaven knows why he didn't take her instead. Not quite the thing, the Langleys. House in Climington Street.'

The women exchanged a knowing look before continuing on their way, none the wiser that Madeline Langley had just witnessed every word that passed their lips.

Mr Rowtcliff and his assistant Mrs Phipps hurried back through, each with an armful of shoes and boots. 'Of course, my lady, once we make your own shoes up they will fit like a glove. These are just some that we have that may pass in the meantime.'

Madeline bit down hard on her lip, pushed the women's cruel words from her mind and chose some footwear as quickly as she could.

The clock struck three and still Cyril Farquharson had not roused himself from his bed. It was not that he was sleeping. Indeed, he had not slept at all since returning home from Tregellas's townhouse last night. Anger had ensured that. The boiling of his blood had diminished to a simmer. At least now he could think beyond the desire to grind Tregellas's face into the dirt. The Earl had outwitted him, snatching the girl to an elopement before Farquharson had realised his intent. And Farquharson's best-laid plans lay in ruins. Madeline Langley would not be his. Her tender innocent flesh belonged to Tregellas now.

He had dismissed his initial instinct to call Tregellas out and kill him. Farquharson was no fool. Tregellas was bigger, stronger, his aim truer, his shot straighter. In a one-on-one confrontation, Tregellas would always win, just as he had won their duel five years ago. Farquharson's leg still carried the scars to prove it. But one victory did not win the war. There were better means to that, underhand means that involved stealth and bribery and corruption. Farquharson had ever relied on others' stupidity and greed.

Stealing Farquharson's betrothed from beneath her mama's nose at Almack's was a stroke of genius. Even through his anger, Farquharson had to admire Tregellas's move. It was an action worthy of Farquharson himself. And it sent a message loud and clear. Farquharson knew what this was about. Hadn't he always known? A mirror of past events. Farquharson smiled. No, he would not call Tregellas out. There were easier ways to catch the Earl. He thought of Madeline Langley and the way that her hand trembled beneath his. He thought too of the fear in her pretty amber eyes and how she struggled within his grip. He wanted her and he would have her, and the fact she was Tregellas's wife would serve to make the experience all the sweeter. After five long years, the game had begun in earnest once more.

The journey to Earl Tregellas's country seat in Cornwall was long and tiresome. It did not matter that Lucien's travelling coach was of the most modern design, sprung for comfort and speed. Or that the man himself had filled it with travelling rugs and hot stone footwarmers to keep her warm. Madeline's bones ached with a deep-set weariness, not helped by the fact she had not slept properly for the past few nights. Every night was the same. Nightmares in which Cyril Farquharson's face leered down at her, whispering that he was coming to catch her, promising that there would be no escape. She woke in a cold sweat, terror gnawing at her gut, afraid to let her eyes close lest Farquharson really did make true on those nightmarish oaths.

Lucien sat opposite her, long legs stretched out before him, looking every inch as if he was sitting back in the comfort of an armchair. The bright daylight shining in through the window showed him in clarity. The stark blue eyes were hooded with long black lashes, the harshness of his handsome features relaxed in sleep. Gentle even breaths sounded from his slightly parted lips. Madeline's gaze lingered on that finely sculpted mouth. All signs of tension around it had vanished. No tightly reined control remained. Just hard chiselled lips. She wondered what it would be like to place a kiss upon them. Madeline licked her own suddenly dry lips, gulped back such profoundly unsuitable thoughts and concentrated on looking out of the window. The countryside surrounding the Andover Road swept by in a haze of green and brown. The daylight was white and cold. Madeline found her eyes wandering back to Lucien once more.

His skin was a pale contrast to the darkness of his angular-shaped eyebrows and the black dishevelment of his hair. Sleep stole the severity from Lucien's face, imposing on it a calm serenity, as if it was only in sleep that he found peace. The fine lines around his eyes and mouth seemed to disappear. Indeed, the more that Madeline looked, the more she found she could not drag her eyes away. Her fingers itched to touch against that blue-stubbled jawline, that bold strong nose, those lips. Although the air within the carriage was cool, Madeline began to feel rather warm. She stared and stared some more. She was just considering the length of his legs and how muscular his thighs were through those rather tight pantaloons when she noticed that Lucien's eyes were no longer closed. Indeed, he was regarding her with something akin to amusement.

Her eyes raised to meet that lazy stare.

He smiled, and it seemed that something of sleep must still be upon him for his face still held a peaceful look. 'Warm enough?' he asked.

Madeline's cheeks grew hotter still. 'Yes, thank you.' Had he seen her staring?

The smile deepened.

Oh, Lord! Madeline hastily found something that necessitated all of her attention out of the window.

'We'll reach Whitchurch by nightfall and put up in an inn there. The White Hart usually serves me well.'

Madeline didn't trust herself to speak, just nodded.

'Are you hungry? There's still some cold pie left in the lunch basket.'

'No, thank you. I'll wait until we reach Whitchurch.'

'Well, in that case…' said Lucien and closed his eyes once more.

Madeline was careful to keep her gaze well averted.

The White Hart was quite the busiest coaching inn that Madeline had ever seen. Not that she was in the habit of frequenting such places, but there had been that time that Mama had taken her and Angelina to visit Cousin Mary in Oxford. The inn seemed to consist of a maze of dimly lit, winding corridors leading from one room to another. This said, the private parlour that Lucien had arranged for them was clean and tidy, as was the place as a whole. The food that the landlord and his wife brought was simple, but wholesome. A stew of beef with carrots, a baked ham, potatoes and a seed cake. They called her my lady and were polite. No whispers followed her here. No gossip. Madeline breathed a sigh of relief and ate her stew.

'Some ham?' suggested her husband.

'No, thank you.'

'A slice of cake, then?'

'No.' Madeline shook her head.

Lucien's brows twitched together. He seemed to be finding Madeline's dinner plate worthy of a stare. 'You don't eat very much,' he finally said.

'I eat enough,' she replied defensively. In truth, her appetite had shrunk since meeting Cyril Farquharson. She picked at her food, nothing more. Three days as Lucien's wife had not changed that.

He said nothing more, just looked at her with those pale eyes.

Madeline knew she should not have snapped at him. It was not his fault that her bones ached and her head was so tired she could scarcely think. 'Forgive me, Lucien. I'm just a little tired.'

'It's been a long day and we have an early start in the morning. We should go to bed. Finish your wine and I'll take you up.'

His words caused Madeline's heart to stumble. She sipped a little more of the claret, then pushed her chair back.

He looked at the half-full glass but forbore to comment on it.

'We are to share a room?' Madeline glanced up at her husband, surprise clear upon her face as he followed her into the room and closed the door.

'It is not safe to sleep alone,' he said.

'But—'

'No buts, Madeline. It is for a short while only and you'll be safe. I'm not quite the monster society would paint me.' There was a hard cynical catch to his voice. 'I'll go back downstairs that you might undress. Lock the door and do not open it for anyone except me.'

She nodded her head.

And he was gone.

The key turned easily within the lock as if it was kept well oiled. She turned to survey the bedchamber. The bed was situated on the right-hand side, facing out into the room and towards the warmth of the fireplace where a small fire burned. At the right-hand side of the bed and behind the door was a sturdy chest of drawers on top of which sat a pitcher and basin and a towel. A plain spindle chair and a small rug had been placed beside the fireplace.

Madeline walked over to the bed, running her hands over the bed linen, feeling the firmness of the mattress. Everything was clean and fresh, if a little worn. Such humble simplicity seemed a surprising choice for a man who held an earldom. She'd imagined him demanding something more luxurious, more ostentatious. And the landlord and his wife hadn't cowered from Lucien. In fact, when she thought about it, their attitude hadn't been dutiful at all. Friendly was definitely a more accurate description. Strange. Especially for a man with Lucien's reputation.

She sat down heavily on the bed, fatigue pulling at her shoulders and clouding her mind. Her new brown pelisse slipped off easily enough, folding neatly beneath her fingers. Next came her bonnet, shoes and stockings. The dark green travelling dress proved more difficult to remove without assistance, but with perseverance and a few elaborate body contortions Madeline soon managed. She made her ablutions, resumed the protection of her shift, removed the warming pan from the bed, and climbed in. The sheets were warm against her skin, thanks to the thoughtfulness of whoever had placed the warming pan within. She stretched out her legs, wriggled her toes and, breathing in the smell of freshly laundered linen, relaxed into the comfort of the mattress. Bliss. For the first time in weeks Madeline was asleep as soon as her head hit the pillow.

A soft tapping sounded from the door. Madeline opened one drowsy eye and peered suspiciously at the oaken structure.

The knocking grew louder.

The pillow was so soft and downy against her head, the covers so enticingly warm.

'Madeline,' a male voice whispered.

Madeline forced the other eye open, levered herself from beneath the sheets and padded through the darkness of the room towards the sound. Her hand touched to the key and stilled.

'Madeline, it's Lucien.'

Her fingers hesitated no longer. The key turned. The door cracked open by the smallest angle, letting in the candlelight of the well-lit landing. Lucien was looking right back at her. The piercing gaze of his eyes blasted away any remnants of sleep from Madeline's mind. She said nothing, just opened the door wider and watched with a beady eye while he entered. There was only one bed: Madeline waited to see what her husband intended.

He locked the door before moving to the chair by the glowing hearth. First his coat was discarded, followed closely by his neckcloth and waistcoat. The bottom drawer in the chest opened to reveal a blanket. Lucien extracted it, kicked off his boots, sat himself down in the chair, and pulled the blanket over his body. All in less than two minutes.

Madeline's toes were cold upon the floor. She still lingered beside the door.

'Goodnight, Madeline,' he said and, leaning back in the chair, closed his eyes.

Her mouth opened, then closed. 'Goodnight.' She climbed

back beneath the covers, looked again at the figure of her husband slumped awkwardly in the small chair. The bed was spacious and warm. Madeline bit at her lip. Offering to share the bed might be misconstrued. And he could have taken two rooms for the night instead of only one. Madeline stifled the guilt and closed her eyes against the discomfort of the chair, only to open them several times to check upon Lucien's immobile figure. Sleep crept unobtrusively upon her and Madeline's eyes opened no more.

Chapter Seven

'Madeline.' His voice was honeyed, but beneath the sweetness she knew there was venom. 'My love,' he whispered against her ear. His lips, hard and demanding, trailed over her jaw. 'Did you think that you could escape me, my sweet?' Bony fingers clawed at her arms, raking her flesh, tearing at her dress. 'There's a name for women like you.'

'No,' she whispered.

'I know the truth,' he said, his mouth curving to reveal those small sharp teeth. She looked up into the eyes of Cyril Farquharson. 'And I'm coming to get you. Tregellas cannot stop me from taking what is mine.'

'No.' Madeline shook her head, denying the words she dreaded so much. Nausea churned in her stomach. Fear prickled at her scalp and crept up her spine.

The blow hit hard against her cheek. Breath shuddered in her throat. She staggered back, searching for an escape, running towards the door. Her skirts wound themselves around her legs, contriving to trip her, pulling her back to him. She fought against them, reaching out towards the doorknob.

Her fingers grasped at the smooth round wood. Turned. Pulled. The door held fast. The handle rattled uselessly within her clasp. Panic rose. She wrenched at it, scrabbled at it, kicked at the barrier. And then she felt the hot humid breath against the back of her neck and the gouge of his nails as he tore her round to face him.

'No, please, Lord Farquharson, I beg of you. Please do not!'

Cyril Farquharson only laughed and the sound of it was evil to the core. He was laughing as he ripped open her bodice to expose her breast, and still laughing as he raised the dagger ready to plunge it into her heart.

'No!' Madeline screamed. 'No! No!'

'Madeline.'

Madeline's eyes flew open with a start to find herself sitting up in the bed with a man's strong arms around her. Fear surged strong and real. Farquharson? She struggled against him.

'It's all right.' The voice was calm and soothing. 'You've had a nightmare.' Cool fingers stroked at her head and then ran over her cheeks to gently tilt her face round to look at his. 'Farquharson isn't here. It's just a bad dream.'

'Lucien?' The word trembled, as did the rest of her. Her heart still kicked in her chest and her throat felt like its sides had stuck together. Slowly she remembered the room in the White Hart and saw the dying embers of the fire across on the hearth.

Firm lips touched to her forehead, murmuring words of comfort. 'Go back to sleep, Madeline. I'm here, nothing can harm you.'

The darkness was so thick as to mask him. Just the hint of the angle of a jaw and the suggestion of a nose. She moved her hands up to his face, lightly caressing his features.

'Lucien?' she said again, touching her fingers against the stubble on his chin.

'Yes,' came the deep reassuring voice that she had come to recognise. He eased her back down against the bed, pulling the covers up and tucking them around her. 'You should go back to sleep. You're safe. I'll be watching over you.' His fingers trailed a tender caress against her cheek as he moved away.

His skin had felt cold against hers. Madeline sat back up, peering towards the fireplace. 'Lucien?'

'Mmm?' There was the sound of a woollen blanket being arranged and the creak of the wooden chair beneath his weight.

The air within the room was not warm. Madeline shivered against its chill. No wonder he was freezing, sitting in that uncomfortable little chair all night with just one thin blanket against the plummeting temperature. 'You…you could come and sleep over here.'

Silence. As if he hadn't heard what she'd just suggested.

But Madeline had felt his weariness and the chill in his limbs. 'There's plenty of room for us both and it's nice and warm. Much better, I'd guess, than that chair.'

A moment's hesitation and then from the other side of the room, 'Thank you, Madeline, but my honour does not allow me.'

Madeline stifled a snort. Lord, but he had the pride of the devil. She dozed for what was left of the night, stealing looks into the darkness, guarding against the return of Farquharson, even if it was in her dreams.

The next day both Lucien and Madeline were tired and wan-faced. A hasty breakfast and then their journey resumed, moving slowly, increasingly closer to Cornwall and the Tregellas country estate. They travelled along the Dorchester

Road, making good progress despite the chill wind. A brief stop at the Three Swans in Salisbury for lunch and then they pushed on, travelling further south as the daylight dimmed and the dark clouds gathered. The rain, when it started at first, was a collection of a few slow drops. But each drop was heavy and ripe, bursting to release a mini deluge. One drop, then another, and another, faster and faster, until the road was a muddied mess of puddles, and the rain battered its din against the coach's feeble body. They put up for the night at The Crown in Blandford, a coaching inn that had none of the welcome of the White Hart, and was filled with travellers wishing to escape the worst of the downpour. Only the production of several guineas served to procure them a room for the night and the shared use of a small parlour. They ate hurriedly, exchanging little conversation, listening to the hubbub of noise that drifted in from the public room, and the batter of wind and rain against the windows.

Lucien downed the remainder of the brandy and scanned the faces around the room. Old men, young men, peasants, servants, farmers and gentlemen. The weather was an effective leveller of class. Even the odd woman, hag-faced, sucking on a pipe, or young with an obvious display of buxom charm. But thankfully the face that Lucien sought was not present. He wondered how long it would be before Farquharson would come after them, for he had not one doubt that he would. Now he knew that Farquharson would never call him out. The weasel wasn't man enough to face him again across an open field. Farquharson would use different methods altogether. The lure had worked, just not in the way that Lucien might have imagined. Farquharson would be part of the gossip: an object of ridicule, someone to be pitied. That was not something that Cyril Farquharson was likely to suffer for long. With cold and deliberate calculation Lucien had unleashed the demon. Farquharson would come for him now, at long last. Finally, after all these years. The satisfaction was tempered by the knowledge that he would not be Farquharson's only target.

He remembered the expression on Farquharson's face the last time he had looked at Madeline, when he had spoken so cruelly to the woman who was now Lucien's wife. She was a softer, easier target for revenge and one that would enable Farquharson to score Lucien's old wounds afresh. And in that memory he realised that it was Madeline that Farquharson would target. Lucien's mouth compressed to a hard line. He had promised her safety. And, by God, she would have it. When Farquharson came, Lucien would be ready. He blinked the fatigue from his eyes, wondering if Madeline would be beneath the covers yet. Then he sat the glass upon the wooden counter and slowly took himself up the stairs that led to their chamber.

He shifted restlessly in the small hard chair, feeling the ache in his shoulders and back growing stronger by the minute. His head was foggy with exhaustion, his eyes gritty and sore. Yet still merciful sleep eluded him. The memory of Farquharson jabbed at him like a sharp stick, taunting him with the terrible deeds from their shared past. Deeds that had stolen Lucien's peace, destroyed the man he used to be, and made him the cold hard cynic he was now. The mean fire had long since burned out; grey raked ashes lay in a cold pile. Lucien huddled beneath the layers of his coat and the blanket, and tried to breathe warmth into his fingers. He pushed the thoughts far from his mind, struggled to escape from their oppression. Another sleepless night stretched ahead. He should be used to it by now. Then he heard it: the small movement from the bed; the change from her soft even breaths to staccato gasps; a mumbled cry; the twisting of her body beneath the sheets.

He trod quietly across the wooden flooring and leaned towards the bed.

'No, Lord Farquharson...' A whisper of torment that wrenched at his heart.

Lucien's teeth clenched tighter. Last night had not been in isolation then. Madeline too knew what it was to suffer the terror of the night demons. There was an irony in the fact that the same man lay at the root of both their nightmares. He reached a hand out towards her, touched it gently against her face. The skin was wet beneath his fingers. Sobs racked her body. He could feel her fear, understand her terror. 'Madeline,' he whispered, trying to pull her from its grasp.

'No!' she sobbed louder.

His mouth tickled against her ear. 'Madeline, wake up. It's a nightmare. You're safe.'

'Lucien?'

He stroked her hair and wiped the dampness from her cheek. 'You're safe,' he whispered again and again, lying his length on top of the covers, pulling her into his arms.

Gradually he felt the tautness of her body relax as she snuggled into him. Her breathing slowed, the frenzied beat of her heart steadied against his chest. He inhaled the scent of her, revelled in the feel of her softness, of her trust, and knew that he didn't deserve it. He swallowed down temptation and with steadfast resolve gently began to ease a space between them. He had just managed to roll away when he felt the sudden grip of her hand around the flat of his stomach.

'Please stay,' she whispered into the darkness.

And Lucien knew that he was lost. He could no sooner

ignore the plea in her voice than he could cut off his own arm.
She was afraid. She needed him, he told himself, and ignored
the stubborn little voice deep down inside that told him that
he needed her, too.

'Come beneath the covers.'

'Madeline.' There was an agony of denial in his whisper
as he gently shook his head.

'I'm so cold.'

'Oh, God,' Lucien ground out and promptly climbed
beneath the covers of the bed.

She didn't feel cold. In fact, Lucien would have sworn that
she was positively warm. He lay motionless by her side,
trying not to feel the slight body that rose and fell against him.
She snuggled in closer and wrapped her arm around him.
Lucien closed his eyes and enjoyed the soft gentleness of his
wife, basking in her smell and her warmth. Slowly, he floated
on a feather cushion of bliss into the black comfort of sleep.

Madeline felt the chill in her husband's body and opened
herself against him, sharing her warmth. Her hand slid over
the soft lawn of his shirt, resting against the strong muscle
beneath. She noticed how strange a man's body felt in comparison with her own—all taut hardness, large, long and lean,
with such a suppressed strength that her eyes flickered open,
straining through the darkness to see him. He lay rigid as a
flagpole, completely immobile, as if he exerted some kind of
tense control over his muscles and limbs, almost fighting
sleep. It appeared that Lucien Tregellas was not a man who
allowed his guard to slip. He might feign an easiness of style,
as if he did not care what happened around him, but it seemed
to Madeline that there was something dark and watchful about
her husband. What was it that he guarded so carefully against?

The only time she had seen the guard drop was yesterday in the travelling coach when he had fallen asleep. Peace had touched his face then. There was nothing of peace in the large body now lying beside her own.

She lay her palm flat against his ribs and snuggled in close so as to feel the beating of his heart. She breathed in the scent of him—a heady mix of bergamot and the underlying smell that was uniquely Lucien. Cyril Farquharson and the stuff of Madeline's nightmare drifted far away. All she knew, all she felt, was the presence of the man lying next to her, filling her nostrils, beneath the tips of her fingers, against her breast and waist and thighs. Warming. Strong. Sure. No matter that theirs was a marriage of convenience, a marriage in name only— nothing had ever felt so right as the man that she called husband. She closed her eyes against him, felt the tight muscles beneath her fingers relax. His breathing eased, letting go, the guard slipping slowly and steadily, until she knew that he slept. She smiled a little smile of contentment into his chest, placed a kiss through the lawn of his shirt, and gave herself up to follow the same path.

Lucien awoke with an unusual sense of calm contentment. He lay quite still, trying to capture the essence of the fragile moment, reticent to lose it. The first strains of daylight filtered through the thin curtains stretched across the window. Lucien opened one bleary eye and reality jolted back into place. As the warm body beside him nestled in closer, he realised the exact nature of his predicament. A woman's soft body was curved into his, like a small spoon lying atop another. Her feet touched against his leg, her back fitted snug all the way up from his abdomen to his chest. Not only did he find that his arm was wrapped possessively around her, but his hand was resting against the small mound of her breast. As if that were not bad enough, her buttocks were pressed directly against his groin. Worst of all, Lucien was in a state of blatant arousal. The breath froze in his throat.

Madeline gave a little sigh and wriggled her hips closer into him.

Lucien captured the groan before it left his mouth, and gently removed his hand from the place it most certainly should not have been. Sweat beaded upon his brow. No woman had ever felt this good, like she belonged in his arms. He could have lain an eternity with Madeline thus and never wished to resume his life. Except that he must not. Never had he wanted to love a woman as much as he wanted to love Madeline right at that moment. Every inch of his body proclaimed its need. Lucien gritted his teeth. A fine protector he would be if he took advantage of her. Little better than Farquharson. *Not like Farquharson,* a little voice whispered. *She's your wife. You care for her.* Lucien slammed the barrier down upon those thoughts. What he cared about was justice and retribution. He eased a distance between their bodies, but he had reckoned without Madeline.

From the depths of her dream Madeline felt him slipping away and sought to recapture the warm contentment that he had offered. She rolled over and thrust an arm over his retreating body.

Lucien stifled the gasp. Hell, but was a man ever so tempted? For a brief moment he allowed himself to relax back into her, feeling the steady beat of her heart against his, inhaling her scent, sweeping his hand lightly over her back to rest upon the rounded swell of her hips. 'Madeline.' Her name was a gentle sigh upon his lips. In the greyness of the dawn he studied her features: the long black lashes sweeping low over her eyes, the straightness of her little nose, the softness of her lips parted slightly in the relaxation of slumber. Lucien swallowed hard as his gaze lingered over her mouth. He experienced the urge to cover her lips with his; to kiss her long and deep and hard; to show her what a husband and his wife should be about. But he had promised both her and himself that he would not.

He heard again her question of that night that now seemed so long ago, although it was scarcely four nights since: *What do you wish from me in return, my lord?* And he remembered the proud, foolish answer he had given: *Discretion...a marriage in name only...nothing need change.* But as he lay there beside her, he knew that he had lied. Everything had changed. He knew very well what he wanted: his wife. Lucien's jaw clenched harder. That wasn't supposed to be part of the deal. He looked at her for a moment longer, then allowed himself one chaste kiss against her hair, her long glorious hair, all tousled from sleep. Quietly he slipped from the bed.

Madeline reached for the warm reassurance of her husband's body and found only bare sheets. Her fingers pressed to the coolness of the empty linen. Gone. She sat up with a start, eyes squinting against the sunlight filtering through and around the limp square of material that passed for a curtain. His name shaped upon her lips, worry wrinkled at her nose.

'Good morning, Madeline.' He was lounging back as best he could in the small chair, watching her.

Surely she must still be dreaming? Madeline watched while his mouth stretched to a smile. A tingling warmth responded within her belly. Most definitely this could only be a dream. Part of the same nocturnal imaginings in which she had lain safe within Lucien's strong arms all the night through, shared his warmth, and felt his hand upon her breast. Madeline blushed at the visions swimming through her mind, rubbed at her eyes and cast a rather suspicious look in his direction. 'Lucien?'

'I thought I might have to carry you sleeping out into the coach. You seemed most resistant to my efforts to wake you.' He was fully dressed, his hair teased to some semblance of order; even the blue shadow of growth upon his chin had disappeared. Her gaze lingered over the strong lines of his jaw and the chiselled fullness of his lips.

Madeline's blush deepened as she remembered exactly what she had been dreaming about. 'I must have been very tired to sleep so long. I'm normally awake with the lark. I don't usually lie abed.'

'You appear to be mastering the art well,' said her husband with a wry smile. 'Did you sleep well?'

Madeline's heart skipped a beat. Had last night been real? Or a wonderful dream that followed hard on the heels of a hellish nightmare? The touch of him, the smell of him, the chill in those long powerful limbs. No, she couldn't have imagined that, could she? 'Yes. After you…after the nightmare passed, I slept very well, thank you.'

The smile dropped and his voice gentled. 'Do you dream of Farquharson every night?'

'How did you know?'

'You uttered his name aloud.'

They looked at one another. Warm honey brown and pale blue ice.

'I did not mean to wake you,' she said.

'I was awake anyway. As you correctly observed, the chair does not make the most comfortable of sleeping places.' He paused. 'You have not answered my question.'

There was a difference about his face this morning. Nothing that she could define exactly, just something that wasn't the same as yesterday. 'Yes. He has haunted my dreams since I first met him. Even before…before he tried to…' She let the sentence trail off unfinished. 'Every night without fail, he's there waiting in the darkness. I know it sounds foolish, but sometimes I'm afraid to fall asleep.'

Understanding flickered in Lucien's eyes. 'He would have to come through me to reach you, Madeline, and that will only happen over my dead body.'

It seemed that in the moment that he said it a cloud obliterated the sun, and a cold hand squeezed upon her heart. 'Pray God that it never happens,' she said.

'It won't,' he said with absolute certainty. 'I'll have stopped him long before.'

'We'll be safe in Cornwall, though. He won't follow us there, will he?'

Lucien did not answer her question, just deflected it and changed the subject. 'Put Farquharson from your thoughts. The fresh water was delivered only a few minutes ago; it should still be warm.' He gestured towards the pitcher. 'I'll go and order us breakfast. Will fifteen minutes suffice to have yourself ready?'

Madeline nodded, and watched the tall figure of her husband disappear through the doorway. So, even down in Cornwall, so far away from London, the threat of Cyril Farquharson would continue.

The hours passed in a blur. At least the weather held fine until the light began to drain from the day. Then a fine smirr of rain set up as the darkness closed, and they sought the sanctuary of the New London Inn in Exeter. It was the same pattern as the previous two nights. He had promised that they would reach Trethevyn by tomorrow. This would be their last night on the road, his last excuse to share her bedchamber. Lucien thrust the thought away and denied its truth. His presence was just a measure of protection. Or so he persuaded himself. If Lucien had learned anything in the years he'd spent waiting, it was to leave nothing to chance. The busy throng within a coaching inn provided opportunity for Farquharson, not safety from him.

Sharing a bed with Madeline had been an unforeseen complication. Lucien's loins tightened with the memory. He tried to turn his mind to other matters, but memory persisted. No matter how damnably uncomfortable the chair, or the sweet allure of her voice, or, worse still, her soft welcoming arms… Lucien's teeth ground firm. He'd be damned to the devil if he was stupid enough to make the same mistake twice. Take the chair, not the bed, he thought, and made his way up the scuffed wooden staircase of the New London Inn.

Surprisingly the room was not in darkness. The fire still blazed and a candle flickered by the side of the bed. The small room welcomed and warmed him. Still hanging grimly on to his determination, he made his way over to the chair and slipped out of his coat. Not once did he permit his gaze to wander in the direction of the bed and the woman that lay within it. He just kept his focus on the chair, that damned wooden chair, and started to undress.

'Lucien,' she said in a quiet voice.

He stilled, his boot dangling in his hand. Temptation beckoned. His eyes slid across to hers…and found that she was sitting up, watching him, her hands encircling the covers around her bent legs, her chin resting atop her blanketed knees. 'Is something wrong?' he asked, hoping that she would not notice the huskiness in his voice.

'I wondered if you might…if you would…' The candlelight showed the rosy stain that scalded her cheeks.

Oh, Lord! Lucien knew what it was that his wife was about to ask.

'I thought perhaps if you were here that…that Farquharson…that the nightmares might not come.' She glanced away, her face aflame, her manner stilted.

Lucien felt her awkwardness as keenly as if it were his own. How much had it cost her to make such a request? Hell, but she had no idea of the effect that she had upon him. She was an innocent. The boot slipped from Lucien's fingers. He raked a hand roughly through his hair, oblivious to the wild ruffle of dark feathers that fanned in its wake. 'Madeline,' he said gruffly, 'you don't know what it is that you ask.'

She gestured towards the empty half of the bed. 'It seems silly that you should be cold and uncomfortable on a hard rickety chair when there is plenty room for both of us in this bed.'

Better that than risk the temptation that lay in what she was so innocently offering. Lucien opened his mouth to deny it.

'I do trust you, Lucien.'

She trusted him, but the question was—did he trust himself? The warmth of her sweet gaze razed his refusal before it had formed.

'Madeline,' he tried again, raking his hair worse than ever.

She smiled, and pulled the bedcovers open on the empty side of the bed, *his* side of the bed. 'And it's not as if my reputation can be ruined by our sleeping in the same bed. We are at least married.' She snuggled down under the covers and waited expectantly.

Lucien knew that he was lost. Could not refuse her. Swore

to himself that he would not touch her. Still wearing his shirt and pantaloons, he climbed in beside her.

Madeline felt the mattress dip beneath his weight. Safety and excitement in equal dose danced their way through her veins. She knew that she should not have asked. Perhaps he thought her wanton to have done so. But the need for him to be close was greater than the shame in asking. And so she had spoken the words that Madeline Langley had never thought to utter and asked a man to come into her bed. They lay stiffly side by side. Each on their backs, careful not to look at the other, determined that no part of them should actually touch. His warmth traversed the space between them, so that the full stretch of the left-hand side of her body tingled from his heat. She wondered that he could have brought himself to marry a woman that he found so…lacking. For all that she was neither his social nor financial equal, he did not despise her, for surely something of that would have communicated itself in his manner? When he touched her she felt warm, happy, breathless with anticipation. Clearly Lucien did not feel the same. He did not want to touch her. The gap between them widened. That was when a glimmer of understanding dawned upon Madeline.

'Lucien.'

'Mmm?' Still he did not turn his head towards her.

It probably was the very question that she should not ask of her new husband, especially when he was lying in bed beside her. Indeed, any sensible woman would not have dreamed of so foolish a folly. But as the prospect of monumental guilt began to blossom, Madeline had to know. Whatever the cost. 'May I ask you something of…of a personal nature?' She felt him edge infinitesimally away from her.

'You can ask, Madeline. It does not mean that I will answer.'

A pause, while she searched for the right words. Eloquence of speech had never been Madeline's strong point. She sneaked a glance across at her husband. 'Before you married me…before Lord Farquharson…' She stopped, unsure of how best to frame her question. And started again. 'I know that you did not wish to marry me, that you only did so to prevent Lord Farquharson from…to keep me safe from him.'

It seemed that the large body next to hers tightened with tension.

'Was there another lady that you…' she took a deep breath '…that you had hoped to marry?' An ache tightened across her chest as she waited for him to answer.

Lucien looked at her then, a look of icy incredulity in those blue eyes.

She swallowed. 'I beg your pardon, I should not have asked, but…' Why had she asked? *To find if he has given his heart to someone else,* came back the little whisper.

'Then why did you?' he said curtly.

She shook her head. 'I-I thought that…' *It might explain why you seem so determined to keep this distance between us,* the silent voice came again. She stoppered her ears to its treachery.

'Don't think. The details of my past life do not figure in our arrangement, Madeline.' Then he rolled away on to his side, turning his back on her, and blew out the candle.

The sting of his rejection wounded her. She knew that she was not pretty, not like Angelina. The message was loud and clear. He might have taken her for his wife. He was prepared to share her bed…under duress. But he did not want her as a woman. Could not bring himself to touch her. But last night… Dreams, only silly foolish dreams, from a silly foolish girl. A marriage of convenience. A contract of protection. Safety from Farquharson. That was what he had offered. Clearly. In terms that could not be uncertain. That was what she had accepted. She had no right to expect anything else.

The bed was warm and blissfully comfortable. The first hint of grey light crept around the curtains. She wriggled her toes and sighed a sigh of utter contentment. Lucien's arm was draped around her, holding her against him as if to protect her from the world. Her cheek rested on the hardness of his chest, the material of his rumpled shirt soft against her skin, rising falling in slow even breaths beneath her face. The scent of him surrounded her, assailing her senses: cologne and something else that was undoubtedly masculine. Where her breasts crushed against him she could feel the beat of his heart, strong and steady like the man himself. Madeline revelled in the feel of him. Everything about him filled her senses and triggered some current of underlying excitement that she did not understand. Their legs were entwined together so that she could not have freed herself even had she wanted to. His arm was heavy and possessive. She resisted the urge to open her eyes, wanting to hold the dream for a little longer before she awoke to find that the bed was empty.

Inquisitive fingers explored across his body, sneaking beneath the loose linen of his shirt. Even in sleep his muscles were hard, with nothing of softness. A light sprinkling of hair dusted across the breadth of his chest. Her fingertips lightly swept through it, dancing in small circles against his skin. Madeline obeyed her instinct and followed her fingers with her mouth, touching her lips against his chest. A sleepy sigh escaped him as she pressed a small kiss against his skin. Lucien groaned, the rumble of the sound vibrating against her lips. So real, too real. Madeline's eyes flickered open. Warm contentment vanished in a second, to be replaced with utter shock.

Lucien's shirt was pushed up to expose his naked skin, and she was kissing him! Lucien groaned again and swept a hand down to caress her buttocks. Madeline froze, desperate to escape the situation she had created, yet afraid to waken Lucien. Slowly she tried to ease herself away from him. Lucien murmured something and slid his fingers against her hip. The material of her shift was no protection against him. His touch branded her with its heat. Another attempt to extract herself, gently easing her legs from his. 'Sweetheart,' he murmured and in one smooth motion rolled over to press her beneath him.

She felt him probe against her, something that willed her thighs to open. Madeline wanted nothing more than to comply, to give herself to him. The strange compelling need that burned in her, that made her crave his touch, his kiss, stoked higher, chasing reason and sensible thought from her head. Madeline fought back. She wanted him, but not like this. Not when he was sleep-drugged and did not know what he was doing. One magical hand stroked across her thigh. She gasped, knowing that this was all wrong, part of her wanting it just the same. 'Lucien!' His name was thick upon her lips. His hand moved to capture her breast, fingers teasing across the soft mound of skin, hardening its tip, until she thought she would faint for the need of him. Need. Her thighs burned with it. Her pulse throbbed with it. 'Lucien!' she cried out with the one last strand of sanity that lingered where all others had fled. 'Lucien!' a cry of desperation and of longing.

Lucien came to with a start to find that the glorious dream in which he was making love to his wife was a horrendous nightmare. He stared down aghast at the sight of Madeline lying half-naked beneath him. 'Madeline?' The word was raw and disbelieving. Her hair splayed across the pillows, long and straight, framing her face. Huge wide eyes that stared back at him in shock and disbelief, lips parted, panting small breaths of fear. And he, like a great beast, swooping over her, with his arousal pressed against her softness. 'Hell!' he swore and rolled off her as quickly as he could. Disgust tore at him, sickening him to the pit of his stomach. He was every bit as bad as Farquharson. He had become the devil that everyone thought him. A man about to rape his own wife— had it not been for his breeches. A thrust of the covers and he was out of the bed, standing staring at her. She looked as shocked as he felt.

'Madeline—' his voice was harsh and gritty '—forgive me. I was sleep-addled. I did not know what I was doing.' It was a feeble excuse, even to his own ears. As if that could justify what he had been about to do, what he would have done if her pleading shouts had not woken him to the villain he was. He wiped a hand across his mouth.

'It was not your fault,' she said.

God in heaven! What had he done to her? 'It won't happen again. I give you my word, Madeline.'

'No.' She shook her head as if to clear the daze from her mind.

How could he expect her to believe him when he had so glibly given his word before and broken it just as easily? 'It was a mistake to share the bed. I shall not do so again and you shall be perfectly safe.' His throat tightened. His jaw clenched.

'But—' Desolation struck at her beautiful eyes.

'Forgive me,' he said again, and gathering up the rest of his clothes in his arms, walked out of the room. It was the best he could offer her. His absence. He could only hope that through time Madeline would come to forgive and to forget.

Chapter Eight

The rest of the journey, from Exeter to Liskeard and then on past Tregellas village, was made in sullen silence. Lucien attended to her every need: ensured she was warm enough, that she was not hungry, that she was not too tired. But there was a formality between them, a distance that could not be breached. He did not touch her, or smile or even lounge back in his seat as he had done during the journey so far. Instead, he sat rigid and stern-faced, as if an anger bristled beneath the surface. His words, the few that he actually spoke to her, were not unkind. But his eyes sparked with something that she could not name. Loathing? Disgust? She did not blame him. He had made it very clear that he did not want her and she had behaved like nothing short of a trollop, tempting his kisses, craving his touch. Her face flamed just at the memory. Little wonder that he could hardly bear to look at her. Shame flooded her soul. She bit down hard on her lip, and averted her face.

Clearly he was a man to whom honour was everything. Why else throw himself away on a marriage to the likes of her? He had sacrificed himself to save her and all because of something in the past with Lord Farquharson. This was how she repaid him. Wanton. The word taunted her, playing again and again in her head, until she thought she would scream from it. Her teeth bit harder, puncturing the soft skin. She didn't even realise she was doing it until the metallic taste of blood settled upon her tongue. The road passed in a blur of mud and field and hedgerow. Madeline was blind to it all, concentrating as she was on holding herself together. His voice echoed through her mind, disgust lacing his every word. *It won't happen again... It was a mistake to share the bed.* She wanted to weep tears of shame and loss. Instead she took a deep breath, and sat calmly, steadfast and enduring, as if her heart wasn't bruised and aching. Strength rallied. She had survived a betrothal to Farquharson with his wandering hands and cruel promises. She could survive Lucien's disgust.

A shameful situation and each believing themselves to be to blame, neither Madeline nor Lucien noticed that both their dreams had been free from the presence of Cyril Farquharson.

Trethevyn was a large manor house that stood on the edge of a great, barren stretch of moorland. Madeline's heart sank as she caught sight of it through the cloud and rain. A huge imposing structure of grey stone, as dismal as the bleak countryside that surrounded it.

She supposed that Lucien must have sent word that he would be arriving, for the staff were assembled in the black-and-white chequered hallway to welcome the master of the house. An austere elderly butler and a large-boned elderly woman who answered to the name of Mrs Babcock seemed to be in charge. Mrs Babcock, who Madeline soon learned was the housekeeper, had a huge bun of wispy grey hair clearly displayed without the pretence of a cap of any kind. Her cheeks were rosy and her eyes were as dark as two plump blackcurrants. As far as Lord Tregellas was concerned, she showed not one iota of the respect that one might have expected. Indeed, she was of a rather no-nonsense approach. She eyed the new mistress with obvious curiosity.

Lucien kept his distance. If the servants thought there anything strange in the fact that his lordship barely looked in the direction of his new wife, they made no hint of it. What would be said below-stairs was quite a different matter all together.

'No doubt you will wish to rest after such a long journey. Mrs Babcock will show you to your rooms.' Madeline was dismissed into the care of the housekeeper without a further word. Lucien disappeared into a doorway on his immediate right, closing the door firmly behind him.

Madeline looked at the large woman.

Mrs Babcock stared right back, and then a huge smile beamed across her face. 'Come along then, m'lady. Best get you settled upstairs and warmed up before anythin' else.' The housekeeper hobbled up towards the staircase that veered off to the right.

Madeline hesitated for a moment longer.

'This way, if you please, Lady Tregellas,' came Mrs Babcock's voice. The kindly blackcurrant eyes peered round at Madeline. Mrs Babcock's ample girth set off at a dawdle up the stairs. She turned her head with frequent regularity to check if the lady of the house was following in her wake, and struggled up stair by stair with her uneven stomping gate. 'Oh, my word, these stairs get steeper all the time,' complained Mrs Babcock, her breath coming in wheezes.

Madeline followed with mounting concern. The housekeeper certainly seemed to be labouring. 'Mrs Babcock, perhaps you should take a short rest.'

'Nonsense!' exclaimed Mrs Babcock cheerfully. 'Up and down these stairs all the day long, I am. Not too old to be showin' the new mistress to her rooms.'

'No. I didn't mean to suggest—'

Mrs Babcock cut her off. 'Trethevyn is a lovely house. I'm sure you'll come to love it as much as his lordship does. Not the best of weather to be arrivin' in, but old George reckons as the weather will turn cold and fine again in the mornin', and then you'll see the place in all its glory. Expect you don't want to be bothered thinkin' about nothin' 'cept gettin' some nice warm food down you. But don't you fret, m'lady, Cook has got a special treat prepared, a lovely selection, and his lordship's favourite apple puddin' an' all.'

Madeline absorbed all this in silence. Her stomach felt small and tight and not a bit hungry. She forced a smile to her face and tried to sound enthusiastic. 'That sounds lovely.'

The wheeze of Mrs Babcock's breath grew louder. From down below there was the bustle of footmen unloading the baggage from the coach. Voices shouted and the fast flurry of footsteps on marble and wooden floors sounded. Madeline followed the housekeeper as the stairs swept back on themselves to reach a landing. From there Mrs Babcock turned to her right and followed down a dimly lit passageway.

'It seems a pleasant house,' said Madeline.

'Once you're settled, m'lady, you won't want to leave. I can promise you that,' replied the housekeeper.

Madeline sincerely doubted the truth of that remark, but said nothing.

Eventually they stopped outside a door, a door that looked to be the same as every other dark mahogany door along the passageway. Mrs Babcock reached forward, turned the handle, and swung the door open.

'The bedchamber of the mistress of the house. In you go, m'lady.' She waited for Madeline to move.

Madeline hesitated, peering in through the heavy mahogany doorway with a feeling of awe.

'Just as her ladyship left it,' said Mrs Babcock.

Madeline looked round with a start. 'Her ladyship?'

The housekeeper chuckled. 'The dowager Lady Tregellas. His lordship's mum, 'fore she passed on, that was. God rest her soul.'

'Oh.'

'And now the bedchamber is yours,' beamed Mrs Babcock, linking her arm through Madeline's and walking her into the room. 'I'm sure you'll be very happy here, m'lady.'

Madeline bit at her lip. 'Yes,' she murmured, unable to meet Mrs Babcock's eye.

The room was large in the extreme, bigger even than the one in Lucien's London house. Even the four-poster bed seemed small in comparison.

Mrs Babcock nodded towards the full-length window in the middle of the opposite wall. 'Have a care if you go out on the balcony until them there railings are mended. There was a right bad thunderstorm a few nights past and lightnin' hit the ironwork. All of a crumpled mess it is.' An ancient finger pointed to the side. 'Dressing room and bath's through there. His lordship even has one of them new water closets installed. Newfangled falderal, if you ask me. A chamberpot was good enough for his father and his grandfather before, but Master Lucien always was rather headstrong. Wouldn't listen as a boy. Still won't listen.' Mrs Babcock sniffed loudly to show what she thought of Lucien's wilful ways. 'Sit yourself down, m'lady. I'll have Betsy bring you a nice strong cup of tea with plenty of sugar. You're lookin' a bit pasty, if you don't mind me sayin'.'

Madeline found herself being steered towards the sofa, an elderly hand patting at her shoulder.

'I'll stop my chatterin' and let you catch your breath then. Anythin' you want, just ring. Betsy'll be right up.' Mrs Babcock got as far as the door before turning her face back towards Madeline. 'Took his lordship long enough to find himself a bride. But I reckon he's made the right choice with you, m'lady. Welcome to Trethevyn.' Then she was off and lumbering back along the length of the corridor.

Madeline stood where she was, listening to the scuffling of Mrs Babcock's shoes against the wooden flooring, eyes scanning what lay before her. A rose-coloured bedchamber, warm from a fire that had clearly been burning for some time within the centre of the carved white marble fireplace. Rain battered against the large full-length window in the centre of the room, and would have lent a greyness to the light had it not been for the warming yellow glow from a multitude of lighted candles. The room did indeed have a peaceful air to it, just as Mrs Babcock had said.

Madeline surveyed the furniture. There was a matching desk and chair, a small bookcase, a large wooden box on top of a stand, and an easel. There was even a vase of snowdrops, bowing their shy white little heads low towards their green stems. She pushed the door shut and walked quietly across the pink patterned rug. A pale brocade-covered sofa with matching cushions was positioned before the fireplace, a corresponding armchair by its side. A tallboy and a wardrobe in the left-hand corner. Two bedside tables. Symmetrically placed in the walls of both the left- and right-hand sides of the bedchamber were two identical doors, painted the same pale rose colour to merge with the walls. Madeline moved first to the right, the side that Mrs Babcock had indicated. The door led into a dressing room complete with dressing table and mirrors, and from there into a bathroom. She looked across the length of the bedchamber towards the matching door on the other side. Madeline suspected what lay behind that. She walked steadily towards it, placed her hand on the smooth wooden handle and turned. The door was locked. She backed away from it. Only in her retreat did she notice the walls.

Every inch of space upon the walls had been hung with framed paintings: paintings of woodland scenes, paintings of dogs, paintings of wild sweeping moorland, and colourful bright studies of flowers. Two children playing in the sunlight, a man walking through the snow. A rainbow lighting a dark sky, and a rugged ruined castle on a cliff edge so sheer as to plunge into a white-foamed sea. They drew Madeline like a magnet. Chilled fingers soon warmed, tension and unease melted away. Madeline forgot all else as she studied the works. Delicate translucence of watercolour, and bold rich oils. Absorbing her into the scenes, drawing her in with the artist's eye. At the bottom of every paper, every canvas, were the same entwined initials: A and T. The same artist had rendered all these paintings, and with such love and passion and clarity. Everyday scenes immortalised for ever by the careful strokes of a brush.

A quiet knock sounded, timid knuckles tapping on wood. 'Come in.' Madeline looked up to find a young woman carrying a tray hovering by the doorway.

'Beggin' your pardon, m'lady, but Mrs Babcock sent me with your tea.' The girl hunched her lanky frame and smiled a nervous little smile.

Madeline returned the smile. 'Thank you. You must be Betsy.'

'Yes, m'lady. Betsy Porter.' Another nervous smile. 'Shall I set it down here on the table by the fire?'

'Yes, please.' The girl's hair was fair, not unlike Madeline's own, but the eyes that looked back were blue washed with grey. 'Betsy, I was just admiring the pictures on the walls. Who painted them?'

'Oh, that was old Lady Tregellas. Mrs Babcock says that her ladyship painted all her life. 'Cept at the end. Wasn't well enough to paint 'fore she died.'

'When was that?' asked Madeline, intrigued to learn something more of Lucien's family.

'Long time 'fore I started work here,' answered Betsy. 'Perhaps five years, or so, ago.' A little silence before she said, 'I hope you like the flowers, m'lady. Mrs Babcock had me pick them specially for you.'

Madeline glanced towards the vase holding the snowdrops. 'They're beautiful, Betsy. I like them very much, thank you.'

Betsy pleated her apron and smiled. 'Mrs Babcock says to tell you that dinner will be served at five o'clock, so there's time for a short nap if you're tired. I'm to come back to help you dress at half past four. There ain't no lady's maid here. Mrs Babcock thought you would be bringin' your own.' Betsy ground to an awkward halt.

'No,' said Madeline, and then, making a spur-of-the-moment decision, 'Perhaps you might like to be my maid?'

Betsy looked as if she'd been struck by lightning. Then the blood rushed with a fury to heat her pale cheeks. 'But I ain't trained, m'lady. I don't know how to do hair stylin' or…' The words trailed off.

'I don't know how to be a countess,' confided Madeline. 'Perhaps we could learn together.'

'Oh, m'lady!' burst out Betsy. 'I won't let you down, that I won't, m'lady.'

Madeline was left with reassurances from Betsy that she only needed to ring and the maid would be straight there. If Betsy and Mrs Babcock were anything to judge by, it seemed that perhaps Trethevyn's staff were a great deal more welcoming than its master. 'Betsy, please can you send up some—'

But Betsy had gone.

Madeline jumped up and half-ran out the door to catch the maid, but of Betsy there was no sign. She'd drink her tea and then ring for warm water to wash in, giving poor Betsy time to catch her breath. She left the door ajar and went to pour the tea. A hot cup of tea and she would feel much better… perhaps.

'Max, come back here at once,' Lucien bellowed. 'Confound that blasted dog!' Lucien strode out of the library, dressed casually in only his shirt and waistcoat. The superfine black coat lay disregarded upon the library chair. 'Back five minutes and the hound deserts me,' he told an amused-looking Mrs Babcock, who just happened to be hobbling past the library at the time.

'Dear, oh, dear,' she said, casting a beady eye over the dark circles beneath his lordship's eyes and the stubborn tilt to his chin. 'Whyever that might be I just wouldn't know.' She surveyed the new leanness to his face and the tiny worry line that always appeared between his brows when he was at his most aggrieved…and wondered. 'Savin' that you look like you've been suckin' lemons. Bad journey down from London, was it?'

Lucien's glare would have had most other women beating a hasty and apologetic retreat.

Mrs Babcock was made of sterner stuff. 'Surprised you

haven't frightened that poor girl to death if you've been glarin' at her like that.'

'Mrs Babcock…' began Lucien with indignant pomposity.

Obviously a raw nerve had been touched if his lordship had abandoned the use of her pet name in favour of full formality. Mrs Babcock placed her hands on her ample hips and sniffed. 'Now, don't you Mrs Babcock me, m'lord. That dog's not daft. Knows a sourpuss when he sees one and seeks out better company up them stairs.' Mrs Babcock shook her head. 'Cook's down there makin' you your favourite apple puddin' an' all and you're up here with a face like thunder.'

'Did you say Max ran upstairs?'

'Disappearin' up there like he'd caught the scent of a rabbit, he was.'

Lucien raked a hand through his hair. 'But Madeline's up there and you know how Max hates strangers.'

Mrs Babcock chuckled, 'Nearly took Lady Radford's hand off the last time she called.' She delivered Lucien a hefty pat on the arm. 'Now don't you worry, her ladyship's door will be shut. He won't get into her room. And besides, don't you think we would have heard by now if it wasn't?'

Earl Tregellas's face was still creased into a frown. 'True. But the dog's too quiet. No doubt up to something he shouldn't be. I'd best find him.'

'Dinner at five, m'lord,' said Mrs Babcock, and limped off in the direction of the kitchen.

Blasted dog. Probably chewing on his favourite top boots. Ten years hadn't diminished Max's taste for good quality leather. Lucien took the stairs two at a time, reaching the upper landing in a matter of seconds. He scanned the corridor running in both directions. Thankfully the door to his own room appeared to be closed. Indeed, every other door along both passageways seemed to be in the same position, save for one. And that was the door that led into the bedchamber of the Countess Tregellas. A sudden trepidation gripped Lucien. 'Max!' he shouted and hurried down the length of the hallway to reach the room. He thrust the door open and barged in, fully expecting to find his wife backed into a corner by a snarling Max. Really, the dog could be a bad-tempered brute at times.

The sight that greeted his eyes could not have been more different. His jaw dropped. For there on the sofa was Madeline with the great black dog lying docilely across her lap, angling himself so that she could scratch his head in just the right spot. Lucien's entry brought only the most casual of glances from Max. Madeline looked up with a start.

'Lucien? Is something wrong?' She tried to stand, but Max showed no inclination to move from the warm comfort of her lap.

Lucien cleared his throat, feeling a turnip for dashing in to solve a crisis that did not exist. He fixed Max with an accusatory stare. 'I thought that Max might have found his way in here, and he can be somewhat…aggressive with those he doesn't know.'

Max turned his best sad expression towards Madeline and gave a pathetic little whimper.

'Oh, poor old boy,' said Madeline, tickling the dog's ears. 'Do you hear what he's saying about you? Look at those eyes.' The innocence in Max's liquid brown eyes intensified. 'As if he could even know what aggression was.' Max's tail set up a thumping wag against the pink brocade of the sofa and he laid his head on Madeline's thigh, looking up at Lucien with as smug an expression as is possible for an old dog to give.

'I assure you, he can be a brute at times,' said Lucien.

'Really?' said Madeline, raising her clear brown eyes to his.

Lucien had the feeling that they were talking about something else altogether. A small silence stretched between them. He made an abrupt change of subject. 'Is the room to your liking? If not, you have free rein to change it as you see fit. The same goes for the rest of the house, excepting the library, which is my…which I would prefer to remain as it is.'

First he ignores her for the whole day's coach travel, then he tells her she might redecorate his entire house if she wants! 'I love this room,' she said. 'I will not change it.' Her fingers scratched a massage against Max's head.

Lucien found his eyes drawn to the slender white fingers moving rhythmically against the dog's sleek black coat. He felt mesmerised, a strange relaxation creeping across his scalp.

'Your mother's paintings are beautiful.'

Lucien dragged his gaze away. 'Yes, they are. I'm glad you like them.' Her face was raised to his. Not angry. Not afraid. Just peaceful.

'Madeline…'

'There you are, you naughty boy!' Mrs Babcock heaved herself into the room.

Both Lucien and Madeline's heads shot round, unsure whether the housekeeper was referring to the master of the house or his dog.

'Ah, would you look at that,' cooed Mrs Babcock. 'I believe he's fallen in love.'

Lucien felt the tips of his ears begin to burn. 'Mrs Babcock,' he said coolly, 'was there something that you wanted?'

'Oh, don't mind me,' the housekeeper said. 'I just popped up to tell her ladyship that Betsy will bring her up some warm water to freshen herself in, shortly. I'll be off then.' And she promptly disappeared.

The moment was lost. 'I'll leave you to enjoy your tea in peace,' said Lucien. 'Come on, Max.' Then, to Madeline, 'I don't know what's got into him. He's normally so obedient.'

Max yawned and snuggled closer into Madeline.

'Max,' Lucien persevered. 'Come on, boy!'

Max shot him a speaking look. It said, loud and clear, *Are you mad?*

'Can't he stay?' asked Madeline.

One last-ditch attempt from Lucien. 'He'll cast hairs all over your dress.'

'I don't mind a few hairs,' said Madeline.

'Well, in that case…'

Max gave a little grunt of triumph.

Traitor! Lucien turned and walked alone from the room.

Lucien dozed fitfully, his dreams interspersed with Far-quharson and the ever-present past. The muted sound of a woman's voice pulled him free of the torture. He knew the words beneath that hushed mumble, had heard them every night over the past weeks since the journey down from London. Correction, every night save for when he had… That was something Lucien could not bring himself to think about. Guilt was not assuaged by the desire that burned low and steady for the woman who was his wife. He had not thought that he, Lucien Tregellas, could have lowered himself to the base level of Farquharson. It seemed that he was wrong. He had taken Madeline to save her from a fate that had befallen another young woman not so very different from herself. That, and as part of his scheme to deliver retribution to Farquharson.

He'd thought he could control that carnal part of himself. He had not slept with a woman in five long years. Since meeting Madeline, Lucien had found himself suddenly obsessed with the longing. Try as he might to deny it, he wanted his wife in his bed. He pushed the thought away, just as he had on every other occasion, and lay listening to her muffled cries.

God, but it rent at his soul! He found himself standing by the door that connected his room with hers. Hand resting on the doorknob, cheek pressed against the smoothness of the wood, listening and listening, fighting his every instinct to stride right in there and take her into his arms. He wanted to kiss away the worry and the fear, to tell her it was only a nightmare and that he would protect her. But who then would protect her from him? *I do trust you, Lucien,* she had said. He had taken that trust and destroyed it, like everything else in his life. So he stood and listened until there was silence once more and he knew that the nightmare had passed.

Every night was a torture. Every day, too. They dined together. Nothing else. The strain of keeping such a rigid formality between them wore at him. To make matters worse, Guy had written to say that Farquharson was still in London, feeding the *ton* a story that the Wicked Earl had abducted Farquharson's bride-to-be and forced a marriage upon her. Little wonder that sleep evaded him. Lucien pulled on his dressing gown and quietly made his way down to his library, and the bottle of brandy that would deaden the sting of his thoughts.

'Gravy soup, skate with caper sauce, kidney pudding, boiled potatoes, leeks, and apple pie on Wednesday. Onion soup, jugged hare, baked ham, turnips in white sauce, and sago pudding on Thursday. And on Friday, lentil soup, roast beef, pork pie, roast potatoes, carrots and stewed prunes. Good. Well, now that we've sorted them menus there's the linen mendin' to think about.' Mrs Babcock swept on regardless. 'But I shall fetch us a nice cup of tea and some scones to sustain us.' Mrs Babcock never missed an opportunity to attempt to fatten up her mistress.

'Thank you, Mrs Babcock, I don't know what I would do without you.'

'Get away with you, doe!' cried Mrs Babcock, beaming a face full of pleasure. 'I've been meanin' to ask you,' she said. 'Are you plannin' anythin' for his lordship's birthday?'

'His birthday?' echoed Madeline in surprise.

'Didn't he tell you? What a man he is! Would try the patience of a saint, he would.'

Madeline shook her head. 'It must have slipped his mind. He is very busy with the estate work.'

Mrs Babcock snorted at that. 'Never too busy for birthdays,' she said. ' Always loved 'em when he was a boy. Apple puddin' and spice biscuits, lemonade an' presents. We used to set a treasure hunt for him and young Guy to follow. Like two little scamps they were. Babbie this, Babbie that, tryin' to get me to help them solve the clues. Little rascals!' The housekeeper chuckled. 'You just let me know if you want a special dinner or the like, m'lady.' Mrs Babcock beamed a smile of reassurance at Madeline. 'I'll be off, then.'

'Mrs Babcock,' Madeline said before she could think better of it.

'Yes, m'lady.'

Madeline nipped at her lip with her teeth and then asked,

'Would you be able to organise one of those treasure hunts again?'

'Me? Heavens, no!' said Mrs Babcock. 'I was a fine children's nurse, and I'm a fine housekeeper, but I could never set them there clues. Was her ladyship that saw to all that. I wouldn't know where to start, doe.'

'I could help you.'

Mrs Babcock didn't look too convinced. 'It's a lot of work.'

'I'm sure that we would manage if we worked together,' said Madeline.

'Very well, then, m'lady.'

'Thank you.' Madeline smiled.

Mrs Babcock gave Madeline an affectionate pat on the arm and then she was off and exiting the parlour at a speed surprising for a lady quite so plagued by infirmities.

Madeline was left alone in the small drawing room, wondering what on earth she had just got herself into.

The days passed and Madeline found herself busy planning the treasure hunt for Lucien. He ate breakfast and dinner with her every day like clockwork, enquired about her welfare, and gave her copious amounts of pin money. But that was the extent of their relationship. Lucien kept a distance even when he was only seated at the other end of the table. Farquharson's name was never mentioned, and neither was a return to London. Madeline had to confess that she was happy in Trethevyn—well, as happy as a woman could be whose husband did not love her. She missed Angelina and her parents. She wondered how they were managing amidst the scandal she had left behind, and wrote to them each week. No replies were ever forthcoming. Madeline had to accept that her family had yet to forgive her. But with spring in the air, and the secret excitement surrounding Lucien's treasure hunt, Madeline could not be blue-devilled for long.

'Oh, m'lady, you are clever!' Betsy said with a giggle. 'Won't his lordship be surprised when he finds what you've done.'

Mrs Babcock hunched her broad shoulders with all the excitement of a small child. 'Such a way with words, doe!'

A surprised smile slipped across Madeline's face. No one had ever uttered such a compliment.

Mrs Babcock wrapped her arms around Madeline's shoulders and pressed a kiss to her cheek.

Madeline blushed with pleasure.

'It reminds me of the old days when her ladyship planned the treasure hunts, and the master was just a youngster wanderin' about the place with jam all round his mouth, his shirt tails hanging out and hair sticking up like a bird's nest. Always was a mucky pup. Her ladyship used to say he was like a little ruffled raven. How we laughed.'

Madeline was having difficulty imaging her austere, most serious husband as a small, sticky, messy boy. The picture conjured up was quite unlike a child that could have grown to become a man feared by half of England.

'It would be good to have little 'uns about the place again,' said Mrs Babcock, unaware of the more intimate arrangements within Madeline and Lucien's marriage.

Madeline stilled.

'What little 'uns?' asked Betsy in all innocence.

'Master and mistress's, of course,' said Mrs Babcock as if it were the most obvious assumption in the world.

Madeline's face flamed. She rose hastily, and cleared her throat. 'I've just remembered that we said we would visit the parson's wife over by the village. I had best be away if I'm to be back before dark.'

'Right you are, then, m'lady,' said Mrs Babcock and trundled off to let Betsy fetch Madeline's pelisse, cloak and bonnet, and, of course, her stout walking shoes.

If Madeline thought to escape embarrassing talk of babies she was to be disappointed, for Mrs Woodford, the parson's wife, was only too keen to reveal the good news that she was increasing and another addition to the Woodford brood could be expected late in the summer.

Madeline sipped her tea and hoped that Mrs Woodford would restrict the conversation to her own breeding. Her hopes were in vain. For it soon transpired that the entirety of the village of Tregellas had an avid interest in the prospect of a Tregellas heir. Indeed, Mrs Woodford's euphoria at her own joyous anticipation led her to divulge that Mr Turner in the King's Arms inn was running a sweepstake on when precisely Lady Tregellas would produce a son and heir for the estate. Madeline paled and heard the cup rattle against her saucer.

Reverend Woodford chose this precise moment to wander in from the garden with Lucien. The two men were still deep in conversation about the parson's plans for Lady Day as they strolled into the small drawing room.

'Ah, Lady Tregellas, I trust that Mrs Woodford has informed you of our expected happy event?' Reverend Woodford's eyes twinkled.

Madeline found her throat suddenly very dry. 'Yes, indeed. It's wonderful news.'

Lucien looked from his wife's pink cheeks to Mrs Woodford's bubbling happiness, and finally to the proud swell of the parson's chest. Comprehension dawned. 'Let me extend my wife's sentiment and offer my congratulations to you both.'

Reverend and Mrs Woodford beamed their pleasure.

Madeline could bear it no longer. 'Please do excuse us, Mrs Woodford. We must be back at Trethevyn before darkness.' She bit at her lip and threw Lucien a pleading look. 'Thank you so much for the lovely tea. S-such wonderful news,' she managed to stutter. 'If there's anything I can do to help, please just ask.'

Mrs Woodford's two-year-old daughter scampered in to the room at that very minute, running full pelt towards her mother before the sight of Madeline brought her up short. She stopped and pointed a small chubby finger at Lady Tregellas, her tiny pink lips forming an expression of surprise.

'Sally!' chided Mrs Woodford, looking anything but displeased. 'Naughty child.' With one scoop of the arms the small girl was resting on her mother's lap. 'No pointing,' said Mrs Woodford, and kissed the miniature extended finger. 'This is Lord and Lady Tregellas, come to visit your mama. Say how do you do, very pleased to meet you, my lord and my lady.' Sally giggled at the absurdity of this, her big blue baby eyes staring first at Lucien and then at Madeline.

Madeline found that the lump in her throat had become a veritable boulder in danger of choking her, and something gritty was nipping at her eyes, so that she had to blink and blink to stop them watering. 'Goodbye, then.'

But escape was not so easy. For little Sally had taken quite a shine to the nice Lady Tregellas and insisted upon placing a kiss on the lady's soft cheek.

Madeline practically ran out to the waiting coach.

'What's wrong? Why did you wish to leave?' Lucien enquired as the door slammed shut.

Madeline swallowed hard, but the lump refused to be dislodged. 'I have a headache,' was all she managed to say, and hoped that Lucien would not press the matter.

He nodded, and, aware of the moist glisten in her eyes and

the quiver of her lips, lent her the space and the silence that she needed to fight whatever it was that was distressing her. Somehow he did not believe her story of the headache.

She stared blindly from the window, willing herself not to cry, and all the way back on the narrow winding road to Trethevyn Madeline began to realise just how much she wanted what she could never have.

Chapter Nine

Fortunately the next day was taken up in hiding the clues that Madeline had written, and Mrs Babcock organising the kitchen for the preparation of the secret birthday lunch, so much so that there was little time to dwell upon such things. Madeline slumped exhausted into bed, wondering what Lucien would think of his birthday surprise.

The day of the birthday was fine and dry with a cold weak sun to brighten the morning room. She rose especially early so that she would be seated at the breakfast table before Lucien even entered the room. She sat quite still at the table, basking in the sunlight that flooded in through the large window. Tiny particles floated on the sunbeam, suspended like small specks of silver within the air. Everything was quiet, so quiet that Madeline could hear the sound of her own breath. She waited with a calm easiness, surprised at her own hunger. A whole plate of eggs, ham and mushrooms had been devoured before she heard the tread of her husband's footsteps. She was sipping her coffee, with Max lounging at her feet, when he entered.

'Madeline?'

She heard the question in his voice.

He glanced towards the clock as if to check that he had not mistaken the time. 'You're up early this morning.'

'Yes,' she said, trying not to look at the neatly folded note that lay beside his place setting. She smiled, a warm anticipation surging through her veins. 'Happy birthday, Lucien.'

Surprise widened his eyes, and then he recovered himself to thank her most politely, and went to help himself to breakfast from the warming plates. It was only when he sat down that he noticed her scraped-clean plate. 'You've already eaten?'

'I couldn't wait for a certain slug-a-bed or I might have starved.'

That drew the vestige of a laugh and eased the tension between them. He found the note beside his plate and scanned the contents. The severity in his face fled, replaced instead with something of the boyish delight she imagined he must have had all those years ago as a child. 'A treasure hunt.'

'I thought you might like it.'

Lucien laughed again, and she couldn't help but notice how it transformed his face. It was like looking at two different men. One cold, handsome and remote, the other, warm and lovable. 'And you were right.'

For the first time since arriving at Trethevyn Madeline saw a glimpse of the man who had swept her off her feet from a dance room and married her before a clergyman that same night.

Lucien held the piece of paper between his fingers. The sun dazzled his eyes, forcing him to squint to make out the words.

First follow beneath me where strong winds blow. I am a cock that cannot crow.

He raised a quizzical eyebrow and looked at Madeline.

Madeline returned a look that belied innocence.

'Do you mean to give me an extra clue?'

'Certainly not,' retorted his wife. 'Mrs Babcock warned me of your lazy ways. You are to solve the clues by yourself.'

Lucien smiled.

They were standing out in the patchwork garden at the rear of the house, with Max in between them. Lucien scanned the surroundings, his eye alighting on the small summer-house built on the top of a grassy knoll in the distance. 'I think perhaps a stroll to the summer-house is in order.' He held out his arm to Madeline and the two wandered off towards the small buff-coloured structure. The weathervane in the shape of a cockerel atop its peaked roof glinted in the sunshine. Max ran off in search of rabbits.

The second does not live and cannot be found above the ground.

Lucien puzzled over that, watching the happiness light his wife's face. He had not seen her looking so relaxed or happy, since before... He pushed that thought away, and continued to look at the warmth radiating out from those sherry-gold eyes. 'Cannot be found above the ground,' he repeated softly as if mulling the clue.

Madeline laughed and clapped her hands together.

He looked directly at his wife. 'I hope you are wearing stout walking shoes, for the Trethevyn mausoleum is on the other side of that woodland.'

Madeline lifted her skirt and dangled a foot encased in a most sensible shoe. 'I think perhaps that my clues are too easy for you.'

'Quite the contrary,' he said, averting his gaze from the slim, shapely ankle that had just presented itself before his eyes.

* * *

By the tenth and final clue, it was time for lunch, and Lord and Lady Tregellas had traced a path that intertwined every feature of the Tregellas estate, even if it did require a two-mile walk there and back. They were standing in the wine cellar beneath Trethevyn, straining to read the clue beneath the light of a solitary flickering candle.

The tenth, and last, can be found where love and peace abound. In golden swathes and purple hues, the answer simply lies in 'you'.

Lucien's brow knitted and something of the old tension returned to his face.

'Have I beaten you at last?' Madeline asked softly.

Their eyes met, and lingered. Hearts beat loud in the silence.

'It would seem so,' Lucien replied. But it was not the treasure hunt to which he was referring. He stepped towards her.

A scrabbling sounded at the cellar door, followed by an inquisitive woof.

'Max!' laughed Madeline. 'He's worried that he's missing something.' She moved to open the door.

Lucien watched his wife stoop to pat the snuffling dog. *He very nearly did,* said the little voice in his head.

'Come on, I'll give you another clue. You should look more closely in the gardens.'

Lucien cocked an eyebrow and followed his wife back up the narrow stairs into the daylight.

Cool spring sunshine bathed the couple as they meandered through the gardens, Madeline's hand tucked within Lucien's arm. There did not seem to be the need to talk. A peaceful companionship had settled upon them. They were happy just to feel the warmth of the sun upon their faces and the nip of fresh air within their noses. A blackbird scuttled beneath the box hedge, a spindle-legged fat-bodied robin whistled its cheeky challenge from the safety of the handle of Old George's gardening fork over by the herb garden. The sky was a clear pale blue, revealing a new clarity of colour to the countryside surrounding them: cold brown earth that crumbled beneath their feet; lawns of green grass; bare branches on ancient old trees; the first hint of buds upon the bushes. They walked towards a battered old wooden seat, and sat down, together.

Madeline breathed in the cool spring air, feeling it cleanse the last of the cobwebs from her lungs. Over the past few weeks tension had just melted away, starting from that very first day when she entered Lady Anne's bedchamber and admired her paintings.. There had been a sense of coming home, with the house and all its occupants making her welcome. Max and Babbie and Betsy, Old George and Mr Norton, whose beady butler eye missed nothing. Even Lucien seemed to have allowed his guard to slip a little.

She felt the warm strength in his arm beneath hers and rubbed her fingers against the wool of his coat. Beneath that cold exterior lurked a kind and loving heart. With every passing day she'd watched as her husband saw to his tenants with a fair hand. He was interested in his people, cared enough to know their names, and what happened in their lives, from the birth of the first lamb to Bob Miller's wife's dropsy. No one in Tregellas was afraid of him; no one called him the Wicked Earl here. Was it her imagination, or, since coming home, had something of that cold handsome austerity thawed? Madeline glanced up at her husband's face. He was looking at her and smiling.

'Love and peace,' he said. His smile deepened as his gaze

moved to linger on the statue that stood behind the small colourful patch of spring flowers. A stone Cupid looked back at him, complete with stone dove perched upon his bow. 'Golden swathes, and purple hues.' The blue eyes twinkled as he saw what she had done. Daffodils and crocuses had been planted to spell out his name—LUCIEN. He chuckled, shaking his head as if he couldn't believe what was before him. In the middle of the letter U, lying on the damp brown soil, was a battered old box. He moved towards it, pulling Madeline up with him. The simple hook latch opened easily, the lid swung open. Inside, a lady's lavender silk scarf had been wrapped around something. His fingers eased under it, lifting it carefully out. Slowly he unwrapped the scarf, to find a small embroidered portrait of a young boy. It had been fitted into a simple wooden frame.

Madeline held her breath while her husband stared down at the needlework that she had laboured at secretly for the past weeks.

His fingers touched the small neat stitches that had been worked with such care.

'Do you know who it is?' she asked.

'I should do. You have captured the likeness very well.' He regarded her quizzically. 'But how on earth did you…?'

Specks of gold glittered in her amber eyes. 'One of your mother's paintings on my bedchamber wall shows two small boys playing together. It was not difficult to work out which one was you. Babbie was happy to confirm my suspicions.'

Lucien grinned.

'George made the frame. We…we hoped that you would like it,' she said shyly.

'I like it very much.' Then he snaked an arm around her waist and dropped a kiss to the top of her head. 'Thank you,

Madeline. It's a fine and thoughtful gift.' Clear blue eyes met lucid brown and smiled until little lines creased their sides, and the warmth of his smile engulfed her so that her heart swelled and her head felt light and dizzy. And when his hand covered hers she thought that life had never been so good.

Hand in hand they strolled back into Trethevyn and the birthday lunch that awaited.

The fire blazed upon the hearth, every candle in the massive crystal chandelier had been lit, and the small drawing room was cosy and warm. Madeline and Lucien sat together on the sofa. Lucien's birthday gift had pride of place on top of the mantelpiece, the stitched boy looking with a cheeky grin over proceedings. Max lay at their feet, beating the edge of the sofa with his tail, and chewing on what had been one of Madeline's dancing slippers.

'I see that his appetite is not limited to my footwear.' Lucien decanted the sherry into two small glasses and handed one to his wife.

Madeline laughed and tickled a black silky ear. 'I made the mistake of leaving my slippers on the floor and he sneaked off with one before I noticed. I salvaged the other before he came back for it, although quite what good one slipper is, I do not know.'

They chuckled together and sipped at their sherry.

Lucien dropped his hand on to his wife's. 'Thank you, Madeline.'

She looked up in surprise. 'What for?'

'For today. For understanding.' His thumb stroked small circle over the back of her hand. 'For…forgiving.'

'Lucien…' her fingers closed around his thumb, trapping it, stilling its motion '…there is nothing to forgive. You saved me from Farquharson.' Her fingers slid from his thumb up to stroke against the inside of his wrist. 'You are my husband,' she said softly.

His eyes closed at her words, struggling against the sensation that her fingers conjured up. Would that he were her husband in every sense of the word. 'That does not mean that I have the right… We had an agreement. I promised you protection, Madeline, not—'

'Not what, Lucien?'

'Not what happened that night in the inn.' He thought he saw wounded anger flash in her eyes and then it was gone. God, he was a fool to have hurt her.

Her teeth nipped at her lower lip, as she entwined her fingers between his. 'I'm sorry that I—'

Lucien felt the constriction in his chest. 'Married me,' he finished for her.

'No!' she gasped. 'Never that.'

Relief loosed the breath from his throat.

Their fingers clung together with a gentle desperation.

'You've nothing to be sorry for, Madeline. You've done nothing wrong.'

The teeth bit harder against the small pink lip. 'I'm sorry that I made you angry that night. I know that you do not want…that you don't want to—'

Lucien could stand it no longer. He pulled her into his arms, tilting her face up to his. 'It was my fault,' he said harshly. 'I should have known better, but found to my shame that I was wrong. Let's put it behind us, Madeline. I wish only for you to be happy.' He touched his lips to her temple in a chaste kiss and put her away from him. Temptation was a terrible thing. And he was determined not to spoil this most precious of days.

* * *

Three weeks had passed since Lucien's birthday and signs of new life sprouted everywhere from small green shoots in the soil to tiny buds upon bare brown branches. Lucien was consideration itself. He smiled more. Laughed more. Held her hand, took her arm. He told her stories of his and Guy's boyhood, carried her with him on most of his estate calls, even walked with her to visit the nearby Neolithic stone burial tomb and the mysterious stone circles called the Hurlers. He bought her a beautiful docile bay mare and rode out with her most days. He accompanied her on visits to the local gentry and took her dancing in Bodmin and shopping in Truro. With each passing day Madeline grew to love the man who was her husband.

What had been naïve pleasure at his touch in London had grown to a burning need. She craved him. Didn't understand why his merest glance caused a flutter in her stomach. Just knew that she needed more of him. The memories of that one night when she'd kissed him in the bed of the New London Inn tortured her. She wanted him. Every last bit of him. To touch his naked skin. Trace a pathway through the hairs upon his chest. To feel the strength of his body moving over hers. Wanted him, despite knowing that the desire was not reciprocated. Madeline blushed at her wantonness.

The exact nature of the marriage bed remained a mystery but Mama had hinted often enough that a wife's duty lay in it. Henrietta Brown, from the ladies' sewing group, had delighted in telling them all that she had heard it from her sister that a woman must do her duty and submit to her husband. Duty and submission did not beckon. Memories of what she had shared with Lucien, however, did. Maybe she had done something wrong to disgust him. Maybe women weren't supposed to kiss their husbands. She lay in the great four-poster bed and pondered the problem. As if sensing her mood, Max crawled up from the bottom of the bed to lie next to her, licking her face with a warm pink tongue, and whining.

'Go to sleep, Max.' Madeline patted his head and took comfort from the old dog's presence. But as she drifted off to sleep she couldn't help but wish that it was Lucien by her side.

'Oh, m'lady, I'm so sorry, the ribbon just slipped an'…I'm not usually so butter-fingered!' Betsy burst into tears and ran from the room.

Madeline started after her in alarm. 'Betsy!'

But Betsy had disappeared down the servant stairwell at the far end of the landing. Madeline quickly plaited her hair back from her face in a queue, securing it with the ribbon that had fallen to the floor, and set off in pursuit. She almost ran straight into Mrs Babcock at the bottom of the stairs. 'Mrs Babcock, have you seen Betsy?'

'What's all this Mrs Babcock?' demanded the large woman, elbows akimbo. 'I thought we'd agreed I'm Babbie.'

'And so you are,' Madeline consoled. 'It's just that Betsy seems rather upset this morning. She only dropped a ribbon and that prompted a flood of tears. She hasn't seemed herself for a week or so now. I'm worried about her, Babbie.'

Mrs Babcock sucked at her bottom teeth, a sure sign of stress. 'It's Mrs Porter,' she said in a loud whisper. 'Betsy's mother. She's not been keepin' well. Right poorly she is. In her bed for nigh on a fortnight and not lookin' any better for it. There's only the two of them. Mr Porter was a real scoundrel, ran off and left the pair of 'em high and dry when Betsy was still a little 'un. Betsy's been lookin' after her mum. An' she's real worried.'

'Why didn't she say something? She should be at home with her poor mother, not here combing my hair!'

'Needs the money,' confided Mrs Babcock. 'Poor as church mice. Mrs Porter normally takes in mendin', but with her illness that's stopped. Betsy's wage is their only income.'

Madeline stared at the housekeeper. 'Then we must do something about that.'

'Now, m'lady, there's no need for you to go worrying yourself about them.'

But Madeline was worried. 'Has Mrs Porter seen a doctor?'

'Old Dr Moffat's been out. He's a real gent. Don't take no money from them that can't afford to pay. A consumption of the lungs, he said, accordin' to Betsy.'

A determined look came over Madeline's face. 'Has Lord Tregellas returned from the Granger farm yet?'

Mrs Babcock shook her head. 'Not as I know of.'

'Then have Cook pack up a basket of food: bread, eggs, pie and the like, and if she's made any soup so much the better. Ask Boyle to harness the gig and tell Betsy to wait ready by it.' Madeline whirled and ran back up the stairs.

'M'lady!' shouted Mrs Babcock at the receding figure. 'Don't you be getting any ideas like. His lordship wouldn't want you doin' nothin' silly, m'lady!'

But Madeline was gone.

When the housekeeper saw Madeline again she was heading for the front door, wearing a warm pelisse and cloak, and carrying two large folded blankets on top of which her reticule was balanced.

'M'lady!' Mrs Babcock hobbled across the marbled floor of the hallway at a surprising speed.

Madeline halted in her tracks. 'Oh, Mrs Babcock, there you are. I'm going to take Betsy home, and visit her mother. Has the gig been brought round yet?'

Mrs Babcock ignored the question. 'You might catch that dreadful disease. Best to stay here, m'lady.'

Madeline pressed a hand to her arm. 'Babbie, it's the very least I can do for them. Poor Betsy has been worrying herself sick all week and saying not a word about it. They're probably not eating properly and the weather has been so very cold.'

The housekeeper's brow furrowed. 'His lordship won't like it. He gave strict instructions that you weren't to be out alone.'

'I won't be alone. Betsy and Mr Boyle will be with me,' Madeline said. 'Besides, Lucien will understand.'

Mrs Babcock looked very much like she knew exactly what Lucien's understanding would be. The furrow across her brow deepened. 'Well, at least let me come with you.'

Madeline shook her head and smiled. 'Dear Babbie, I know how very busy you are today, and the weather's enough to smite the ears from your head. You know what the cold does to your knees. Stay here and keep warm. Somebody needs to check if Cook is making those delicious scones.'

The housekeeper mumbled.

'My stomach's rumbling at the very thought. I swear I'll be ready to eat a horse when I get back.'

Mrs Babcock nodded. 'Off with you then, but mind you don't stay too long. Scones won't take long in the makin' and you'll be wantin' them nice and warm from the oven.'

Madeline laughed and disappeared out of the door, running down to meet Betsy, who was waiting patiently by the gig.

'What do you mean, she's gone out?' Earl Tregellas did not look to be in the best of moods.

Mrs Babcock faced him with a defiant calm. 'Gone to visit Mrs Porter, who is poorly in her bed. Taken Betsy with her, a hamper of food, blankets and a purse of money.'

'And when did she go?'

'Ten o'clock, m'lord,'

'That was two hours ago,' said a poker-faced Lucien.

'She's only out the other side of the village. It's safe enough there.'

'Babbie,' he said with barely concealed exasperation, 'there is a very specific reason that I have tried to ensure that Madeline is always accompanied on her every outing. I would not have her safety compromised.'

'Lord Tregellas,' said Mrs Babcock a little more gently, 'there ain't nothin' goin' to happen to her at Mrs Porter's. Time's moved on; her ladyship's in no danger.'

Lucien turned the full strength of his gaze upon the old woman. 'Madeline is not unknown to Cyril Farquharson. Indeed, he has what might be termed a special interest in her. Only here in Trethevyn is she truly safe.'

Mrs Babcock tightened her lips and sucked hard on her bottom teeth. 'Oh, Lord! You should have told me.'

'I'll take Nelson and ride out to find her.'

Mrs Babcock clutched a veined hand to Lucien's arm. 'Forgive me, I'd never have let her go had I but known.'

A nod of his head, and Lucien stepped away.

Carriage wheels crunched against the gravel of the driveway outside.

Lucien and Mrs Babcock looked at one other. Lucien was out the door before the gig had even come to a halt.

Madeline clambered down from the gig and looked at the two tense faces regarding her. 'Lucien, you're back.'

Lucien said nothing.

The housekeeper eyed the empty gig behind Madeline.

'I thought it best that Betsy stayed with her mother until the poor woman felt better. I'll manage without her for a few weeks.'

A welcoming bark sounded and Max trotted down the stairs to greet her, jumping up at her skirts until she scratched at his head.

Two pairs of eyes continued to stare at her with blatant accusation.

'Is something wrong?'

'You mean something apart from you sneaking off unaccompanied in the gig?' said Lucien.

Madeline blinked in surprise and continued to stroke the dog's head. Her husband's mood had been fine at breakfast. Evidently matters had altered that. 'I didn't sneak. Betsy's mother is ill. I merely went to visit her, that's all.' Puzzlement was clear upon her face as she glanced at Mrs Babcock.

The housekeeper looked every bit as cross as Lucien.

'We'll discuss this inside, Madeline.' Lucien stalked back inside the front door.

She followed him to the large drawing room, Max dogging her every step.

Not one word was said until he had closed the door carefully behind him. Then he turned and raked her with a blast from those piercing eyes. 'Do you mean to explain yourself?'

'I beg your pardon?' Madeline stared at him as if he had run mad. 'I have not the least notion of what you mean.'

'Then let me remind you of a certain man who displayed an unhealthy interest in you. Can it be you have forgotten him so easily?'

'What has Cyril Farquharson to do with my visit to Mrs Porter?' She perched herself on the edge of the chair, while Lucien loomed before her.

'You gave me your word that you would not go out alone.'

'And I didn't. Betsy and Mr Boyle were with me.'

'A lady's maid and Boyle hardly count as adequate defence against someone like Farquharson. Boyle's seventy if he's a day. And even at that you came back without Betsy.'

'You're exaggerating the danger,' said Madeline.

Lucien arched one dark eyebrow. 'Really?'

Max looked from master to mistress in confusion and gave a loud booming bark.

'Yes, you are!' Madeline stood up and glared at him. 'Farquharson is far away in London. He's hardly likely to just pop up in Mrs Porter's house. I don't see what the problem is.'

'Then let me enlighten you.'

'There's no need. I think I begin to understand.' Madeline turned on her heel and walked towards the door.

'Madeline,' he said in a soft, deadly voice.

Madeline walked on regardless, not even showing that she'd heard. Her fingers had reached the handle when she felt herself gripped in a pair of strong hands and spun round to face him.

'Cyril Farquharson hasn't been in London for two weeks. It's likely that he's here in Cornwall.' His hands held her firmly, but without hurt.

Her eyes widened at that. Her heart skipped a beat.

A high-pitched whine sounded in the room. Madeline and Lucien looked down to find their normally docile pet in a state of distressed confusion.

'Max?' Lucien said.

Max whined louder and then set up a raucous barking.

'Good God!' exclaimed Lucien and, letting his hands drop, backed away.

The barking stopped and Max trotted quickly in to fill

Lucien's place, taking great delight in sniffing around the hem of Madeline's skirt.

Madeline gave a quick raise of her eyebrows and a little sheepish smile. 'Perhaps I should take Max with me the next time I go visiting. He's really a rather good guard dog.'

Lucien did not return the smile. His pale eyes bored into hers. 'Let me make it crystal clear, Madeline. You are not to leave Trethevyn unless it is in my company. You may under-estimate Farquharson. I do not.'

In the weeks that followed, spring blossomed in all its glory, warming the earth and setting everything in growth. Lambs gambled in the fields and what had been bare and barren and brown when Madeline arrived in Cornwall turned green. Since the day of their argument Lucien had shown no signs of changing his mind. As the days wore on with no sign of Farquharson, her husband grew increasingly wary rather than more relaxed. Madeline began to question what lay behind her husband's zealous guarding. She stood at her bed-chamber window, watching the stark outline of his dark figure riding out down the sweep of the driveway. Betsy sat noise-lessly in the chair close by, trying her best to repair the damage inflicted upon a shawl by Max.

'Naughty dog,' said Betsy. 'You've nigh on ruined her ladyship's good shawl.'

Max raised innocent eyes as if to say, *Who, me? Impos-sible.*

Madeline chewed on her lip and followed the dark figure until it disappeared from sight. 'Betsy…' she began.

'M'lady?' Betsy concentrated on making her stitches small and neat.

It was probably not an appropriate subject to discuss with

the maid, but other than Babbie, Madeline had no one else to ask, and Babbie was desperately loyal to Lucien. Much as the housekeeper bossed and harangued Lucien in a way that no one else dared, Madeline couldn't imagine the old woman standing to hear a word spoken against him. 'Do you not wonder on his lordship's preoccupation with danger, Betsy?'

'Ain't my place to wonder, m'lady.'

'We've been here over two months, yet still he rides out every day to check across the length and breadth of the estate. It's as if he expects the imminent arrival of Lord Farquharson.'

'Who's this Lord Farquharson, then, m'lady?'

Madeline plucked out a hairpin that was pressing uncomfortably against her scalp. 'A villain of a man who has a disagreement with Lord Tregellas,' replied Madeline. There was no need for Betsy to know the full details of what had happened in London. 'I cannot help but wonder over Lord Tregellas's response. What happened with Farquharson is far behind us. He cannot harm us now. Yet Lucien would keep me a practical prisoner in this house for fear that Farquharson means to exact some revenge upon my person.'

'If he's an evil man, then perhaps his lordship has a right to be worried,' reasoned Betsy.

'But the passage of time should diminish the threat, not make it worse. If Farquharson were here, we would have known of it by now. No one can arrive in the village, or leave for that matter, without one of Lord Tregellas's men reporting it back to him. I'm worried about him, Betsy,' confessed Madeline. 'He thinks of nothing but Farquharson. I believe it's an unhealthy obsession, something that has grown out of all proportion. Perhaps the threat from Farquharson is not what he would have me believe. Perhaps it never was,' she said quietly.

'Stands to reason, though,' said the maid, 'that he's likely to be a bit overreacting about such things, given what happened.'

'What do you mean?' Did Betsy know that she had jilted Farquharson to elope with Lucien? And if Farquharson was of a mind to call Lucien out, he would have done so before they left London. He had told her Farquharson had killed a woman, but it wasn't Farquharson that London whispered was a murderer. For the first time Madeline began to doubt the truth of what Lucien had told her. She had married him on the basis of his assertion that she was at risk from Farquharson, that and her own instinct that there was something intrinsically rotten about the Baron. Looking back, she began to see that she had been blindly trusting of a man that she had not known at all. And now that she knew him, had come to care for him... His behaviour towards Farquharson smacked of something more, something dark and obsessive. Madeline shivered, and waited for the maid's answer.

'What happened with his betrothed, all them years ago.'

Foreboding prickled across Madeline's scalp. 'His betrothed?' she whispered.

Betsy looked up and blushed beetroot. ''Cept we're not supposed to talk about that, m'lady.'

'Betsy?'

But Betsy had suddenly remembered an urgent appointment with Mrs Babcock and was off and away before Madeline could say another word.

Madeline rubbed her arms against the sudden cold that chilled her. She thought she had come to know her husband, to learn something of his childhood, of his life before he had met her. Now she realised that she knew nothing at all, save for a queer, hollow dread that had opened within her heart.

Chapter Ten

The letter arrived at midday while Lucien was still out on the estate. The writing comprised spiky narrow letters that were vaguely familiar. Something tickled in her memory, lurking just beyond recall. Faint unease shimmied down Madeline's spine.

'Somethin' the matter, doe?' enquired Mrs Babcock, topping up Madeline's cup with tea.

Madeline shook her head. 'No, nothing at all. What kind of soup did you say?'

'Mock turtle, and as well as that George brought in a lovely brace of partridges fresh this morning.'

'That sounds fine, Babbie.' The seal broke easily beneath her fingers and she opened the letter. A glance over the first line, then her eyes leapt down to the signature and she quickly closed the piece of paper back over and tucked it beneath her leg.

'You sure you ain't sickenin'? You're lookin' a touch pale, m'lady.' Mrs Babcock stared with concern as the blood drained from Madeline's cheeks, leaving her ghost white.

'No, no,' gasped Madeline. 'Just a little light-headed, that's all. It will pass. I'm fine.'

'Light-headed?' Babbie said, her blackcurrant eyes growing rounder by the minute. 'Can't be due to lack of food. You've developed a right healthy appetite since you come here. I remember when you first arrived, picked at your food like a little sparrow, you did. Not good for a body, that is. Got a bit more meat on you now, I'm glad to say.' Babbie's brain weighed up the evidence, feeling faint, increased appetite, weight gain, and a new closeness between the master and mistress…and reached quite the wrong conclusion.

'Yes,' said Madeline rather weakly. 'I think I might just go and lie down for a little. Will you manage the rest of the dinner arrangements?'

'Course I will, doe,' replied Mrs Babcock, beaming. 'You got to get your rest, m'lady. Don't want you takin' too much out of yourself. I'll leave the scones and tea here in case you want to finish them later. Got to keep your strength up.'

Madeline waited for the housekeeper to leave and wondered why Mrs Babcock seemed so pleased. She didn't ponder the problem for long. As soon as the door shut the letter was hauled from its hiding place and, with a dry mouth, she began to read each and every one of the words penned upon it, hearing once again that cruel voice that Trethevyn had made her forget. For the sender of the letter was none other than Cyril Farquharson.

London
April 1814
My dearest Madeline
I hope that this letter finds you in good health, and that Tregellas has not yet subjected you to the worst of his nature. I write to tell you that I bear you no malice for marrying that scoundrel—indeed, the blame lies en-

tirely upon his head. For what choice had you in the matter, my love?

I strike my breast and deliver myself a thrashing when I think how you misinterpreted my eagerness for our union. Forgive my cruel words that I last threw at you, I was overwrought. I love you, Madeline. I have loved you from the first minute that I saw you. But I should have realised that my very great consideration for you would overwhelm such a fragile flower as yourself. I beg your forgiveness, most humbly, if I ever acted as anything but a gentleman. You should know that I have ever held you in the highest regard, and I truly regret if I let my passion frighten you. It was my dream to make you my wife and care for you in the manner you deserve. Alas, Tregellas has destroyed all of my hopes.

I wish you well, Madeline, but my conscience could not sit easy if I did not at least try to warn you of Tregellas's true nature. I am afraid that there is, indeed, substance behind his reputation as the Wicked Earl. Although I do not wish to increase your hurt any more than it is already, as a Christian gentleman it is my duty to tell you the truth of what lies behind your forced abduction and marriage.

Many years ago, as a young and impetuous man, I met a young lady who captured my heart. She was sweet and good in much the same way as you, my dear Madeline. We fell in love and wished for nothing other than to be married. But the lady was betrothed to Tregellas and he would not release her from their contract. For the sake of our love we had no other choice than to elope. Perhaps it was wrong of me to return her love when she was promised to another, but I cannot be ashamed of some-

thing so pure. Tregellas was like the devil with rage. He came after my sweet wife, and...pen and ink tremble at the words I know I must write...killed her.

Forgive me, Madeline, for breaking such a harsh and horrible truth to you. I can do nothing else but warn you of his terrible evil. From that day until this, he has stalked me, desiring nothing more than my death. He hates me with the haunting compulsion of the insane. You must realise by now that he cares nothing for you, and, indeed, that he wed you in an act of selfish revenge. I do not know the extent of the lies he has told you, but I truly fear for your safety, Madeline. Should you need my help at any time, you have but to send me a message and I will come. I did not think to love again in this life, but God blessed me with you. I could not stand to live if Tregellas were to kill you, too, my darling. I pray with all my heart that you will be safe from danger.
Ever your servant,
Cyril Farquharson

Madeline read the letter, and reread it, until the words blurred upon the page. His love, his darling? Never. She remembered the biting grip of his fingers bruising against her skin, the hardness of his mouth as it sought hers. One close of her eyes and she could see the cruel promise in his face. She shuddered and set the letter down upon her desk. Yet time and again as she sat there her eyes drifted back to catch at the page. He wrote of a woman who had been betrothed to Lucien. Betsy had let slip those same words. Lucien's betrothed. Her stomach knotted at the very thought. *He came after my sweet wife, and...killed her.* The words stood out boldly on the paper before her. It was not possible. Not Lucien. Not when he had only ever treated her with kindness and care. That, at least, could not be denied. He might not desire her, he most definitely did not love her, but Madeline knew in her heart of hearts that Lucien would never hurt her. From the first time she had looked into those intriguing pale eyes, she had trusted him and felt safe. Surely her instinct could not be so wrong?

But Farquharson was right in certain aspects: Lucien's increasingly obsessive behaviour; Lucien's hatred of Farquharson, so intense as to be almost palpable. Could Farquharson be right about the others? Her teeth gripped hard at her lip, contemplating what she had learned. She wondered what truth lay behind Cyril Farquharson's letter. Had Lucien wed her solely for revenge? Was he guilty of Farquharson's accusation? Or was it Farquharson who had murdered the woman, as Lucien had claimed that night so long ago in London? Madeline's head whirled dizzy with the thoughts. Cold fingers touched again and again to the letter before, at last, she folded it up and placed it carefully in the bottom drawer of her bureau, beneath a pile of fresh writing sheets. She rose to stand before the window in her bedchamber.

Farquharson made her flesh crawl. Lucien engendered different emotions altogether in her breast. For all the dark mystery that had surrounded Earl Tregellas, that still surrounded the man she called her husband, she trusted him over Cyril Farquharson. From what she knew of Farquharson, it was likely that he had fabricated the entirety of the story. Lucien might have been betrothed once upon a time, in the past. It was hardly a fitting subject to raise with his new wife. Little wonder he had not spoken of it. There would be no link between Farquharson and the woman promised to marry

Lucien. And as for Lucien killing anyone…well, the whole idea was just preposterous.

Madeline lifted her face to the sun, letting the brightness of its rays through the pane glass warm her and banish the dark suspicions from her mind. Cyril Farquharson might think to fool her, but Madeline refused to be so easily hood-winked. She would not let her worries over Lucien's beha-viour add substance to Farquharson's lies. She thought once more on how increasingly bedevilled her husband was becoming with Farquharson. The letter would only make things worse.

A wood pigeon soared high in the sky, heading for the trees at the far end of the drive. Madeline watched the hurried beat of its wings and felt the freedom that surrounded its flight. In the clarity of the moment she knew what she should do. Lucien had tried to protect her. Now it was her turn to protect him. Whatever reason lay behind Cyril Farquharson's torment of her husband, Madeline meant to see that it would go no further. She lifted the pen and opened the lid of the inkpot. By the time she was finished, Lord Farquharson would be under no illusion as to where her allegiance lay.

It was early the next morning when Madeline received the news that Mary Woodford was unwell. She ceased her rummaging amidst the linen cupboard and scanned the hur-riedly scrawled note pleading that she attend Mrs Woodford at the parsonage.

Madeline nipped at her lip and pondered the problem. It was clear that she should visit Mrs Woodford to offer what help she might. But Lucien had left at dawn to travel to Tavistock and would not return to Trethevyn until late. And since her visit to Mrs Porter, Lucien had ensured that she did not leave the house unless he accompanied her. What to do? Madeline worried some more at her lip, concern about the kindly parson's wife snagging at her conscience. Mary Woodford was a friend. The woman would not plead for help without good reason. Surely Lucien would understand why she could not just sit here uselessly while heaven only knew what Mary Woodford was going through. If she were to be accompanied by one of the grooms, as well as Betsy, and have Mr Boyce to drive the carriage, and they were to carry a cudgel with them… He could not be angry that she had taken no precautions against danger. Besides, he need never know that she had gone. She would be back well before him.

'The linen can wait. Mrs Woodford is unwell and has asked that I visit her. We must make ready.' Madeline replaced the bedsheet back upon the neatly folded pile on the shelf closest to her within the press. 'And, Betsy—' she delivered her maid a worried look '—ask John Hayley to accompany us and to bring a large cudgel with him.'

'J-John Hayley?' stuttered a suddenly rather pink-cheeked Betsy.

'Yes, the groom with the blond, curly hair, arms like a cooper, looks like he's made of solid muscle, bright blue eyes.'

Betsy's face flushed a deeper hue. 'Why ever should he accompany us, m'lady?' Her hands plucked at her apron in a decidedly flustered manner.

'As our guard,' answered Madeline, gaining an inkling as to the reason for her maid's rosy complexion. 'Do you know him at all?' she asked rather wickedly.

'A little,' admitted Betsy with an averted gaze.

Madeline tried hard to keep a straight face. Only the hint of a smile tugged at the corners of her mouth. 'Then this will be a good opportunity for you to get to know him better. He looks very strong, does he not?'

'Yes, m'lady, quite strong indeed.'

'And I suppose that some ladies might even describe him as handsome.'

'Very handsome,' agreed Betsy.

'Well, then, it's settled. You run down and ask Mr Boyce and John Hayley to make ready in, say, half an hour. I will speak to Babbie. That sounds like a good plan, does it not?'

Betsy grinned. 'Yes, m'lady, a fine plan.'

The two women laughed together before setting off downstairs to make the necessary preparations for their journey.

Four hours later neither Madeline nor Betsy were laughing. They stood by the side of a muddy road, a fine drizzle soaking through their clothes and ruining their bonnets. Mr Boyce and John Hayley were hunkered down examining the axle of the carriage, scratching at their heads. One large wheel lay forlornly in the middle of the road. A sea of mist had gathered on the horizon and was creeping closer towards the little group.

'Well, at least Mrs Woodford is feeling better. Dr Moffat said that the baby is fine. She's to rest for the remainder of the week. Poor little Sally does not know what to make of her mama tucked up in bed.'

But Betsy had other things than the parson's wife on her mind. She gave a shiver. 'They say the ghost of Harry Staunton haunts this moor, puttin' the fear of death into any wayfarin' travellers who he happens to chance upon.'

'Who was Harry Staunton?'

'A ruffian and a highwayman. Hundred years ago they hanged him, they did, and when they cut him down and placed him in his grave he was still breathin'. But they buried him anyway…alive, and he's haunted the moor ever since. A wanderin' soul, robbin' and terrorisin' them he meets on the moor, him and his great black stallion, appearin' out of the mist and disappearin' just as easily again.' Betsy wiped a hand across her runny nose, then rubbed at her eyes. 'Oh, m'lady, what are we to do? Harry Staunton's out there, I knows it.'

'There's no such thing as ghosts, Betsy. It's just a story told to frighten people. Even if this Harry Staunton was ever a real person, he's dead and buried, not haunting Bodmin Moor.' Madeline placed a comforting arm around the maid's shoulder. 'You're just tired and cold and wet. Things will seem much better when we get back to Trethevyn.' She pulled a clean pressed square of white linen from her reticule and placed it into Betsy's hand. 'Here, take my spare handkerchief.'

Betsy sniffed. 'Oh no, m'lady, I shouldn't.'

'Of course you must,' insisted Madeline before turning to Mr Boyle. 'How fares the repair, Mr Boyle? Will it take much longer?'

The elderly retainer scratched at his head. 'Not lookin' too good, m'lady. Need some tools to sort this. Young Hayley could run back to fetch 'em and bring the coach back out to collect you. But that'll take some time, and I don't like the look of that mist. Ain't too much shelter on the moor neither. Master won't be best pleased when he finds out 'bout this.'

Guilt twinged at Madeline. It was her fault, not the servants. She didn't want them getting into trouble. Especially when Lucien had forbidden her to leave the house without him. 'Lord Tregellas need not know of our trip. Could not the wheel be repaired this afternoon before he returns?'

With a great deal of effort, and some help from John Hayley, Mr Boyle clambered to his feet. He wiped the dirt from his hands down his breeches and gave her a look that was enough to make Madeline shrink with shame. 'Are you askin' me to lie to his lordship?'

She felt her face colour with embarrassment. 'No. I just thought…I was thinking that, perhaps—' The muffled drum of horses' hooves in the distance stopped her.

The fine bays still attached to the carriage pricked up their ears and whinnied.

Betsy gave a shriek. 'It's him, m'lady. Harry Staunton and his black devil horse. God help us all!'

Mr Boyle armed himself with an ancient blunderbuss and John Hayley grabbed the cudgel from the interior of the carriage. 'Stand behind us, quickly, m'lady, Betsy,' ordered Mr Boyle, his gnarled old hands aiming the gun at the bank of thick white mist into which the road disappeared.

Betsy started to sob.

'Come along, Betsy,' Madeline urged. 'There's no need to cry. It's just another traveller. Perhaps they will be able to help us.' She did not miss the look that passed between the two men.

Betsy whimpered even louder.

Madeline tried again. 'Mr Boyle and John will protect us.'

Betsy's whimper turned to a wail.

Madeline patted at the tearful maid's shoulder, then wrapped an arm around her, to no effect. 'Hush now, Betsy.'

But Betsy would not be hushed.

'He's comin', I knows it!' she wailed again and began to tremble from head to toe.

John Hayley stepped back briefly. 'It'll be all right, Betsy,' soothed the young groom. 'We won't let nothin' happen to neither of you.' A large hand touched against the maid's arm, a bright smile flashed, and Betsy's crying miraculously ceased.

'Promise?' she hiccupped through breaths still small and panting from her sobbing.

'I promise,' said the young man.

The mist closed in around them. The hooves grew louder. John Hayley stepped forward to be level with Mr Boyle. They waited in silence, tension crackling all around them, eyes trained upon that spot where the road had been. Waiting. Poised. Afraid. Knowing that the encroaching mist distorted sound, aware that the horseman could be closer. They strained their attention towards that one single point. Both wishing and dreading his appearance.

Suddenly, from out of the mist, the horseman appeared. A large dark shape astride a huge black horse.

Betsy screamed. 'It's Harry Staunton!'

An almighty flash and a loud explosive crack burst forth from the blunderbuss, the recoil of which knocked Mr Boyle to the ground. The air was heavy with blue smoke and the stench of gunpowder. It seemed that the shattering noise echoed amidst Betsy's incessant screaming. Raising the cudgel John Hayley prepared to protect them all from the attack of the ghostly highwayman.

'What the blazes…?' Lucien saw the flash of gunpowder ignite and threw himself flat against his horse's back, bracing himself to control the petrified beast. From behind he heard the shout of alarm from his man Sibton, and reined the gelding in hard. Nelson reared on to his hindlegs, eyes rolling back in terror. Lucien clung on for dear life, whispering calming reassurances in the horse's flattened-back ears, using every ounce of strength to stop the beast bolting directly into the small huddled group before him. Nelson skittered forward and reared again, sending deadly hooves crashing down dangerously close to the fair-haired man standing to their fore. The bodies scuttled backwards, the woman's piercing screams unnerving both Nelson and his master. With a firm press of the knees Lucien managed to quiet the great black horse enough to draw the pistol from the pocket of his greatcoat. He jumped down from Nelson's back, throwing the reins to Sibton, and pointed the muzzle at the shape before him. 'Unhand that woman or I'll fire.'

The screaming intensified.

'What the hell are you doing to her?' He prowled forward, the mist thinning as he did so. The pistol cocked beneath his finger.

'Lord Tregellas?' a familiar elderly voice sounded. 'Can it be you?'

'Boyle?' One more step and he saw them clearly. Young Hayley with cudgel raised, standing before Boyle, who lay upon the ground. Two women, one trying to help the old man up, the other huddled in a frightened ball, screaming and sobbing in terror.

The stick dropped from the young groom's hand and the defensive stance relaxed. 'M'lord, thank God it's you. We thought…'

Lucien surveyed the scene before him closer, his eyes moving quickly from one face to another, until it came to rest on that of his wife. 'Madeline.' Her eyes were huge and dark in the pallor of her face. He stepped past Hayley. 'What happened?' He saw the blunderbuss down by Boyle's side.

'Forgive me, m'lord I didn't know 'twas you. Thought you were a villain comin' out of the mist. Couldn't take no chances on account of her ladyship bein' present,' Boyle murmured, clutching at his shoulder.

Comprehension dropped into place. 'You mean it was you that shot at me?'

Boyle nodded weakly. 'Praise the lord that the shot went high. I could have killed you.'

'Never mind that now. Let me have a look at that shoulder.'

'Just a bruise,' gasped Boyle from between gritted teeth. 'See to her ladyship, I'll be fine,' he whispered, cheeks turning chalkier by the minute. Lucien had to bend an ear close to the old man's mouth to catch the faint words amidst Betsy's hysteria. Lucien turned an irritated eye towards the maid. 'By Hades, will someone quieten that girl before I do it myself?'

'Lucien!' exclaimed his wife. 'Don't be so unkind. Betsy is distraught. She thought you were a ghost coming out of the mist.'

Lucien's gaze swivelled to Madeline. He raised one dark eyebrow. 'If that bullet had been an inch lower, I damn well would have been.' He looked into her eyes and saw fear mixed with relief. He caught back the words from the tip of his tongue. 'See to your maid,' he said and turned to Hayley. 'Help me get Boyle up to a sitting position. I think he may have dislocated his shoulder.' Between them, Lucien and the young groom manoeuvred Boyle until Lucien had a gentle grip upon the coachman's shoulder. 'Hold him tight, this is going to hurt like hell.'

The one short grunt that issued from Archie Boyle's lips were more distressing than all of Betsy's screaming put together.

Madeline averted her face, holding her arms around Betsy, until the sobbing was nothing more than a series of shudders through the maid's body.

Lucien spoke to Hayley. 'That should have done the trick,

but I want Dr Moffat to look him over when we get back. Stay here with Boyle and Betsy.' He rose and, walking over to Sibton who was still holding the horses, pressed a pistol into his servant's hand. 'Just make sure you know who's coming out of the mist before you fire it. I'll take Lady Tregellas back to Trethevyn with me, and send the coach out for Boyle and the others. Tether the bays and bring them back in at the same time. We'll come back for the carriage once everyone is safe.'

Sibton nodded his compliance.

Lucien returned to stand before his wife. Not trusting himself to speak, he just reached a hand down towards her and pulled her up into his arms. He felt the subtle resistance, saw the flicker of her eyes towards the maid.

'I cannot leave Betsy,' she murmured.

'Hayley will look after her,' he said, and steered Madeline towards his horse. 'We're going home.'

Home. Madeline realised that she had indeed come to think upon Trethevyn as her home. It offered safety and comfort, and a whole lot more. Despite the threat of Far-quharson, and the mystery surrounding Lucien, Madeline ac-knowledged that she was happier in the large country house than she had been at any other time in her life. The strength of Lucien's arm curled around her waist, securing her firmly to both the saddle and himself. She felt the warmth of his chest press against her, chasing away the worst of the damp chill. One hand clung tight to him, the other gripped the edge of the saddle. He was angry. She could see it in the tense muscles around his mouth, feel it in his body's rigidity. Yet every so often his arm squeezed a little tighter around her, as if to reassure himself that she was still there, still safe. Nelson's steady canter enabled her to keep her seat easily enough. But the mist was thickening so that they could barely see the road before them.

'Nelson knows his way home, Madeline. We can trust that he will keep to the road easily enough.'

'Lucien…' she looked up at his face '…I'm sorry. Mrs Woodford is unwell and I was so worried… I did not anticipate that the visit would turn out in this way.'

'We'll discuss the matter when we get home.' His voice was firm, but the fingers that caressed her waist were gentle and reassuring.

The smirr of rain grew stronger. She nestled in closer, trying to shield herself from its seeping dampness. Lucien stopped the horse, unbuttoned his greatcoat, and, unmindful of her wet clothing, pulled her against his body, inside the shelter of the coat. And that was how she stayed all the way back to Trethevyn, her cheek pressed against the hard muscle of his chest, listening to the beat of his heart.

It was an hour later and all of Lucien's staff were safely back at Trethevyn. Lucien made his way upstairs. A curt knock and, without waiting for a reply, he swung the door open. He entered the bedchamber silently, dismissed Betsy, ensuring that she took a grudging Max with her and closed the door quietly behind them. His wife had at least changed from her wet clothes into something warm and dry. She knelt on the rug before the marble fireplace, head bowed, drying her hair by the heat of the flames. Her hair tumbled in a tousled waterfall, pooling around her shoulders in a sensual reminder of what he was missing. Lucien banished such thoughts, forcing himself to remember exactly why he had come here and what he meant to say.

'Lucien.' She looked up and smiled. Her cheeks were pink

with warmth and her eyes sparkled a clear golden brown. A thick cotton nightdress showed above her dressing gown. Lucien's eyes flicked down to take in the bare feet that peeped out from under the cotton, and rose to take in a very shapely pair of hips. Stirrings of a highly inappropriate nature made themselves known. Lucien cleared his throat and strolled over to survey the view from the window until he could regain control over his body. Lord, but she looked so adorable he longed to just pull her up into his arms and kiss her. He swallowed hard. If he was entirely honest, that's not all he wanted to do. It would be so easy to scoop her up into his bed and keep her there the whole night through. Such thoughts were not helping his problem. He glanced down. Indeed they seemed only to be making it worse. He strove to think of Farquharson and the danger that he presented. And from that to Madeline's blatant disregard of his request that she did not travel from Trethevyn unless in his company. That seemed to do the trick.

'Is something wrong?' The soft pad of bare feet sounded behind him.

'Nothing apart from the fact you seem determined to place yourself in the worst of situations.'

The clear honey eyes blinked back at him. 'I've said my apologies. Mary Woodford is my friend. She might have lost the baby, Lucien, so I went in response to her note, to offer my help. Thankfully, matters were not so bad as she had thought. The doctor has said that the baby is safe.' A tenderness came into her eyes.

He swallowed back the reciprocal feeling that it engendered. 'I asked you not to leave Trethevyn without me.'

'Would you have had me ignore her plea and just sit here while she was enduring such agonies?' Madeline looked up at him. 'They are your people, Lucien. Do you not care for their welfare?'

'That's an unfair question. You know that I do. Besides…' he raked a hand through his hair '…I have no issue with you visiting the parsonage, or anywhere else for that matter, as long as I'm with you. And you understand the reason that I've asked such a thing.'

She sighed, and moved to stand beside him.

'You should have waited until I got back. We could have gone together, tomorrow.'

'It might have been too late by then. I was worried and she asked me to go as soon as possible.'

'I know you were, Madeline, but not half as worried as I was when I heard that blunderbuss and saw you stooped over Boyle's body.'

'I'm sorry.'

But 'sorry' would not save her from Farquharson. 'You play a dangerous game, Madeline. Farquharson could have plucked you as easy as a berry from a bush.'

A little line of pique appeared between her brows. 'I took John Hayley and a cudgel. My Boyle took his blunderbuss. I thought we would be safe.'

'Indeed?' he said. The memory of the pounding of his heart and the dread when he saw her through the drifting mist and gunpowder plume spurred him on. 'Had I been Farquharson, or any other villain, do you think that Boyle would have stopped me? I could have put a bullet through Hayley before the cudgel was even raised in his hand. Then where would you have been, Madeline? Completely at my mercy.'

Madeline's chin tilted in defiance. 'You are obsessed with Farquharson. Of all the places he is likely to be, Bodmin Moor late on a damp misty afternoon is not one of them.'

'And you know that beyond all reasonable doubt, do you? You are willing to take the risk? Believe me, Madeline, I know, better than most, the evil of which that man is capable. I will not have you expose yourself to such danger.'

'We weren't going far. I did not know that the wheel would come off.' She turned from the window so that they were facing one another.

'That does not matter.' He pushed her excuses aside. 'You disregarded my request not to travel alone.'

'I wasn't alone,' she protested.

'You understand my meaning well.' Exasperation lent an edge to his voice. 'You seem intent on trying to throw yourself into Farquharson's path.'

'Oh, don't be so silly!' she replied, anger lending her a foolhardy courage. 'I'm just getting on with living. I cannot forever be looking over my shoulder. Would you lock me behind these doors, never to venture out again for fear of him?'

'That's not what I'm saying, Madeline.'

'Then what are you saying?'

'It's not too much to ask that I accompany you.'

Madeline's breast rose and fell beneath the dressing gown in a flurry. 'I'm beginning to feel like a prisoner, Lucien. I love Trethevyn, but I should be able to at least visit a friend when she is ill without waiting for you!'

'Under normal circumstances I would agree entirely. But the circumstances are far from normal. Until I have dealt with Farquharson, we must both live by certain constraints.'

She hesitated. Dealt with Farquharson. The claims of Farquharson's letter came back to her. *He has stalked me, desiring nothing more than my death.* 'What do you mean to do to him?' she asked.

'Whatever it takes to stop him.'

Madeline shivered.

He reached across and pulled her into his arms. She was so small, so vulnerable. 'Farquharson's more dangerous than you realise.' He stroked a hand over the damp tumble of hair, smelling the sweetness of her and her orange fragrance. 'He will come after you in the most unexpected of places.'

'But if he meant to hurt us, would he not have done so by now?'

Lucien shook his head. 'He's biding his time. But our waiting is nearly at an end. Farquharson will strike soon. And when he does, I want us both to be ready.'

It should have been her husband that she asked, but it wasn't. Madeline was desperate and so she asked Babbie about the woman Lucien was to have married.

'Terrible affair it was,' said Mrs Babcock. 'Almost drove Master Lucien insane. It's not my story to tell, but what I will say to you, m'lady, is please don't judge him too harshly. He was a young man and he made a mistake like all young men do. 'Cept his mistake cost him dearly. Can't forgive or forget. Blames himself even yet, though it weren't his fault.' Mrs Babcock's eyes dampened with a terrible sadness. Her eyelids flickered shut as if gathering the strength to carry on.

Madeline touched cold fingers to Mrs Babcock's hand. 'What happened?' she asked carefully. 'Will you not at least tell me that? Please, Babbie.'

'She was a young lady. I won't divulge her name. Wealthy, titled, only daughter of a viscount. Quiet and shy. Beautiful she was, tall and slender with long black hair and big blue eyes. The most beautiful girl in all of Cornwall.'

Beautiful, tall, black hair, big blue eyes—in short, everything that Madeline was not. A little ball of nausea rotated in

Madeline's stomach. She didn't want to hear the words. She knew that she had to.

'And the most foolish. She was just eighteen when they were betrothed.'

Madeline pressed a hand to her stomach and swallowed hard.

'Even so, she went up to London for her first Season. Met a gentleman there. Next thing she ran off and married him, even though she were under age and had not so much as a word of consideration for Master Lucien. Whisked off with the gent in the middle of a dance. Most out of character for her, by all accounts. Needless to say, it was a right scandal.'

In the middle of a dance! 'Oh, God!' Madeline could stop the expletive no longer. For she had a horrible premonition of where this story was heading.

Mrs Babcock's hand balled to a fist tight against her own lips. 'I've said too much. You should hear the whole of it from his lordship. He'll tell you when he's ready, m'lady. Please, give him some more time. He don't mean to be high-handed. He's just worried and wants to keep you safe.'

Madeline bit down hard upon her lip. 'Who was the gentleman that the girl ran off with?'

'That's for his lordship to tell,' said Mrs Babcock.

'It was Cyril Farquharson, wasn't it?' Madeline stared at the housekeeper.

Mrs Babcock's mouth stayed firmly shut.

'Wasn't it?' said Madeline, and there followed a deadly hush.

'Yes,' said Mrs Babcock miserably, 'Lord Farquharson was his name.'

Madeline gazed in anguish for a moment longer. 'Please can you go now? I'm tired and would like to rest.'

'But, m'lady, you don't know the full of it. It weren't just that. There's more. Much more. And—'

Madeline shook her head. 'I've heard enough, Babbie. Please just go.'

Mrs Babcock rose and hobbled out of the room, closing the door quietly behind her.

Chapter Eleven

It seemed to Madeline that her heart had ceased to beat. She sat stunned, unable to move, barely able to breathe for the tightness that constricted her throat. Everything suddenly made sense. Cyril Farquharson had told the truth. The pieces of the puzzle had fallen into place to reveal the picture in full. She knew now why Lucien had been so determined to save her from Farquharson, why the wealthy Earl Tregellas had plucked a plain little nobody from beneath that fiend's nose to make her his wife. For in truth it was not Lord Farquharson who was the fiend at all—that title belonged to her husband. He had married her for nothing more than to exact revenge upon Farquharson, to do unto Farquharson precisely what the Baron had done unto him. Madeline Langley was just the silly little fool who had lent herself as the weapon of his vengeance. And that vengeance had not been for her. It had never been for her. It was for another woman from across the years who had betrayed him.

All talk of saving her from Farquharson, of protection, was just a lie. With the harsh brutality of realisation she knew that everything he had said had been a lie. Lies and more lies.

Madeline blinked back the tears, determined not to cry. The tip of her nose grew numb and cold. A lump balled in her throat. London had called him the Wicked Earl and with good reason. Madeline had thought she knew better, had refused to believe the rumours. And Madeline had been proved wrong. Now she knew why he would not share her bed. Lucien Tregellas would never love her, for he loved another woman, a tall woman with big blue eyes and long dark hair…the most beautiful woman in all of Cornwall.

Blood trickled down from Madeline's lip and still she did not realise the pain or the pressure of her bite. 'Damn him,' she whispered. 'Damn him for the devil he is.' She had thrown common sense to the wind, risked all to avoid a marriage with Cyril Farquharson. Now that she had made her bed, as Mama would say, she would have to lie in it. Madeline screwed her eyes tight against the tears that threatened to fall. She'd be damned if she'd let him see just how much he'd hurt her.

Then a little thought made itself known. If Farquharson had told the truth about Lucien's betrothed, was it also true that Lucien had killed the woman? That he meant to kill Madeline too? No matter how angry she was, no matter how hurt, she could not bring herself to believe either. If Lucien wanted a wife in name, then that's exactly what he would get. That meant no more allowing him to dictate what she could and couldn't do. What had he said the night that he asked her to marry him, or at least when she believed she had a choice in the matter? *You would be free to live your own life.* That was his bargain. A cold-hearted bargain. And, by God, she would hold him to it!

Guy, Lord Varington, was concentrating on the two piles of cards on the table when the sensation of someone having walked across his grave shivered across his shoulders. He glanced up to find Cyril Farquharson watching him from across the room. Guy delivered him an arrogant sneer and switched his attention back to the game. Ace. He won the last turn and bowed out with a sense of unease still upon him. It was quite out of character for a man whose lazy arrogant confidence was renowned the length and breadth of London. He meandered towards the fireplace, ignoring the call of several voices for him to rejoin the game of faro. The night was still young, but curiously White's seemed to have lost its atmosphere of indulgent relaxation. He ordered a brandy, sat himself down in a comfortable armchair, and started to browse through a copy of *The Times*.

'Varington…' a familiar voice feigned pleasance '…the very man I was hoping to see.'

Guy looked up into the face of Cyril Farquharson. Without showing the slightest hint of surprise he answered, 'Back in London so soon, Farquharson? But then again, I had forgotten your need to trawl the marriage mart.'

The barb hit home as Farquharson's cheeks ruddied, but he controlled his temper well. 'What ever made you think that I had departed the metropolis? Gossip can be so misleading.' He sat himself down in the chair opposite Guy's. 'Don't mind if I join you, do you?'

Guy became aware of the murmur of interest in the room around them. He smiled a smile that did not warm the ice of his eyes. 'You have five minutes to say what it is you that you've come to say, and then…' Guy's smile deepened '…if you're still here I feel I must warn you that I'm not endowed with my brother's restraint.'

'Five minutes shall more than suffice,' said Farquharson. The grey of his snugly fitted coat mirrored the smokiness of his eyes.

They looked at one another, dislike bristling beneath a veneer of civility.

'How fares Lady Tregellas in Cornwall?'

A dark eyebrow arched in sardonic surprise. 'All the better for choosing my brother over you as her bridegroom.'

Farquharson's lips narrowed. 'That's not what I've heard, sir.'

'Then you ought to have a care to whom you listen.'

The closed face opened with mock-innocence and he leaned forward in a confidential manner. 'Even if it comes straight from the horse's mouth, so to speak?'

Guy smiled his deadly smile again. 'Your time is running out, Farquharson. Waste the remaining minutes in riddles if you wish.' But the chill of anticipation was upon him and Guy knew that Farquharson would not be sitting there attracting the attention of White's patrons if he did not have something worth revealing.

'Perhaps it would be better if you saw the evidence yourself.' Farquharson reached into his pocket and produced a letter, ensuring that no one in the room missed him pass the paper into Varington's hand. 'I should tell you that I've had my lawyer make a copy signed as a true representation of the original…should anything untoward happen to the letter while it's in the possession of another.' A row of teeth was revealed.

Even before he touched it Guy could see that the broken wax seal was that of Tregellas. The note opened to reveal a tidy flow of ink script upon his brother's headed writing paper. Guy's eyes followed each and every word down to the flourish of the neat signature. He balked at the letter's contents, but the face he raised to the red-haired man seated opposite showed nothing but a bland disinterest. 'Another one of your efforts at amusement.' Guy let the paper fall to his lap and proceeded to examine his fingernails. 'And another failure. May I remind you, sir, that forgery is a crime.'

'Indeed it is. That's why I've had the authenticity of the paper and seal checked. I wouldn't want anyone to believe any misrepresentations that may have been circulated about me. The letter verifies what I've said all along about Tregellas. That's why I plan to publish it in a certain London newspaper, so that all may see it.'

Pale blue eyes locked a focus on smoky grey.

'But as you are aware, Varington, I'm a just and fair man, and even though Tregellas has wronged me I'm prepared to give him the chance to do the right thing.' A slim white finger stroked his upper lip. 'Take the letter and show it to him. If I hear nothing from him within the next fortnight, then I'll go ahead and publish.'

'Go to hell, Farquharson. I'll not be your messenger.'

Farquharson's mouth stretched to a semblance of a smile. 'Then you forfeit your brother's chance to prevent publication. Thank you for your time, sir.' Farquharson reached to retrieve the letter, but Guy's fingers were there first, removing the letter, tucking it safely inside his coat, knowing that he had no other option.

Farquharson stood and made to leave. 'Just one more thing, Varington. When you see Tregellas, ask him if he has come to appreciate Madeline's acting skills. She is really rather good, but then again I did train her myself. Tregellas is so very predictable. I couldn't have "guided" his actions nearly so well without her.'

Guy rose quickly, but Farquharson was halfway across the room, making his escape, smiling his gratitude at the captive audience that allowed it. There was nothing that Guy could do without causing a scene, and that was the last thing that Lucien needed right now. Guy forced himself to sit back down, to finish his brandy and read a few more news articles in *The Times* before strolling out of the gentlemen's club as if he had not a care in the world. It was only when he reached the haven of his townhouse that the affected air of boredom was cast aside.

At first light next morning, Viscount Varington was seen leaving his house, travelling light on the fastest horse in his stables, with only his trusty valet for company.

When Farquharson heard the news that Varington had left town he could scarcely contain his glee. The bait had been swallowed. He knew there was only one place that Varington would have gone, and that was exactly where Farquharson wanted him to be: Trethevyn. Farquharson smiled. The first aim of the letter had been achieved. The second would follow soon, when Tregellas read the words penned upon that paper. Farquharson's smile deepened. Contrary to his threats, he was not ready to publish, not until matters in Cornwall were completed. Publication of the letter would meet its third and final aim: a fitting end to Tregellas. Farquharson sniggered. The five years of waiting would almost be worth it. His plan was coming together nicely…beginning with Varington. The last of Farquharson's valises was carried from his bedchamber. He made his way down the stairs and out to his waiting carriage to begin the journey to Cornwall. And the thought of just what he planned to do there excited Cyril Farquharson almost to a frenzy.

The woman who faced Lucien over dinner that night was not the woman he had come to know in the months since he'd married her. It seemed that the light in Madeline's eyes had dimmed and a new coolness had crept into her manner.

'I met Mr Bancroft while I was out today. He invited us for dinner tomorrow evening. Mr and Mrs Cox will be there, along with Mrs Muirfield, Reverend and Mrs Woodford, and Dr Moffat.'

'Unfortunately I shall be unable to attend,' said Madeline in the voice of a stranger.

He couldn't help but notice that her cheeks looked pale tonight. Indeed, something of the bloom that had settled upon her in the past weeks seemed to have faded. She was once more picking at the food set upon her plate. 'Why might that be?'

'I'm planning to return to London tomorrow morning. It's a while since I have seen my family, and I would like to visit them.'

The sudden silence within the dining room grated. Only the clock upon the mantel sounded.

Lucien dismissed Mr Norton and the footmen. Only when the door had been closed behind their departing bodies did he speak. 'I'm sorry to disappoint you, but it does not suit me to leave Trethevyn so soon. Perhaps in a week or two we shall make the journey. I'm sure that your parents will understand.' Lucien waited for his wife's reaction.

Madeline did not look up from her dinner plate. 'I'm perfectly content to travel alone. You may stay here.'

Another silence.

Was she so keen to be rid of his company as to risk exposing herself to Farquharson? A sliver of hurt stabbed at Lucien's heart. Even as he closed his mind to the pain, he wondered how she had managed to pierce the protective numbness that the years of torment had forged. 'I'm afraid I cannot allow that, Madeline,' he said.

Her knife and fork were set down upon her plate, the pretence of eating the food forgotten. Gone was the warm biddable woman, replaced instead by someone that he did not know. 'Cannot allow?' For the first time he saw a spark of anger in her eyes. 'Did we not have an agreement, sir?' Without waiting for a reply she rushed on. 'I have fulfilled my side of the bargain—do you seek to renege on yours?'

Lucien found himself frowning across at her. 'I'm doing exactly what I said I would.'

'You said that I may visit my family whenever I wished. Well, I wish to do so now.' A hint of a pink stain stole into her previously pale cheeks.

Lucien gritted his teeth. 'You may also recall that I promised to protect you. And I cannot do that if you are insistent upon exposing yourself to danger. It's not that I do not wish you to see your family, but I won't have you put your life at risk to do so. Patience is a virtue, Madeline. The visit will be all the sweeter for waiting a few weeks more.'

'You would know all about patience, wouldn't you? Please do not presume to lecture me on it, for I would rather act on one foolish impulse after another than have your cold, calculated patience!' A deeper blush flooded her cheeks and her chair scraped back hard against the polished wooden floor. 'And as for protection and safety…please spare me any more of your untruths. I know full well what this is about, sir. You may cease your game.' She rose swiftly, threw her napkin down upon the table and started to walk towards the door.

In one seamless motion he was out of his chair and across the floor, his hand grasping her arm, pulling her back to face him. He was aware of the tension that resonated through them both, of the pulse that throbbed at her neck. 'I think you had better explain your words, Madeline.' The softness of his voice belied the turmoil of emotion that roared beneath that calm façade.

She looked up into his cold pale eyes and felt a tremor flutter deep within, but it was too late to pull back. She had fired the first shot and now she would have to finish the fight. 'You know of what I speak. There is no need for me to spell it out.'

'Humour me,' he said in a flat tone. 'Every word, every letter.'

His fingers burned against the flesh of her upper arm. He was so close she could feel the brush of his breeches against her skirt, smell the scent of soap and cologne upon his skin, see the detail of the dark shadow of stubble upon his chin. Her heart hammered in her chest. 'I know the truth,' she whispered.

His eyes bored into hers. 'Pray enlighten me with it.'

'I know why you married me.' She saw a muscle twitch in the tightness around his jaw. 'I was never in any danger from Cyril Farquharson, was I?' she said in a low voice. 'Only from you.' She thought she saw shock and something else in the depths of those ice-blue pools, a reflection, there, then gone.

'You really have no idea of the lengths to which Farquharson will go, the depths to which he will plummet, to have you. He means to kill you, and he will, unless I stop him.'

'No, Lucien! I won't listen to any more of your lies.' She tried to pull back from him but he made no effort to release his grip. 'Why did you not just call him out and have done with it?' she shouted at him. 'It would have saved us both a lot of trouble.'

'I did, albeit too damned late. Have you not noticed his limp? My aim was flawed. A leg is a poor substitute for a heart. I shall not make the same mistake again.' His face was white and bloodless against the stark black of his hair

'Your fight with him has nothing to do with me. Just let

me go. You may seek a divorce at the Consistory Courts. I will not stop you. I'll return to my family until I'm able to think of what to do with my future. You need not fear I will speak of the matter—I give you my word that I will not.'

Lucien's hands tightened around her arms. 'Divorce? By heaven and hell, Madeline, if that's what you're hoping, then I tell you now that I will never divorce you. You knew when you agreed to marry me that there was no going back. I haven't gone through all of this to hand you to Farquharson on a plate. If he has his way, you won't have a future.'

'Cease this pretence, Lucien. Can you not forget what he did, carry on with your own life?'

A gasp of incredulity escaped Lucien's lips. His eyes burned with cold blue fire. Anger coiled tight. 'I will never forget, and I will never rest until Cyril Farquharson is dead.'

'He was right,' she whispered. 'Jealousy has driven you mad.' She struggled to release herself from him.

He hauled her closer. 'Jealousy?' The straight white teeth practically bared. 'And of what is it that you think I would be jealous? Rape? Torture? Murder?'

Disbelief blasted at her from every pore of his body. The breath grew ragged in her throat. They stared at one another with the frenzied ticking of the clock in the background goading the squall of emotion higher. The mask slipped. Raw and bleeding hurt showed clear upon his face. All her beliefs of what lay between him and Farquharson, of his callousness in using her for revenge, turned on their head. 'Lucien…' she reached a hand towards him, but it was too late.

Letting his hands fall loosely by his sides, he stepped back from her. 'Good God, you really don't believe me, do you? You think I'm lying about protecting you? About what he means to do to you?'

She shook her head. 'I…I don't know.' She watched the harsh shutter drop back across his face, shielding whatever he was really thinking from her view. 'He stole your betrothed. So you stole his. *Quid pro quo.*'

His eyes held hers. There was about him an agony of tension that reached across the small distance between them. 'Never think that,' he said. 'I will not let him hurt you in the way that he hurt Sarah.' He reached across and with a featherlight touch caressed her cheek. 'I failed before and two women died because of it. I will not fail again. Hate me if you will, but I'm the only thing that stands between you and Farquharson, and I have no intention of giving up an innocent to him again. You're my wife, Madeline, and while Farquharson still breathes that's the way it's going to stay.'

The gentleness of his fingers stilled against her cheek, transfixing her, wooing her against her will. But beneath it all she heard the steely determination of his tone.

'Lucien, I cannot…I will not…' She was determined to finish what had to be said. 'You loved her.' Madeline ploughed on through the weight of crushing pain that had settled upon her chest. It pricked at her eyes and tightened around her throat as if to choke her. 'I didn't know it, that night in the inn…in the bed. I would never have…I wouldn't have done what I did, had I known.' *And I wouldn't have married you had I known that your heart had already been given, and I would lose my own to you,* the little voice inside her head whispered. She would not hear it, could not allow herself to. Tonight she would say everything she must, for tomorrow she would be gone—whatever Lucien said to the contrary.

'You did nothing. I was the one who forgot myself, not—'

'No, Lucien. That's not true.' She looked at him a moment

longer. The blush scalded her cheeks. 'I understand why I dis-gusted you.'

She thought she disgusted him? Lucien reeled at the frank admission. 'What ever gave you such a ridiculous idea?' But as the question formed upon his lips, he remembered his reaction on waking to find himself in the throes of making love to his wife. He'd been disgusted all right, but with himself, not Madeline.

The amber eyes looked up to his.

'I can assure that you do not disgust me, Madeline. Quite the reverse, in fact.'

'Then why—?'

Lucien's fingers slid round to cradle the nape of her neck. In one step he closed the space between them, his other hand sweeping down to press against the small of her back. She felt the superfine of his coat brush against her breasts. His head lowered towards hers until his breath tickled against her neck, licked against her cheek, her chin, her nose, igniting a trail of passion. Ice-blue eyes locked with warm amber. The words died in her mouth. Madeline found she could not move, could not breathe for drowning in the cool blue water that was his eyes. 'Lucien…' The word was nothing more than a hoarse breath between them. She watched his gaze drop to her mouth and linger. Felt hers do the same, cleaving to that finely sculpted mouth. 'Lucien…' Need grew stronger.

The sweet allure of her lips beckoned. Moist. Pink. His lips moved to capture her protestation, claiming hers. Sliding together in possession as his fingers stroked against the skin of her neck. Her mouth opened beneath his, responding to his call, answering with a passion of her own. His tongue teased against her lips, then probed further, seeking within, until it touched against her own small hesitant tongue. Urgency exploded between them.

Madeline arched her back, instinctively driving her breasts against the hardness of his chest, gasping with the sensations taking over her body. She moaned a protest as his mouth left hers. Her hands entwined themselves around his neck to pull him back down to her. But Lucien had other ideas. He pressed a trail of hot kisses to her nose, eyebrow, temple and ear, tracing the delicate line of her jaw with his tongue.

'Lucien!' She gasped his name aloud, dizzy with desire, blind to everything save the man that pressed against her, deafened by the thud of their hearts.

His fingers moved to close around her breast. His palm scorched the mound, his finger and thumb teasing against her nipple until it hardened and peaked between them, as if the silk of her dress was not there. And still the madness continued. It was not enough. She wanted more. Needed more. Her breasts ached with need. And it seemed that her thighs were on fire, burning her, scalding her with desire. His hands slid down across her stomach, following over the curve of her hips round to cup her bottom. She nestled in closer, feeling her own desperation echoed in his body. His mouth raided hers once more, hard, demanding, needful, but the hands that stroked against her were gentle and giving.

His breath was ragged against her ear. 'Madeline!' The ravaged whisper sounded against the hollow of her throat, against her lips.

Her legs trembled as she gave herself up to him, lost in the ecstasy of the moment. Strong arms supported her, would never let her fall.

He pulled back enough to look into her face and she

wondered that she ever could have thought his eyes cold, for they held in them such a look of warm tenderness.

'Madeline,' he said again, more gently this time, 'you make me forget myself and all of my promises. Disgust, indeed!' A wry eyebrow arched and a wicked smile curved his mouth. His fingers caught a tendril of hair that had escaped its pins to feather across her cheek, and tucked it back behind her ear. 'If you are set upon returning to London tomorrow, then I will take you. But as long as Farquharson lives then I will never let you go. And, Madeline, if you really did know the truth of what happened here five years ago, then you would understand why. Idle gossip weaves lies with truth in equal measure. I thought you knew that. You would have done better to ask me.'

He still held her, close and intimate. Her body burned for want of his touch. 'Would you have told me?' she whispered the words against his chest.

Lucien's chin rested lightly on the top of her head. He hesitated. 'In truth, I do not know. It's a difficult matter for me to speak of.' She deserved the truth about that at least.

'Will you tell me now?' She looked up and shyly touched a small kiss to his throat. Palms laid flat against the muscle of his chest, feeling the strong steady beat of his heart.

His gaze held hers as he moved his thumb against the soft cushion of her lips. 'It does not make for a pleasant story,' he said. 'Are you sure that you want to know?'

She nodded once. 'I need to know, Lucien. All of it.'

She felt the slight tightening of his muscles beneath her hands, saw him swallow hard.

'Very well, then,' he said. 'But not here. Let's go to the library.'

The library. His special place into which she had never

before been invited. She knew then that he meant to tell her everything.

His hand closed over hers and together they walked towards the dining-room door.

They had almost reached it when a stiff little knock sounded against the wood. Lucien swung the door open to reveal the portly figure of Mr Norton. The butler recovered well, hiding his shock. In all the forty-seven years Mr Norton had served the Tregellases, he had never had the Earl open the door in person. 'M'lord,' he said with only a shade less than his usual aplomb. A slightly horrified expression flitted across his face as he caught sight of the barely touched serving dishes and food-laden dinner plates upon the dining table. 'Perhaps the meal was to not to your liking?'

'It was very good, thank you, Norton.'

Mr Norton showed not the slightest intention of moving. He stared with barely disguised confusion first at Lord Tregellas, and then at his wife.

'The meal was lovely, thank you, Mr Norton.' Madeline smiled at the butler.

'We are retiring to the library and are not to be disturbed,' said Lucien, and, taking her hand in his, swept Madeline off in the direction of the library.

Madeline sat in one of the battered old wing chairs positioned close to the hearth. The library was not a large room. Down the full length of the wall opposite the fireplace were shelves of books. All were bound in a burgundy-leather cover, with gilt lettering upon the front cover and spine. There was a desk that was bare save for a writing slope, some cut paper, and a pen-and-ink set. A small drum table between the two wing chairs held a decanter and two balloon glasses.

Madeline's fingers rested against the worn and cracked leather of the chair arm and she watched her husband push the small table back towards the book shelves, then pull the other chair closer to hers.

He reached across, lifted her hand from the chair leather and held it gently within his own. 'I didn't mean for you to discover the history of what lies between Farquharson and me. It is, as I said before, hardly a pleasant subject…especially so for you, Madeline.' He lifted each of her fingers in turn, rubbing them, playing with them as he sought to find the words to tell her what needed to be said. 'But half-truths are a dangerous opponent, and so I find I've no choice but the one to which I'm pushed. I ask only that you hear what I would say in full and that you promise never to reveal what passes between us this evening.' He paused, watching her, waiting for the oath that would bind her to secrecy, afraid of what the truth might do to her.

'I promise.' Madeline felt the warmth of his hand around hers, saw the hesitation in his eyes. 'Lucien, you may trust that I will spill your words to no one. I give you my word on all that is holy.'

His gaze held hers a moment longer, then shifted to the golden glow of the fireplace. 'As you must know, it happened five years ago, although sometimes it seems that time has stood still since that night.' His profile was austerely handsome. 'I was betrothed to Lady Sarah Wyatt, daughter of Lord Praze. My father and Lord Praze were friends. It seemed a good alliance for the families to make.' He paused. 'I did not love Sarah, but through time perhaps I would have come to care for her.'

Madeline bowed her head and tried not to be glad.

'She was a very quiet and reserved young girl. Even though it was agreed that we would marry, Sarah had always longed to go to London and be presented for the Season. I saw no reason why she shouldn't do so. The winter had been hard that year and none of the family knew that my father's heart had weakened. I'd been in London only a fortnight when I received the news of his death.'

Madeline squeezed his hand. 'I'm so sorry.'

Lucien gave a barely perceptible nod of the head and continued in the same controlled tone as before. 'My parents didn't care for the town, preferring to spend their time here at Trethevyn. Naturally Guy and I returned with haste. My mother was distraught.' He glanced at her then. 'Theirs had been a love match, you see.'

Madeline briefly touched her cheek to the back of the hand that was still wrapped around hers.

'Sarah didn't return to Cornwall. She sent a letter expressing her condolences and carried on as before.'

'Did you not mind?'

'Not really. She was young and enjoying all that London had to offer.'

Sarah Wyatt also sounded to be a rather selfish young lady to Madeline's mind, but she held her tongue and did not offer her opinion.

'It was two weeks after the funeral when the first rumours reached us. Cyril Farquharson had been seen too frequently in Sarah's company. Their behaviour was giving London something to gossip over. My mother insisted that she would manage and bade me return to London to speak to Sarah,'

'So you went back.'

'Yes, I went back to find that Sarah had been beguiled by Farquharson and was set upon marrying him.'

Madeline shivered. 'She would willingly have wed him?' Her voice rang high with incredulity.

'Indeed, yes,' replied Lucien with surprising calm. 'She told me that I might sue her all I wished, but it would not convince her to marry me or stop her loving Farquharson.'

Madeline's jaw dropped open, her eyes opening wide. 'Love? How could anyone love such a man?'

Lucien shrugged. 'She barely knew him. It was not Farquharson that she loved, but the false image that he played her.'

'What happened?' she whispered the question, wondering what was to follow. Sarah Wyatt was dead, of that she was sure. But by what means and had Lucien played any role in that terrible event?

The stark blue eyes moved to hers. 'The time comes when I must confess my guilt, Madeline, for had I acted differently that night, things would not have unfolded in the same manner. Both Sarah and my mother would still be alive.'

Cold dread crept up Madeline's spine. Her teeth nipped at her bottom lip. She waited for what he would say.

The firelight flickered upon Lucien's face, casting sinister shadows across its hard angular planes. And still he said nothing. A log crackled, sending a cascade of sparks out on to the marble slabs.

'What did you do?' Her throat was hoarse with aridity. It was the question she most feared to ask, and the one question she knew that she must.

'I killed her,' he said softly.

Madeline's heart stopped. Breath trapped in her throat. Time shattered. Her eyes slid to him, gaped in horror at the stillness of his profile.

'Or as good as,' he said, still staring into the flames as if he were locked into some nightmare of the past.

As good as? A sigh of relief. *Then he hadn't, he didn't...*

'Tell me, Lucien,' and she pulled him round to face her. 'Tell me,' she said again.

His eyes held hers. 'I cast her out. Sent her to him, willingly. Told her that I would not sue her because I did not want her.' And still he faced her with defiance. 'I didn't even call Farquharson out over it.'

'But you shot him. I thought—'

He shook his head in denial. 'That was later, after I knew what he had done to her.' The pain was clear upon his face. 'I sent her to her death, Madeline. The guilt is mine.'

'No! She loved him. She wanted to marry him. You did nothing wrong.'

'She was a foolish, innocent young girl. What chance did she have against Farquharson? She couldn't have known what manner of man he was.'

'Did you?'

'There was always something unsavoury about him. But I did not know the extent of it. Not then.'

'Lucien, what else could you have done? You couldn't have pushed her to a wedding she did not desire.' Clear honey eyes stared into pale blue. Both knowing that the conversation was overlapping on to more recent events.

'Not even to protect her?' he said with a harsh cynical tone. 'To save her life?'

The heavy beat of Madeline's heart thudded in her chest. 'Like you did me,' she whispered.

'Yes.' He raked a hand wearily through his hair. 'Exactly like I did you.'

Only the slow ticks of the clock punctuated the silence.

'How did she die?'

'Horribly.'

The single word hung between them.

'I don't understand.'

'It's better that you don't.'

'Lucien…' a wrinkle crept across her brow '…I should know it all, however bad it is.'

He sighed, and opened his palm beneath her hand. 'Madeline, once you know there's no going back.'

'Tell me,' she said again and laid her hand over his. 'I'm your wife, Lucien, and nothing is going to change that.'

He gave a slight nod. 'Very well. Cyril Farquharson—'

A knock sounded.

Madeline jumped. Lucien glanced round at the library door.

Another knock, slightly louder than the last.

'Come in.'

The door opened to reveal Norton. 'My apologies, m'lord. I know you didn't wish to be disturbed, but Lord Varington has just arrived. I've taken the liberty of placing him in the drawing room.' The butler gave a mild clearing-of-the-throat noise. 'If I may be so bold as to observe that Lord Varington has come only with his man, and that his horses have been ridden long and hard.'

A prickle of foreboding traversed Lucien's scalp. 'I'll come immediately,' was all that he said before turning to Madeline. 'It appears that we must postpone our…conversation until another time.' He waited until the butler's footsteps receded into the distance. 'Guy wouldn't have arrived unannounced, on horseback and at this time of night, if something wasn't wrong. Perhaps it would be better if you waited upstairs.'

He could see the look of hurt in her eyes. 'My brother will not speak bluntly in front of you and I need to discover what's happened to bring him down here at such speed.' His fingers squeezed hers in a gesture of reassurance. 'Guy hates the country. I can't remember the last time he left London.' He stood.

Madeline got to her feet. 'Then matters must be serious.'

'That's what I'm afraid of. Go up to your room...' he spoke gently, his hand still intertwined with hers '...I'll come to you later. We should finish what we've started this evening.' He stared into her eyes. 'There will be time later to speak of it in full.'

'Lucien.' She raised her face to his. 'You will come... tonight, won't you?'

He traced the outline of her cheek with his thumb, regarding her with something akin to wonder.

'Are you sure that you want me to? Perhaps it would be better kept until another time.'

She shook her head and, standing on the tips of her toes, reached up to place a shy kiss upon his mouth. 'No. What happened with Farquharson wasn't your fault.' The thrum of her heart pulsed in her chest. 'Tonight.' She pulled back to look into the cool blue pools of his eyes. 'Please.'

'I'll come to you tonight.'

Their lips touched, lingered together, parted reluctantly. Both knowing that it was not only the end of the story for which she was asking.

He followed her out, watched while the slender figure mounted the stairs. Subtle sway of her hips and rustle of silk. He breathed in the subtle scent of oranges that surrounded him, felt his heart swell with a long-forgotten tenderness, acknowledged that he wanted her, every last inch of her, from the heavy dark gold of her hair to the tips of her toes. Not only her body, but also her respect, her affection, her love. She did not blame him for the terror from across the years. Would she, once she knew it all? Lucien did not think so. Her belief in him eased the heavy burden of guilt. Her warmth thawed the ice in which he had been frozen. And the realisation that she wanted him was a salve to his soul. After tonight, the possibility of a divorce *a vinculo matrimonii* would be no more. A consummated marriage could not be nullified. But first there was the small matter of his brother.

Chapter Twelve

'What were you doing speaking to him?' Lucien raked a hand through his hair, oblivious to the mayhem he was wreaking upon his valet's hard work.

Guy lounged back in the wing chair, swinging a muddy booted leg over the arm. 'Your concentration seems to be elsewhere, Lucien,' he said. 'I already told you, he approached me in White's. I couldn't very well break the bastard's jaw without drawing a smidgen of attention to the fact. Believe me when I say that I was tempted in the extreme. But I didn't want to give that snake any further fuel to burn upon the fire he's stoking.' Guy looked at his brother's face and took a swig of brandy. 'You'd best prepare yourself, Lucien. The matter's not over.'

'I never believed it was. I've been waiting for him to strike, watching closer with each passing day.'

'Farquharson was ever the coward, Lucien. He's coming after you, all right, but not in the way that you think. He means to convince all of London that Madeline was an unwilling party in your marriage. He's been working on it since you left.'

Lucien paced the length of the small library. 'Let him. Arthur Langley will vouch for his daughter's story. Madeline spoke before Farquharson and her father. She assured them of her willingness in the matter and confirmed the validity of the marriage.' A vision of a tousled-haired Madeline wrapped in his dressing-gown, asserting before both her father and Farquharson that she had married and bedded him because she loved him, swam into his mind. His heart swelled with tenderness. He'd be damned if he would let either man take her from him by whatever means.

Guy's leg ceased its lazy swing. 'That may have been what she *said*. It's what she has *written* that is the problem.'

A sinking feeling started in Lucien's chest. 'Go on.'

A short silence. Brother looked at brother. And Lucien knew that what Guy was about to say would change everything.

'How certain are you of your wife, Lucien?'

'What do you mean?' A dark frown drew his brows close. 'She's the innocent in all of this mess.'

'Is she really?' asked Guy softly.

'What the hell are you getting at? Farquharson had her in his sights. I married her to protect her.'

'And lure Farquharson to a confrontation.'

'Yes, I admit it, that as well. None of us are safe until he's dead.'

'And Farquharson isn't safe until you're out of the way either. You've never left him alone in all of these years. Everywhere he's gone you've dogged his steps, waiting for your chance.'

'Ensuring that there would never be a repetition of what happened to us five years ago.'

'You knew what you'd do if he found another woman, a woman like Sarah.'

'You know that I did.'

'While you were watching and waiting all those years, did

it never occur to you that Farquharson might be hatching his own plan, to rid himself of you?'

Lucien looked into the eyes that were so like his own.

'That he might use an "innocent little victim" to lure *you?*'

'Are you saying that Farquharson never had any intention of marrying Madeline? That he deliberately set matters up to make it appear that he meant to?'

Guy's lip curled. 'Knowing full well that you would rush to her rescue, even if it meant marrying her yourself.'

The coldness started in his toes and spread up through the core of his body. 'Even if it was all a ploy, I still won't yield her to him. She's my wife now. He may have used her. I have no intention of doing the same.'

'Even if she accuses you of abduction and begs him to rescue her.'

'Don't be absurd! Madeline would never do such a thing.'

Guy set the empty glass down carefully on the table before standing to face his brother. 'She already has,' he said quietly; retrieving the letter from his pocket, he handed it to his brother. 'Farquharson has a copy and means to publish it unless you come to some kind of agreement with him within the next two weeks.' He placed a hand on Lucien's shoulder. 'I'm sorry, but, with Madeline's assistance, Farquharson cannot fail to make you the villain of the piece while he comes out as the unfairly wronged victim of the whole affair, just as he did before.'

'It's not possible.'

'Oh, I assure you that not only is it possible, but that Farquharson and Madeline have their little plan well under way.'

'Are you suggesting that Madeline is somehow complicit in this absurdity?' Lucien's eyes narrowed and everything about him stilled: the calm before the storm.

Guy squeezed Lucien's shoulder, his fingers conveying the sympathies that he knew his brother would never let him voice. 'Farquharson bade me ask you if you appreciate her acting skills. Said he trained her himself. She's tricked you, Lucien. She's in league with that devil.'

'You would believe *his* word?' Aggression snarled as Lucien batted Guy's hand away.

Guy dropped his hand loosely to his side. 'Look at the letter, Lucien. It bears the Tregellas name and crest at the top of the paper. Even though the seal is broken, it is clear that it is yours. Unless you are in the habit of allowing Farquharson to use your writing desk, I fail to see how he could have faked such things.'

Guy refilled two glasses; the brandy spilled down the decanter, splashing unnoticed against the cherrywood of the table and over the base of the branched candlestick that sat behind it on the table. 'Is the writing from Madeline's hand? Have you nothing against which you can compare it?'

'No.' Then he remembered the letter lying on his desk to be sent; the letter she had written to her mother. Woodenly he moved towards the desk, taking the neatly folded paper up in his hands, dread and disbelief eating at him in equal measure. 'A letter she would have me dispatch to Mrs Langley.'

Guy brought the branched candlestick close.

The two men looked from the incriminating letter to the neatly penned address on the letter to be franked. A short silence. The words did not need to be said—it was quite clear to see that the writing was identical in both cases.

Guy looked with saddened eyes towards his brother and nodded. 'You had best check that the letter within is indeed to her mother.'

Lucien broke the seal, unfolded the paper, scanned the lines of small neat words that stacked tidily, one row upon another. 'It's to Amelia Langley all right. Nothing in it that I would not expect her to say.'

A log crackled upon the fire.

'She must have sneaked her letters to Farquharson through the village post. Your servants are loyal. It should be easy enough to find if anyone carried such a letter in recent weeks.' Guy emptied the contents of the glass down his throat. 'I'm sorry, Lucien.'

'Not as damned sorry as I am,' came the reply, as he settled down to read exactly what his wife had written to Cyril Farquharson.

He sat by the fire for an hour after Guy had gone to bed, trying to make sense of the words, following every avenue of hope, exploring alternative explanations for a letter written in his wife's hand, on his crested paper, and bearing his own seal. A letter that spoke of mistakes and distrust; that accused him of obsessive hate, verging on insanity. A letter that begged Farquharson's forgiveness and pleaded with him to rescue her from the clutches of a madman who held her prisoner. Had she not voiced the very same doubts on his honesty and his sanity earlier that evening? Lucien felt like his ribcage had been levered open and his heart ripped out. Surely Madeline's response to him, her passion, her warmth, could not have been feigned? Could it?

The brandy burned at his throat, searing a path down to his stomach, but did nothing to numb the pain. It was a raw pulsating hurt beyond anything that he ever thought to allow himself to feel again. This had to be Farquharson stirring trouble, seeking some way to blacken Madeline's name. What better way to damage both her and the man who had been his nemesis for so long? Had he not seen it with his own eyes, he would never have believed it. The writing was that of Madeline's hand. But writing could be copied, words faked. The seal and paper were that of Tregellas. There were only two Tregellas seals: one adorned the ring fitted firmly on the third finger on Lucien's right hand, the other lay within the top drawer of his desk by the window. Damn Farquharson's eyes! Damn his soul! Guy was right. Quizzing of his staff would soon determine if a letter to Farquharson had left the house. With a heavy heart he pulled the bell and waited for Norton to appear.

Madeline curled her legs beneath her on the sofa and stared into the flickering flames in the centre of the fireplace. He would tell her the truth, she knew it instinctively. The story of how Sarah Wyatt had died. Madeline shuddered at the thought. But then again, Sarah had chosen Farquharson over Lucien. Quite how any woman could have come to make that choice was beyond her.

Lord Farquharson and Lord Tregellas. Two men at opposing ends of the spectrum. One gifted with pretty polished words that tripped too readily from his tongue. Red hair, creamy pale skin peppered with freckles, sharp grey eyes and a slim face that some considered handsome. Madeline could not agree. He reminded her of a fox, all slyness and cunning. The other man, a contrast of dark and light. White skin and pale blue eyes that could not fail to pierce the reserve of that upon which he fixed his focus. Classically sculpted features as handsome and as cold as those of the marble Greek god that represented the ideal of manly beauty. Scant of words. Austere. Hair as black as midnight and, if London was to be believed, a soul to match.

But therein lay the problem. Madeline could not believe it, indeed, had never believed the whispered rumours that fanned in his wake. The Wicked Earl, they called him, but when she looked into his eyes it was not wickedness that she saw, but pain and passion, kindness and consideration. Hidden deep behind his cold façade, but there all the same. Whatever Lucien Tregellas would have the world believe, he was a man who felt things deeply. Hadn't she seen the evidence with her own eyes? Felt the warmth of his arms around her, the strength of his determination, the tenderness in his eyes and the burning heat of his lips? It seemed that for all he said, her husband was not indifferent to her, that he didn't just want the unemotional bargain that he had set out that night in his coach in London, any more than she did. She remembered his words, *I'll come to you tonight.*

Excitement tingled through her. He would tell her the truth and then he would kiss her. Without disgust. Without guilt. Only with gentle possession. He would kiss her until she felt hot and all of a tremble. Madeline smiled, knowing that there was a truth of her own to be told. She loved him. No matter what lies Farquharson sought to spread about him, no matter the chill of his veneer, she knew the warm tenderness of the man beneath it. She loved him. Tonight she would tell him. With a smile she picked up the discarded novel by her side and was soon immersed in the description of Mr Darcy proposing to Miss Elizabeth Bennett at the parsonage in Kent.

'Are you certain, Norton? Might the boy not be mistaken as to the addressee? Can he even read?' Lucien thought he saw the hint of a flush touch the old butler's cheeks.

Mr Norton folded his hands behind his back and regarded his employer with his usual servile superiority.

'Hayley is illiterate, m'lord. Lady Tregellas asked him to take the letter to the post office in the village right away. Hayley is sweet on her ladyship's maid, Betsy Porter, and he spent a few minutes in saying his farewells to her before attending to his errand.' Two silver-grey eyebrows raised marginally. 'I noticed the letter lying upon the kitchen table on account of the person to whom it was addressed. Far-quharson is a name I'm not likely ever to forget for the rest of my days, m'lord.'

Lucien touched a solitary finger to the hard square line of his jaw. 'Did my wife ask anything else of Hayley with regard to the letter? Not to speak of it before me, for example?'

'No, m'lord.' The old butler shook his head. 'Nothing like that, but she did give him half a crown for his trouble.'

'I see.'

'Will that be all, m'lord?' Mr Norton did not like the dark brooding look that had settled upon his master's face.

'Yes, thank you, Norton. You may retire for the night.'

Only when the butler had gone and the library door was firmly closed did Lucien allow himself to fully contemplate the impact of Madeline's dishonesty.

Madeline closed the last page of the book, well contented with the happy ending. Stretching out her back, she snuggled lower beneath the covers and watched the low flickering flame of her bedside candle. The clock struck midnight and a little furrow of worry creased between her brows. Guy's news must be bad indeed to keep Lucien so late. Momentarily she wondered what had brought Lord Varington to Trethevyn with such speed. Lucien would tell her soon enough, when he came to her as he had promised. Madeline smiled at the thought. Soon he would lie beside her in the bed and tell her the rest of his story. She would kiss him and tell him that he was not to blame, that she loved him, that she would love him for ever.

Guilt was a heavy burden to bear and Lucien had carried it for five long years. In truth, he had done nothing wrong. Sarah Wyatt had chosen Farquharson and she had paid the price with her life. Poor, foolish Sarah. Eighteen was too young to die. Madeline could only be glad that Lucien had intervened to save herself from Farquharson.

A pang of conscience tweaked at her. To think that only this evening she had doubted her husband and had questioned the motives behind their marriage. All along he had blamed himself for Sarah's death and determined to save her from the same fate. An image of Lord Farquharson's face stole into her mind. Hard grey eyes, narrow lips that formed such pretty words, and beneath it all a soul as black as the devil's. Even the memory of his moist breath against her cheek and the pungency of his spicy scent made her feel quite sick. How could she have even contemplated the words of such a man?

Instinct had warned her against him from the start. Lucien had described him as unsavoury. Madeline would have used a much stronger and unladylike word. Yet despite it all she had questioned her husband with ungrateful suspicion. He had gone to such lengths to save her from Farquharson. And she had practically cast it all back in his face. It was a wonder that he had not just sent her packing back to London. But Lucien had not done that. He had told her the truth, and kissed her. Tonight he would come to her bed and everything would be all right.

Madeline awoke with a start and as much a feeling of panic as from her nightmares of Farquharson that had long since ceased. The clock on the mantel chimed two. The room was in darkness, the candle long since expired, and the fire nothing more than a pile of warm ashes. She sat up, stared around her, aware of a feeling that something was wrong. Then she remembered that Lucien was supposed to have come. On the covers beside her lay the warm, heavy weight of Max, giving the occasional whimper while he chased rabbits in his dreams. The small seed of dread deep within her began to grow. An unease. What news was so bad as to have kept Lucien from his promise? All around her was the hiss of nocturnal silence, broken only by the ticking of the clock. The night was black with the occasional glimmer of a cold pale moonlight that crept from behind cloud cover to illuminate her bedchamber. It seemed that a hand wrung at her stomach and she could not rid herself of a bleak, unnatural sensation. Something was badly awry. Had Farquharson harmed another woman? Her mother? Angelina? Madeline could not dispel the notion of dread, even when Max opened a sleepy eye and licked her face.

The floor was cold beneath her feet on the edge of the rug. She peered from her window across the darkened gardens, seeking any sign of movement. There was none. An owl hooted in the distance. She moved silently towards the connecting door that led to Lucien's rooms, Max padding by her side. Her fingers closed around the smooth roundness of the handle, hesitated for a minute and then turned. It was not locked. The door opened noiselessly. Madeline waited where she was, heart racing twenty to the dozen, eyes straining to see through the darkness of the room. Lucien's bedchamber was shrouded in a thick black, by virtue of the heavy curtains closed across his windows. No fire. No lit candles. That did not deter Max. The dog disappeared into his master's room, the black hair of his coat merging with the darkness. 'Max! Come here!' Madeline whispered. A snuffling and the click of canine nails against wooden flooring sounded from the other side of the room. 'Max!' she whispered again.

She stepped across the threshold. Gradually her eyes adjusted to make out the shapes of large pieces of furniture, blacker shapes within the darkness, there, but only just. Without some hint of guiding light, she did not dare proceed lest she knocked something over or tripped over some hidden object. 'Max,' she said softly. No reply. Her hands extended, reaching out before her, probing cautiously into the darkness. One foot edged forward, then the other, arms waving before her. But Max was not forthcoming. And it seemed that her husband must be in the depths of a sound sleep, for no stirring came from anywhere in the room. Madeline sighed and knew that she would have to leave Max to snuggle his warmth against Lucien. She retreated as silently as she had arrived, the handle scraping slightly as the door closed. The barrier between the two bedchambers was intact once more.

Her fingers fumbled with the tinderbox as she struggled to strike a light. Eventually the small remnants of her candle by the bedside took, casting soft yellow flickers of light to dance around the paintings upon the walls. Madeline had never felt more disinclined to sleep. Her fingers fanned through *Pride and Prejudice,* but the story had been read. Then she remembered Lucien's library with its complete wall lined with books. She looked at the small lump of candle left within her holder. There would be candles down there, too. A good novel would drag her mind from such melancholic contemplation. Madeline lifted the small spluttering candle and headed towards the bedchamber door.

Lucien stared blindly out of the library window. The fire had long since died and the draught infiltrating the window frames caused a flutter of the curtains he had pulled back two hours since. Lucien noticed neither, nor did he feel the chill that had steadily descended upon the room. He lounged back in the chair and threw some more brandy down his throat. Anything to deaden the pain of betrayal.

Every time his eyes closed it was to see Madeline. Sherry-gold eyes and pink parted lips that curved in the sweetness of her smile. *What happened with Farquharson wasn't your fault,* she said, and reached her lips to his. Warm. Willing. So beguiling, yet traitorous. Farquharson would never get beneath the guard he had so carefully erected in the years that had passed. Madeline had managed it without even trying.

He rubbed long fingers against his temples, replaying the scenes for the umpteenth time. She was good. He had to give her that. Feigning such innocence. Responding to his kisses. Asking him to come to her bed. How far would she have gone to be sure of him? Would she actually have given herself to him for Farquharson's sake?

Another swig of brandy, but the pain hung on grimly, refusing to go. Especially in view of what he knew he must do. A faint noise sounded from the hallway. He thought he heard a woman's voice. A pause, then the library door slowly creaked open. There was a moment of faint illumination and then darkness.

'Wretched candle,' the voice muttered.

Lucien froze in his seat, the smell of candle smoke tickling at his nose.

One small hesitant step sounded and then another. Whoever had decided to visit his library in the middle of the night was coming closer. His muscles tensed for action.

Madeline edged towards the window, thankful that her husband had left the curtains open. Now that she thought of it the curtains had been closed earlier that evening when he had brought her here to tell her of his past. He must have opened them before retiring for the night. And he must have retired, for she had seen no glimmer of light escaping the drawing-room door along the corridor. Fleetingly a break in the clouds revealed a shaft of moonlight. It lit enough of the library to show her the desk by the window and the high-backed chair behind it. Maybe Lucien would keep a candle and a tinderbox on his desk. Her father had always done so.

She moved warily forward, hands outstretched in the darkness. If only the clouds would not keep covering the moon, then she would see readily enough. Progress was slow, but Madeline persevered. She reached the desk, and skimmed her fingers lightly across its surface, seeking the means to make light. Writing slope, paper, pens, ink pots, a small knife, more paper. Nothing of any use to Madeline. She tried the drawers, but they were locked. She withdrew her hand and hesitated where she was, unsure of what to do next. Back to the bedchamber and the thoughts that had forced her down here in the first place. She sighed and looked again at the inky cloud-streaked sky beyond the window. Blues and blacks and deep charcoal grey. And every now and again the peep of the bright white lunar disc. The scene beckoned her. Madeline answered its call. Unmindful of the cold, ignoring the darkness, she moved to stand before the window.

Lucien smelled her before he saw her. The faint resonance of oranges, and then she appeared. A small figure in a flowing white nightdress that stretched down to the floor. Her hair was unbound, sweeping long and straight across her shoulders and down to meet her waist. He knew her feet would be bare. She moved forward until she was right up at the window, staring out at the view beyond, seemingly unaware of his presence. He heard the softness of her sigh, saw the relaxed slump of her shoulders, as if something of night had taken a burden of tension away from her.

The empty glass nestled within the palm of his hand. Three-quarters of a decanter of brandy and nothing of the horror of Guy or Norton's words had faded. And now he had caught her searching around his desk in the dead of night. Hell! The pain bit deep. Farquharson had played him for a fool, thanks to the woman he had tried to save. However hard he tried to deny it, he knew that Madeline had found a route directly to his heart. He reined in his emotions and watched the slight figure before him.

The clouds drifted, ever changing, forming patterns against the night-time sky. Madeline watched in fascination, feeling some sense of relief from the foreboding that had gripped her in the bedchamber. She was being fanciful and foolish. She was just overtired and thinking too much on Lucien's story of Farquharson. Everything would seem better in the morning, in the sunlight, with Lucien by her side. As she turned to go, the moon escaped the cover of the cloud and lit Madeline's route across the library with a soft silver brilliance. She smiled a small smile at her good fortune and glanced down at the floor. Still smiling she stepped forward, raising her eyes…to look directly into the face of her husband.

Madeline gave a small yelp of fright and jumped back. 'Oh, Lucien, you startled me. I didn't know that you were there.' Her hand touched against the embroidered neckline of her nightdress.

'Evidently not.' His face appeared unnaturally pale beneath the moonlight, as if he were a carved effigy in white marble. It contrasted starkly with the darkness of his hair. His coat, waistcoat and neckcloth had been cast aside. His shirt was hanging open at the neck. At least his pantaloons and top boots still appeared to be in good order. An empty glass was cradled within his hand and the look upon his face did not bode well.

'Is something wrong?' She bent and touched a hand to his arm.

Lucien pulled his arm back as if scalded. 'He was right, Madeline. You play the game well. I admit that you had me convinced. Not once did I think to question the innocent Miss Madeline Langley.'

Madeline stared at him as if he was speaking double Dutch. Her eyes dropped to the empty glass in his hand. 'You're foxed!' she exclaimed in surprise. Something of the dangerous glitter in his eyes sent a warning. She knew better than to pursue the conversation. 'I'll see you in the morning,' she said and made to leave.

But Lucien had other ideas. He moved with alarming speed, his hand gripping her shoulder before she had even completed one step.

'Lucien!' Madeline gasped.

He hauled her back so that they stood face to face before the window. 'Did you find what you were looking for?' His voice was hard, with nothing of the tenderness that had softened his words earlier in the night.

Madeline's brow creased in puzzlement. 'No. My candle expired too soon. I had hoped to find a new one before it extinguished.'

One harsh breath of laughter grated. 'What a shame you couldn't see to rummage through my desk.'

'I was not rummaging! I couldn't sleep and had finished my book. I came to borrow one of yours. I didn't think that you'd mind.'

'Looking for anything in particular, or just something that might be of use to you both?'

'Lucien, I was looking for a candle and tinderbox.'

Madeline tried to shake him off, but Lucien held her arms in a firm grip.

'Sorry to disappoint you, Madeline, but you'll only find cut sheets of writing paper there. My documents are thankfully locked away.'

'I don't know what you're talking about.'

He lowered his face towards hers. The first thing she noticed was the strong smell of brandy. The second was the coldness of his eyes. 'Oh, but I think that you do, Madeline,' he said silkily. 'You're in league with Farquharson, aren't you?'

'Lucien?' She lifted her hands to rest against the muscles in his arms. 'You're drunk. You don't know what you're saying.'

'I know all right,' came his reply. 'All along I thought I was saving you from him. I would have forced you to become my wife. That's how determined I was to stop him from harming you. And all along you and Farquharson were playing me for the fool.'

'No!' she gasped. 'How could you think it?'

'That night in the Theatre Royal with your mama, and then again at Lady Gilmour's ball, you were very good at feigning fear. I believed you.'

Madeline just stared up at him, aghast at the words spilling from his mouth. Gone was the man she had come to love, in his place, a cold stranger.

'You married me to please him, didn't you? How much further were you willing to go for him? Would you have let me bed you? Make love to you? What then, Madeline? Would you have borne my child?'

She flinched at his cruelty. 'Stop it, Lucien.'

'Or perhaps I never would have survived that long.' His eyes darkened to something she had never seen before. 'Are you his mistress?' His fingers tightened against the skin of her arms.

'You've run mad!' Fear snaked up her spine. All the old doubts flooded back.

His face lowered to hers so that their lips were all but touching. 'How could you do it, Madeline?' he whispered before his mouth swooped over hers, lips sliding in hard possession. She felt the light insistent nip of his teeth and held herself rigid against the onslaught. There was nothing of giving and everything of taking. His hands slid from her arms, moving to claim her breasts, thumbing at her nipples, pulling her close, hard against him. Her lips parted in a gasp, allowing his tongue to raid within, possessing her mouth with what started as a fervour, but soon gentled. The taste of brandy lapped against her tongue with his. She felt his fingers cup her buttocks, lifting her against the hard bulge in his pantaloons.

'No, Lucien! It's not what you think.'

He seemed to hear her. Ceased his actions. Pulled back to look into her face. Stared for what seemed to be an eternity. His grip slackened. But she could still feel the tension throughout his body pressed against hers. His voice when it came was quiet and harsh and ragged. 'Damn you, Madeline.' With that he released her.

She staggered back, unable to comprehend what was happening.

'Pack your bags. You wished to travel to London to visit your mother. I have arranged for you to leave at the end of the week. Guy will accompany you on your journey to the city.'

'And what of you?

'I'll stay here as you suggested.' He heard the soft intake of breath and saw the confusion upon her face. The brandy lent him courage to continue. 'But before you go, Madeline, tell me just one thing. Did Farquharson tell you what he did to Sarah?'

A little gasp escaped her.

Lucien ignored it. 'Somehow, I doubt very much that he did. If you knew the truth, you wouldn't be standing here right now, you would never have danced to his tune. Ask him one day, when you're feeling brave. I warrant you'll not like what he has to say.' His gaze held hers directly. 'Goodbye, Madeline.'

Her face glowed white beneath the moon, and her eyes were huge dark pools of wounded disbelief. If she did not go soon, he knew he would weaken, give in to the urge to gather her back into her arms and lavish gentle kisses upon her mouth. She waited only a moment more, long enough for him to see the tremble of her lip before her teeth gripped it in a fury, long enough to see the glisten of moisture in her eyes. Then a flurry of white and she was gone, leaving him alone to remind himself that what he had just witnessed was a piece of consummate acting.

Chapter Thirteen

Madeline fled through the darkness, unseeing, uncaring, until she reached the safe haven of her bedchamber. The door shut forcibly behind her and, for the first time since arriving at Trethevyn, she turned the key within the lock. His words still echoed in her mind. Cruel words, words that never should have spilled from Lucien's tongue, and yet they had, all too readily. It was a nightmare from which there was no waking. Tension gripped her muscles so that they contracted hard and tight. Her heart was thudding too fast, too loud in her chest following her hurried flight from the library. Her mouth was dry, and what had started as a faint hint of nausea was rapidly expanding.

Such was her agitation that she paced the floor of the bedchamber, a small white ghost lit only by the transient light of the cloud cast moon. A scratching came from the connecting door. She moved to the spot, heard Max's muted whimpers, and let the dog back into her own room before locking the door. As if sensing something was wrong, Max looked up at her with a saddened expression. His tongue licked his reassurance over her fingers.

'Oh, Max!' Madeline crouched and clutched the warm black body of fur to her. 'What has happened to make him so angry and suspicious? He must truly have run mad.' She stroked the dog's head, lingering over the silky softness of his ears.

Max looked up at her, eyes dark within the muted nocturnal light, and whined.

Madeline could not bring herself to climb back into the bed she had left with such hopes. Lucien's gentle kisses and whispered promise seemed a lifetime ago. What could have wrought such a change in her husband? Then she remembered that he had gone to meet with his brother and that Lord Varington's sudden appearance probably meant that he conveyed news of great importance, news that had turned her husband against her. Madeline curled herself up on the sofa. Max clambered up next to her and laid his head across her legs. And there they stayed for what remained of the night, until the darkness paled to grey and a new dawn had broken. Never asleep. Just thinking, of a love so newly found and now lost.

By the time Betsy tried the door the next morning the faint outline of a plan had formed in Madeline's mind. If Lucien had no mind to discuss his brother's news rationally with her, then she would seek out the Viscount and ask him herself. She might as well know what had happened to bring about such a change in Lucien. If matters had not changed by the end of the week, she had no other choice than to travel to London with Lord Varington, as directed, and deal with the matter as best she could from there. As gently as she could she dislodged Max's heavy weight, finding that the cost of the great beast's warming presence was a numbing sensation in her left leg.

Betsy's knocking became louder. She whispered hesitantly

through the thick oaken door. 'M'lady? It's Betsy. I have your water here.'

Madeline hobbled faster towards the door, the key turning easily beneath her fingers. 'Forgive me, Betsy, I had forgotten that it was locked.'

The maid stared wide-eyed at her mistress, taking in the dark shadows beneath her eyes, the ashen hue of her complexion, and the fact that she appeared to be having difficulty in walking. 'M'lady!' she whispered in shock. Betsy set the basin down on the nearest table and rushed to Madeline's side. 'What has happened?'

'I slept poorly, that's all,' Madeline sought to reassure the girl.

'But your leg?'

Madeline attempted a smile. 'Max was lying on it and has given me pins and needles. He's rather heavy, must be eating too much.'

Betsy did not look convinced.

'I think I might just take a little breakfast here this morning, Betsy. Please could you bring up some coffee and a bread roll.'

Betsy stared some more. Madeline's next words confirmed in the maid's mind that something strange was going on.

'Oh, and can you find out if Lord Varington is up yet.'

'Yes, m'lady.' Betsy beat a hasty retreat to inform Mrs Babcock that Lady Tregellas was not at all herself this morning.

It was Mrs Babcock herself who returned with Madeline's breakfast on a tray. Red-cheeked and panting with quite an alarming volume, the housekeeper hobbled into the room.

'Babbie! I wasn't expecting you to carry that tray all the

way up here. I would have come down to the morning room to save you the trouble.'

'It's no trouble, m'lady,' puffed Mrs Babcock. She peered at Madeline's face. 'Feelin' a bit under the weather, are you, doe?'

'No. I'm quite well, thank you,' lied Madeline.

Mrs Babcock sniffed suspiciously. 'Lord Varington is still abed. Always was a slug in the mornings. Won't see him until this afternoon. Used to keepin' London hours, he is. At least, that's a polite way of puttin' it.' Her lips pursed in disapproval. 'Wayward young puppy!'

Madeline sipped at her coffee. The prospect of waiting for several hours until Lord Varington managed to extract himself from bed was sure only to set Madeline's nerves even more on edge. 'In that case, I think I might spend the morning visiting Tintagel Castle. I've been hoping to see it for some time and I shouldn't like to leave Cornwall without visiting it.'

'Bit of mornin' mist out there, m'lady. It'll be worse on the coast. Best wait until later in the day.'

Madeline poked at her bread roll, but found that her appetite had deserted her. 'Perhaps I could wait a little, but I'd like to be back by this afternoon.' She looked up into the housekeeper's blackcurrant eyes. 'It's likely that I'm to leave Trethevyn at the end of the week.'

'His lordship didn't mention nothin' 'bout leavin' so soon.' Mrs Babcock crossed her arms over her ample bosom.

'No,' said Madeline with the colour rising in her cheeks. 'Lucien shall stay here. I'm to travel with…with Lord Varington.'

Mrs Babcock's beady eyes missed nothing, from the bleakness in Madeline's eyes to the embarrassment warming her otherwise pale cheeks. 'I'll ask the master to make ready for your trip to Tintagel, then?'

'No!' Madeline almost shouted the word. 'I mean, no, thank you. I would rather that you didn't disturb Lucien.'

'He won't be best pleased. Told me in no uncertain terms that you weren't to leave this place without him.'

'I think you'll find that he's changed his mind,' said Madeline softly.

The older woman looked at her strangely. 'As you wish. Betsy will be up shortly.' Mrs Babcock had almost reached the door when she faltered and looked back at the slim figure standing by the newly lit fire. 'It's not my place to speak out, but I'm going to anyway. I've loved Master Lucien since he was a baby and I don't want to see any more unhappiness for him. I don't know what the two of you have had words about, and I won't ask. All I do ask is that you don't just leave him, m'lady. I know he's been a bit, well, high-handed, of late, but then I reckon he's got good reason with Lord Farquharson likely to appear at any minute.'

Madeline saw the opportunity rise before her eyes. 'Farquharson stole Sarah Wyatt from Lucien. Did he...? What happened to her?'

'He killed her.'

A heartbeat, then Madeline asked, 'Who killed her?'

Mrs Babcock looked her straight in the eye, knowing the traitorous thought that lurked beneath the question. 'Why, Lord Farquharson, m'lady. Who else did you think it might have been?'

Their gazes locked, golden on black.

'I had to be sure,' said Madeline. 'Farquharson told me that Lucien was responsible for her death.'

Mrs Babcock's upper lip curled in disgust. 'And you believed him?'

'No.' The word was like a sigh in the room.

'But you asked all the same.' Mrs Babcock turned and limped from the room. The quiet click of the bedchamber door closing behind her was louder than any slam could have been.

Madeline calmly pushed the uneaten bread roll away and drained the cooled dregs of her coffee. Time sounded with the steady strokes of the clock's pendulum. A small shaft of sunlight flooded the room, shining a golden spotlight upon the painting of two small boys from which Madeline had worked her embroidery. Outside in the garden, a blackbird whistled. And inside, Madeline knew she had just lost a friend.

Lucien awoke some time the wrong side of noon. His head ached like it had been cleaved with a wood axe and his mouth tasted as if he had been licking the soles of filth-encrusted boots. Sunlight streamed in through the library window, burning at his eyeballs. He moved the discomfort of his back and the pounding in his head intensified. The reek of stale brandy assailed his nostrils and he noticed the empty decanter and broken glass on the floor by his feet. Tentative fingers probed at his scalp and he winced.

God in heaven, it had been a long time since he'd felt this bad as a result of drink. He pushed himself up out of the wing chair in which he'd spent the night and walked gingerly forward, gripping the edge of the desk as his head thumped worse than ever. He had just focused himself enough to make it to the bell pull, when his eye alighted on two objects that should not have been on his desk. The memory of the night's dealings returned with a cruel and battering clarity. Madeline. Her words played loudly through his poor aching head, *I finished my book and came to borrow one of yours...I was looking for a candle and tinderbox.* And there before his very eyes was the evidence of what she had said. A rather battered copy of *Pride and Prejudice* and a single candleholder, complete with the stubby remains of a long-expired candle.

A knock sounded against the door and Guy walked into the library. 'Thought I might find you here, old chap.'

Lucien peered round, his head suffering from the speed of his movement. 'What the hell are you doing up so early?'

'Good afternoon to you, too. From the state that you're in, I would hazard a guess that you drank the rest of the brandy and spent a cold and miserable night in that chair.'

No reply was forthcoming from Lucien.

'I'm sorry to have been the bearer of bad tidings, but I thought it best that you knew.' He looked at his brother's red-lined eyes and the haggard expression upon his face, knowing that the news had affected Lucien far worse than even he had expected. He tried to salve the hurt as best he could. 'Perhaps there's some other explanation lying beneath all of this. Perhaps Madeline didn't send the letter to Farquharson at all. Have you enquired of your staff yet?'

Lucien turned a jaundiced eye in his direction. 'I've spoken to them all right, and it seems that my wife has been writing to him.'

'Oh.' Guy shut the door firmly behind him. 'Then the matter is proven.'

'No, Guy, it is not.' Lucien ran a hand through the dishevelment of his hair. 'She came here last night. Had the chair turned out to face the window, she couldn't see me, didn't know that I was here. Heard her searching around on the desk.'

'Good God! It's worse than I thought.'

'Said she'd finished her book and came down in search of another.'

'In the middle of the night?' Guy raised a cynical eyebrow.

'Couldn't sleep, apparently.'

'A likely story.'

'I believe she was telling the truth.' Lucien raised blood-shot eyes towards his brother.

A silence stretched between them.

Guy shook his head.

'Look.' Lucien gestured towards the well-thumbed book and the candleholder resting not so far from where his hands leant against the mahogany desk top. 'Madeline isn't stupid. Had she come here with the intent of searching my papers, she would have had a decent candle, one that could at least stay alight long enough for her to see what she was doing. She said that the candle had expired and she was looking for a tinderbox on the desk.'

'It's a lame excuse and you know it. The book could have been a cover in the eventuality that she was discovered rifling through your desk in the middle of the night.'

'If you could have seen the expression on her face…shock, horror, disbelief all rolled into one.'

'Farquharson himself told me that she's an actress. She's playing you, Lucien.'

Lucien looked at his brother. 'But we know Farquharson to be a liar.'

'That doesn't mean that Madeline is innocent.'

'I didn't even give her a chance to defend herself against the accusations. Just judged her as guilty.' The hand raked his hair again. 'I shouldn't have been so harsh, but the brandy clouded my judgement. Hell, I haven't felt so angry since I discovered what Farquharson did to Sarah.' He levelled his brother a direct look. 'I was a brute, Guy. Madeline didn't deserve that.'

'Oh, come on, Lucien. Farquharson is brandishing a particularly loathsome letter, written by her own hand, around all of London. You have proof that she dispatched a letter to him from this very house, and to cap it all you catch her rifling through your desk in the middle of the night! What do you think you should have done? Clapped her on the back? Congratulated her? The evidence is stacked against her.'

'I still cannot believe it.'

'You mean you don't want to believe it.'

'I know her, Guy. It's not in her character to be devious or dishonest.'

Guy gave an incredulous snort. 'She has you fooled, big brother, and no mistake.'

'That's just it. She's done nothing to try to fool me. The first time we met in the Theatre Royal she said not one thing against Farquharson, and at Lady Gilmour's ball she was desperately afraid. Such fear and loathing couldn't be faked.'

'You only have her word for it, Lucien. You don't even know if Farquharson was up in that bedchamber.'

'The terror and panic on her face were real enough. Never once has she used tears or pleading or dramatics. Do you not think she would have resorted to such ploys had she been acting?'

'She's too good an actress for that.'

'I cannot help but feel that we have this all wrong, Guy. In these past months I've come to know Madeline. She's not the woman you would paint her. She's more trusting than you could imagine. The evidence might condemn her as guilty, but instinct tells me otherwise.'

'She has bewitched you. Don't let your attraction for the woman blind you to the truth.'

'Oh, don't be absurd, Guy! That has nothing to do with it.'

'Then you admit that you are attracted to her?' Guy waited for the answer.

'Damn it, yes! I want her, all of her, in my arms, in my bed, and more. Is that what you want to hear? I may desire her, Guy, but I haven't touched her. I'm not that much of a fool.' He thought fleetingly of the tenderness of their shared kisses. Even last night, what had started as a kiss of punishment had ended as something else.

There was a pause as something of the situation communicated itself to Guy. 'It's not just desire that you feel, is it, Lucien?' he asked quietly.

'No,' said Lucien, touching his fingers against the misshapen lump of wax at the base of Madeline's candleholder. 'I'm afraid that matters are a little more complicated than that,' and realised, perhaps for the first time, exactly what it was that he was saying.

Guy gave a sigh and twitched a smile. 'Well, in that case, you had best pour some strong coffee down your throat, eat some breakfast, and set about discovering the truth.'

'I owe her an apology for my behaviour last night…and I would hear what she has to say regarding the letter.' A shameful look washed over Lucien's face. 'I told her that I was sending her back to London with you at the end of the week.'

'Ah. Many a lady might relish the prospect of a few days travelling in my company. Somehow, I don't think Madeline is one of them. I'd best ring for that coffee right away.'

It was some little time later when a clean-shaven and rather fresher-looking Lucien, finally sought out the company of his wife.

'She's gone where?'

Mrs Babcock sniffed. 'Tintagel Castle. Tried to put her off, but she weren't havin' any of it. Assured me that your opinion on her travellin' without you had changed. I came to tell you anyhow, but you seemed to be in the sleep of the dead. Couldn't wake you.' The housekeeper folded her arms. 'She left this morning. Asked after Lord Varington. Said she would be back this afternoon. Reckon she had somethin' she wanted to be speakin' to him about.'

Lucien opened his mouth to speak.

'And before you ask, she took Betsy and John Hayley with her. Mr Boyle's back is painin' him today, but he's still drivin' the coach.'

'Thank you, Babbie.' A spur of unease pricked at Lucien. Madeline had gone to Tintagel, little knowing it was there that Sarah Wyatt met her death.

The morning had been particularly fine, all clear pale sunshine and dry cold, apart from the mist that had hovered around their route past Bodmin Moor. Nothing of that remained in Tintagel. She breathed in the fresh sea air, smelling the salt and the seaweed and revelling in the dramatic sight before her eyes. Tintagel Castle was a sprawling medieval ruin balanced precariously close to a cliff whose edge dropped dramatically through a sheer pathway of jagged rocks into the sea. The water was a wash of pale greens and blues, and hissing heads of white froth where it battered against the riot of rocks. She had spent some time exploring throughout the ruins, knowing that the castle was reputed to be the site of the birthplace of King Arthur.

A story of intrigue and deception surrounded the place. King Uther Pendragon had fallen in love with Ygraine, the beautiful wife of his nobleman, Gorlois, Duke of Cornwall.

Uther could think of nothing else save that he must have Ygraine and when Gorlois would not yield his lady, declared war upon Cornwall and its Duke. Gorlois hid Ygraine in the impregnable fort at Tintagel while he came under siege at another of his castles. Knowing that the fate of all Britain rested upon it, the druid wizard Merlin cast a spell over Uther so that, for a single night alone, Uther would take on the appearance of Gorlois. Thus, out of the darkness the castle guard saw their lord approach, drew up the gate and welcomed him home. Ygraine, too, went gladly to her husband. Before dawn of the next morning, the man she had lain with all the night through had gone. An hour later a messenger arrived to tell them that Ygraine was a widow, for Gorlois had been slain in battle the previous night. Ygraine knew then what had happened. Nine months later she bore a son. His name was Arthur and he was to clear the invading darkness from Britain's shores and become the best and greatest of kings.

From the seeds of such treachery, goodness and salvation had grown. Madeline mulled over Merlin's part in the plot. She sat alone on the simple wooden bench and looked out across the white flecked roll of water, amazed at the ragged chasms in the cliff face and the scatter of sharp stone below. It was a scene she could have looked at for ever, drinking in the rugged beauty, the wildness of sea and wind and the dark dangerous rocks. The rush of the wind filled her ears, chasing the sadness from her soul and the fatigue from her bones. She was glad that she had asked Mr Boyle to stay by the coach. The poor man's back ached more than he was willing to admit. Madeline had not missed the grimaces of pain when he thought that no one was looking. She was glad, too, that she had sent Betsy and John Hayley off to wander the ruins by themselves. If Madeline was right, she suspected that romance was brewing, and even if she had been staying in Cornwall she might soon be in need of a new personal maid. She turned her head and watched the young couple wander hand in hand through the remains. She swallowed down her own sadness and was glad for them. Her gaze fixed upon where the distant roll of waves met clear blue sky and she wondered what it was that Guy had brought with him to Trethevyn, besides an end to all of Madeline's dreams.

As if from nowhere, the wind whipped up one strong gust that pulled the bonnet from her head, tumbling it along the grassy pathway. Madeline leapt up, trying to catch the bonnet before it dropped over the cliff edge, but to no avail. She peered over, watching it swoop down the sheer rock face to meet the white swirl of waves below, tossed on the violent ebb and flow of water. Her feet stood close to the edge of the pre- cipice. Too close, with the wind gusting as it was. She made to retreat. Someone grabbed at her arm. Madeline gave a small yelp of surprise, her feet stumbled and the firm grasp tightened, lifting her up, hauling her back.

'Madeline!' Lucien's voice strained against her ear. 'What the…?' He clasped her against him and dragged her further inland.

Madeline's heart hammered hard against her breast, first from the fright she had just sustained in almost pitching down to join her bonnet, and now from the man whose arms were wrapped around her. Slowly the thudding subsided enough for her to hear the words he was saying

'Madeline,' he whispered against the top of her head, then moved her back to drop kisses against her cheek, the tip of her nose, her chin. One hand cradled the nape of her neck, the other pressed against her back. 'I thought I'd lost you,' he murmured against her eyebrow. 'Thank God…' And then he found her lips and kissed her with a passion beyond anything that Madeline had ever known. Gentle, possessive, loving. As if he would never let her go. As if her nightmare of last night had never been. And in the meeting of their lips were all the words that they had not spoken. 'Madeline,' he said again and moved back to look into her eyes.

Even through the dazzlement of surprise Madeline noticed the pallor of his face. 'Lucien?' Her fingers fluttered against his cheek in mounting concern, unsure of the response that they would meet.

'I didn't think…I wouldn't have you lose your life over my foolish words, Madeline.'

Madeline blinked up at him in confusion.

'Forgive my shoddy treatment. I fear that I'd made too freely with the brandy.' He reached and captured her fingers from his face, imprisoning them with great tenderness within his own, his voice suddenly gruff. 'It's not worth killing yourself over, Madeline.'

Madeline suddenly realised what he thought. Her eyes widened and a rather embarrassed expression crossed her face. 'It was just that the wind…my bonnet… I was only looking to see where the wind had taken it.' She waited for his response.

The bold pale eyes held hers. 'Then you weren't planning to leap from the cliff top?'

She shook her head, inadvertently loosening more of the hairpins. The wind instantly took advantage and pulled what had started as a plain and tidy style into a mass of long blowing locks.

'My pins!' Madeline cried and bent to retrieve what she could.

Lucien pulled her back up to face him. 'Leave them.' He

ran his fingers through her hair, mussing it worse than ever. 'I prefer it this way.'

Madeline felt two spots of warmth grow on her cheeks.

'I should place you across my knee and give you a thorough thrashing for giving me such a fright.'

Madeline saw the twitch of his smile before it was lost.

'But I've been too much of a brute of late. I shouldn't have treated you as I did last night.'

'What happened? Why were you so angry? You thought that I was searching for papers on your desk…for Farquharson.' Her brow crinkled. 'Why? What did Guy tell you?'

'The news is not good, Madeline.' The pale gaze held hers, watching, measuring. 'Farquharson has a letter from you, pleading that he save you from your madman of a husband. It claims that our marriage was the result of forced abduction and rape.'

'No!' The word slipped loudly from Madeline's tongue. 'No,' she said again, a little more quietly. 'It's a lie. I wrote no such letter.'

'I've seen it with my own eyes. It's written in your own hand, on paper printed with my crest and sealed with the Tregellas seal.'

The accusation hung between them.

'How can that be? It's impossible!'

'So you deny sending a letter to Farquharson?' His eyes did not waver from hers.

She paused. 'No. I don't deny that,' she said slowly.

Lucien felt the tension wrap around his heart and start to squeeze,

'He wrote to me, you see, some weeks ago.' Colour flooded her cheeks. 'You were so worried about him, I thought it would only make matters worse to tell you.'

Lucien said nothing, just waited, and all the while the ache in his chest continued to grow.

'The letter is within the drawer of my bureau, if you wish to see it. Farquharson asked my forgiveness and said that he loved me.' She saw something flit across Lucien's eyes. Pain, hurt, anger? Madeline did not know. 'And then he warned me of you. Told me the story of Sarah Wyatt, much as you did. Except that in his version, he accuses you of killing her. He offered to help me escape you, said I need only ask and he would help.'

Lucien's eyes were as pale a blue as ever she'd seen, the black outline of the iris and the darkness of the pupil lending them an unnaturally brilliant appearance. The thump of her heart sounded slow and steady in her chest. 'So I wrote to him and told him that I knew his words for the lies they were and that the man I knew to be a murderer was not my husband. I asked him to leave us in peace.' She did not mention what else she had said in those carefully penned words: that she loved Lucien, that she would never be sorry that she had agreed to marry him, that they were very happy together. 'I gave the letter to John Hayley to take to the post office in the village.'

'And you have never written anything else to him?'

'No, of course not.'

They looked at one another for a moment longer.

'I believe you. I don't know how he did it, but Farquharson wrote that letter, not you.'

He saw relief colour her eyes, felt the tension slacken from her body.

She slumped forward, resting her forehead against his chest and he knew that no actress could have feigned what he had seen in her face.

'Let's go home, Madeline,' he said, and, placing his arm around her, led her towards the coach in the distance.

Chapter Fourteen

All was quiet at Trethevyn.

Mrs Babcock saw the entwined hands of the Earl and his Countess as they entered the hallway and drew her own conclusion.

Madeline blushed and tried to disengage her hand at the sight of the housekeeper, but Lucien was having none of it. He cast Madeline an intensely intimate look and retained her fingers firmly within his own.

'Lord Varington has gone out for a ride,' said Mrs Babcock, 'I'll be in the kitchen if I'm needed,' and promptly left.

'Then we're all alone with the remainder of an afternoon to fill before my brother returns.' His gaze dropped to her lips before returning to meet her eyes. 'There are unfinished matters between us, Madeline, matters that should be resolved.'

Madeline knew from the hunger of his gaze that it was not letters, or Farquharson, or even Guy of which her husband spoke. She felt the heat intensify as Lucien bent closer and touched his lips gently against hers. 'Lucien,' she murmured as he pulled back enough to look into her eyes.

'I know what I promised you, but I can no longer limit myself to our bargain. My life would be the poorer if you were not in it, Madeline.' He moved his mouth until it hovered just above hers. 'I want you as my wife in every way that it's possible: a full marriage, not some half-witted contract of convenience.'

'Oh, Lucien,' she sighed and met his lips with all the passion that had been burgeoning within her for the past months.

'I've been a fool.' His words were breathy and hot against her skin, trailing a path along the delicate line of her jaw and down on to her neck.

Madeline made one last grip at reality before it would slide away for ever. 'No,' she whispered. 'You saved me from Farquharson; for that I'll always be grateful.'

'It's not your gratitude that I want,' he growled against the soft white skin of her throat.

She moved to look him directly in the eye. 'If not my gratitude, then will you accept my love instead?'

He stilled beneath her fingers, his eyes dilating wide and darkening. 'You love me?' His brows arched in surprise. 'After all that I've done?'

Madeline felt the smile creep to her lips. The tall, handsome man before her was not as arrogantly confident as he would have the world believe. 'Yes,' she said simply. 'What you did was save my life, Lucien, nothing less. I love you. And…' she hesitated, feeling the warmth rise in her cheeks '…and I want you, Lucien.'

His lips twitched with amusement. 'In that case, lady wife, I must insist that you accompany me to my bedchamber this very moment.'

'Lucien!' she exclaimed. 'It's the middle of the afternoon, and broad daylight! Retiring at this time of day would be positively scandalous.'

'Indeed, it would.' His mouth swooped down, halting only

a whisper away from hers. 'But not quite so scandalous as being discovered making love upon the stairs.' His fingers teased across the bodice of her dress to rest fleetingly upon her breast. 'The choice is yours, Madeline. What is it to be?'

Madeline shivered at the delicious sensations threatening to overwhelm her. 'Well, if you put it like that, sir, I think I'll choose the bedchamber.'

Lucien delivered her a wicked smile and, without a further word, scooped her up into his arms and advanced up the stairs with some considerable speed. He did not pause until he had deposited Madeline upon the great sprawling four-poster that was his bed.

Sunlight flooded in through the bedchamber windows to bask Madeline in its warm golden glow. She watched in awe while Lucien stripped off his coat, dispensing with it in a heap upon the floor. Next came his waistcoat and a pair of still mud-splattered riding boots. The neckcloth followed, with the same haphazard abandonment. Only when he had discarded his shirt did Madeline protest. 'Lucien, surely you cannot mean to remove all of your clothes!'

Her husband gave her a mischievous look and his grin deepened.

'The sun is still high in the sky!'

Lucien glanced nonchalantly in the direction of the window. 'So it is.' And then he climbed upon the bed.

'But—'

Any further protestations from Madeline were effectively silenced when Lucien claimed her mouth with his own, massaging in a rhythmic slide until her lips parted. His tongue welcomed the invitation and slipped into that intimate cavern, seeking what he knew would be within Madeline's head danced, dizzy in a haze of floating sensation. Their tongues met. Connected. Moist. Warm. Needful. Danced and twisted and lapped until all vestige of rational thought fled. And when Lucien's hands slipped down across her body, a path of tingling fire followed in their wake. She trembled beneath his touch, both revelling in it and all the while conscious of a growing need for more.

'Madeline, my love,' he murmured against her cheek, her throat, her collarbone and lower, until he touched the neckline where her dress began. His breath moved up, scorched hot upon her shoulder and his fingers moved to deftly undo the row of small jet buttons that fastened the dress to Madeline's body.

Contrary to all her expectations, Madeline was neither shy nor embarrassed. Indeed, it was with a degree of impatience that she assisted her husband to shed not only her dress but her petticoats, stays and shift as well. She lay naked on the bed, his bed, exposed in her entirety by the clarity of the sunshine licking warm against her pale skin.

Lucien sat back, gaze sweeping over her, drinking in every inch of her sweetness. When she made to cover her nudity with her hand he captured those slender fingers within his own, met those amber eyes that were smouldering with passion. 'You're beautiful.' Beneath the heat of his gaze she felt truly beautiful: beautiful and desirable and loved. Then their lips writhed together until all thoughts were forgotten. Her fingers threaded through his hair, pulling the dark silken locks as she had so longed to do. His cologne mixed with his own masculine scent, teasing and tantalising her. She breathed in the intoxicating mix. Awareness narrowed, until there was just the two of them. Lucien and Madeline. Husband and wife. Together in a union of love.

His hands stroked gently around the mounds of her breasts, tracing an inward spiral that stopped just short of their rosy peaks. Madeline shifted beneath him, pressing herself up, nipples tingling with need. And still his fingers teased upon the slopes.

'Lucien!' The whisper was urgent, pleading.

He could withhold no longer. Her nipples stood erect beneath the brush of his thumbs. He rolled the hardened buds between his fingers, hearing her gasps of pleasure. His mouth trailed kisses down her neck and on to her breast. She cried out as he replaced his fingers with the hot moisture of his tongue, lapping against the tender pink skin, suckling first at one and then the other. Her hands clutching the dark ruffle of his head closer, harder. The heat grew between her legs, pulsing down to encompass her thighs. There was a wetness there that she did not understand. Instinctively she pressed herself to him, not knowing what it was that she sought, just conscious of an escalating urgency and her overwhelming love for the man who was stoking such powerful sensations within her body. Lucien. Lucien. It seemed she cried his name a thousand times within her mind. Needing him. Wanting him. 'Lucien.' The cry of desperation burst aloud from her lips, but Madeline no longer knew what was real and what was not, caught as she was in an escalating vortex of sensual force.

Lucien could not fail to answer such a plea. He rolled off her long enough to divest himself of his pantaloons, then, in response to the small murmur of complaint, covered her body with his own, taking his weight upon his elbows lest he crush her. Satin-smooth skin flushed rosy where the roughness of his stubbled chin had lingered and caressed. His fingers moved to her breast, teased fleetingly at their peaks then slid down across her stomach and lower still. The soft white skin of her thighs was hot beneath his touch, as he massaged and stroked and kneaded a pattern of pleasure. She jerked against him as his fingers gently probed the silken secret between her legs, her breathing quickening to short greedy gasps.

Nothing else mattered. Everything was here and now. In this moment. Here with the man that she loved. She wanted him. She burned for him. Felt the start of a deep welling pleasure at the intimate caress of his fingers, the heat of his lips on hers, his tongue tantalising her own. Some part of him pressed against her thigh. She moved her hips against him and reached her fingers to feel him. He groaned, his eyes fluttering shut at her touch. His hand captured her wrist. 'Madeline,' he gasped. 'Any more of that and I'll be unable to finish what we've started.' He kissed her tenderly, stroking her hair back from her face, and drawing back to look into her eyes. 'I love you,' he whispered and deliberately moved himself between her thighs.

'As I love you,' Madeline replied.

Blue and amber, ice and fire, locked as he thrust gently into her, accepting the precious gift that she offered.

Madeline felt the pain sear through her, momentarily blighting the pleasure. But then his mouth was upon hers and his whispers of reassurance were in her ear. Pain diminished. Pleasure grew. And as he began to move within her she gave herself up to the ecstasy that bound them, until his seed spilled within her and they lay entwined and sated in the heady glow of loving. There seemed no need for words. Madeline relaxed, feeling the steady beat of Lucien's heart against her back, the protective curl of his palm against her stomach. What had happened between them had changed her for ever. She had given her heart and shared her body. They were as one, each bound to the other through love. Madeline knew in those blissful moments that nothing could ever change that.

* * *

The hours ticked by and Guy still did not return.

'Ask Cook to delay dinner for a further half an hour. He should be back by then.'

'Right you are, m'lord. I'm worried about the youngster. Not like him to be out so long, least not in the country.' Mrs Babcock sniffed, and sucked hard on her bottom teeth with mounting anxiety and disapproval.

Quite how Babbie could describe Guy as a youngster amazed Lucien, but he had to concede that he shared the old housekeeper's concern. His brother was not known for his enjoyment of country pursuits. Indeed, it might even be said that Guy found the countryside abhorrent, describing the peace and clean open air as downright ghastly. But then again, Guy had his own reasons for preferring the town. Not for the first time did Lucien worry over the hedonistic path his brother's life seemed to be taking. Nothing of these thoughts showed upon his face as he sought to reassure the old woman. 'No doubt Guy has forgone the pleasures of cross-country riding for the hospitality of the King's Arms in the village. He might even have ridden into Liskeard or Bodmin. Don't worry, Babbie. He'll be back soon enough.'

Only when the door closed behind the housekeeper did he massage his temples in the action that he knew would reveal his true anxiety to the old woman who had practically raised him as a child.

Madeline rose from the chair and moved silently across the room to stand beside him. 'You're worried, too, aren't you?'

Lucien looked down at the slender figure by his side. The shadowy light from the window spilled across her face, contrasting with the warm glow from the candles. Her cheeks were still pink from their earlier lovemaking and her eyes held a special sparkle. It seemed that she could read him better than he realised. 'Guy is reckless and prone to distraction by…how shall I put it…certain pleasurable activities. But I would have expected him to be back before darkness, especially in light of this morning.'

Madeline gave him a puzzled look. 'What do you mean?'

'He knew I was intent on speaking to you about Farquharson's letter and will be interested to learn your response. Believe me when I say there's no love lost between Farquharson and my brother.'

'He thinks me guilty.' It was not a question, just a plainly stated fact.

Lucien would no longer lie to the woman he loved. 'He doesn't know you as I do. He saw the evidence and drew his conclusion.'

A flicker of pain flitted across her face.

'Together we'll convince him of the truth.' He took her hand in his and gave a little squeeze.

She smiled and the two turned to look out down the length of the driveway.

Only half an hour later and their happiness was destroyed.

Raised voices, alarmed, alert, coming from the hallway, growing louder. Lucien jerked open the door of the small drawing room and strode down the stairs towards the noise. Not far from the front door a group of servants were huddled around something.

'Lord above!' Babbie shouted.

A housemaid began to cry.

'Is he still alive?' Mr Boyle said.

Betsy Porter fainted in a heap upon the floor.

And then Mr Norton's gruff words, 'Fetch his lord-ship—now!'

Cold dread clasped at Lucien. He thrust it away. Strode to the small throng, afraid of what he would see. Clearing the path anyway. 'What's going on here?' His tone was cold, clinical, the tone of a man in control.

The crowd parted. He heard Boyle by his elbow. 'Was tied to his horse to make it back here. Couldn't do nothin' other than ride it right up to the front door. Bleedin' badly he is, m'lord. We got him in here as quick as we could. Young Hayley's taken the beast round to the stables.'

A broad smear of blood across the marbled floor of the hallway showed clearly where the body had been dragged. Something squirmed in Lucien's gut. One hand steered the sniffling housemaid to the side until at last he could see the figure that lay there. The man's clothing was darkened and wet. Great slashes in the material showed skin that had been white, now mottled dark. Lucien's eyes travelled up the tortured body, past the wounds, past the blood, until they came to rest upon the face. A breath escaped him. A rush of air so silent that none around would have noticed. A sound both of horror…and relief. For the blood-daubed face was not that of Guy, but his valet, Collins.

Lucien knelt by the poor battered body, touching his fingers to the neck in search of a pulse. Then he stripped off his coat and balling it as a pillow, carefully inserted it behind the man's head.

The gritty eyelids fluttered open. 'Lord Tregellas.'

The man's whisper was so low that Lucien had to press an ear close to the bruised mouth to hear the words. 'It's all right, Collins, I'm here.'

The valet struggled to speak.

'Take your time,' said Lucien, kneeling by the man's side.

'Was a trap. Walked right into it before we knew.' Collins reached a bloody hand to catch at Lucien's. 'There were too many of them. Ruffians. Brawn hired by the gent. Didn't stand a chance.'

The coldness was spreading throughout Lucien's body. He held Collins's hand and waited for him to continue.

The man's swallow was painful to watch. 'We put up a fight, but they had us in the end. Took us somewhere deep under the ground. No light, just torches. Damp. Horrible. Asked us questions about this place, and you and Lady Tregellas.'

Lucien's lips tightened to a grim line.

'Released me to bring you a message.' Collins paused to gather his strength. 'The gent says if you want to see your brother alive again then you're to meet him tonight at ten o'clock by Tintagel Castle—and take your wife with you. If the both of you don't show, he'll kill Lord Varington.'

'Is Guy…?' Lucien could not bring himself to say the words.

'He's hurt bad.' Collins's eyes filled with moisture. 'Nothing I could do. I'm sorry.'

Lucien patted the man's hand. 'You did your best. Guy will be proud.' He leaned in closer as Collins's eyes began to close. It was a question he did not need to ask, but he wanted to be sure. 'Just one more thing before you rest, Collins. His name—did the one you call a gentleman tell you his name?'

Collins slowly shook his head. 'Said you would know who he was. Hair as red as a fox's pelt. Slim, medium height. Lord Varington called him Farleyson or some such name.'

'Farquharson,' said a woman's voice behind Lucien.

'Yes, m'lord, that was it.' The valet drifted out of consciousness once more.

Lucien slowly turned his head to look over his shoulder, and when the ice-blue eyes raised, they met with the clear amber gaze of his wife.

'Don't be absurd, Madeline! You are not accompanying me and that is final.' Lucien's jaw tightened into what Madeline had come to learn was his stubborn expression.

'And when you turn up to meet Farquharson without me, what then? You'll effectively condemn Guy to death.'

'It's a trap, Madeline. He means to catch us all. If I go alone, at least I have a chance of killing him. To take you along would be to hand you to him on a platter. It's bad enough that he has Guy without giving him you as well.'

'But you mean to walk straight into his trap yourself, and you think that I'll just sit here and let you?'

'We've little choice, Madeline.'

'What about the High Constable. If we inform him, perhaps he could—'

'We're running out of time and, besides, the Constable will be of little use against Farquharson and his cronies. The only chance that Guy has is if I go alone.'

'No.' Madeline shook her head. 'He'll kill Guy anyway, and then he'll kill you.'

'No, Madeline, not if I kill him first. I cannot just leave my brother to die without trying to help him. Farquharson's methods will not result in a quick and painless death. The villain thrives on pain. It gives him pleasure to watch others suffer.'

'Sarah Wyatt…' It was not fair to ask the question with Lord Varington as Farquharson's prisoner.

Lucien's face was a mask of grim severity. 'An endless orgy of torture and rape. He killed her at Tintagel, then brought her here, left her body in the old chapel in the grounds of the house. He thought if her body was found at Trethevyn, then I would be suspected of her murder. My mother found it the next morning. She had been unwell since my father's death. The shock of what she saw that day sickened her more than I can say. She never recovered. Two months later she was dead.'

'Oh, Lucien,' Madeline placed her arm around him. 'I'm so sorry. I shouldn't have stirred such painful memories.'

'It's better that you know the truth,' he said.

'Why did he never stand trial?'

'Farquharson has the cunning of a fox. There was nothing that could link him with the crime. His cronies swore that Farquharson had spent the night of the murder drinking and carousing with them. The High Constable could not proceed. Besides, Farquharson was busy planting the seeds of rumours that I was responsible for Sarah's death. I was, after all, the spurned betrothed, and her body had been found on my property.'

'Was there nothing that could be done to bring him to justice?'

'I employed a Bow Street Runner to investigate the matter, in an attempt to come up with something against him, but there was nothing to be found.'

'How can you be so sure it was Farquharson?'

Lucien sighed. 'At first I wasn't. I suspected him, nothing more. There was always an undercurrent about him, something unwholesome. And then when he knew he was safe, when he knew that there was nothing that could link the grieving husband to Sarah's murder, he approached me in my club one day and told me what he had done.'

'He admitted it?'

'Every detail.'

'But surely you could act as a witness against him?'

'Farquharson had been busy establishing my reputation as

the Wicked Earl. The gossip in London said that I had killed Sarah. He would not have been found guilty.'

Madeline said nothing, just shook her head.

'I called him out, thought that I would kill him. But I allowed my hatred for him to affect my aim. My bullet landed in his leg. His shot landed wide. The matter was closed. There was nothing more I could do…but wait and watch, and ensure that he never struck again.'

'Oh, Lucien…' Madeline pressed her cheek to her husband's hand '…you've had a terrible time.' She raised her head and looked at him. 'If Farquharson killed Sarah at Tintagel, then it explains why he has chosen that same place for an assignation.'

Lucien nodded. 'A repeat of history except that instead of Sarah, this time he wants you. Farquharson's perversion will never diminish. I have to stop him, Madeline. You do understand why I must do this?'

'To avenge Sarah's death.'

He shook his head. 'Once upon a time that's what I lived for, the thought of making him suffer as he did to both Sarah and my mother. Not any more. Vengeance is not mine. Farquharson will reap that in plenty when he meets his Maker.' He took her face between his hands, his fingers resting lightly against the softness of her cheeks. 'I love you, Madeline. For all my denials I think I've loved you since first I held you in my arms and waltzed with you at Lady Gilmour's ball. I will not let him have you. That's why it must stop here, this night. You were right, Madeline, you cannot live your life forever looking over your shoulder.'

She clung to him, pressed her lips to his. 'No, Lucien! I didn't mean that. I love you. Please don't go alone.'

'It's the best way, Madeline.' He looked down into her

eyes, seeing tears falling freely from them for the first time. 'Don't cry, my love. One shot is all I need and this time the bullet shall land within his heart.'

'I cannot let you do this, Lucien. I won't.' Her face was wet beneath his touch.

'Madeline,' he said gently. 'Do this one thing that I ask.'

She sobbed aloud. 'Please…'

'No more tears, my love.' And slowly, tenderly, he lowered his lips to hers and in that kiss was everything he wanted to give her: gratitude and joy and celebration for all that she had brought to his life, peace, and faith and eternal love. 'Promise me that you'll stay here.' Her eyes were a clear light sienna flecked with gold. Eyes to lose yourself in, he'd once thought, and he'd been right. 'Give me your word that you won't seek to follow me.'

Her teeth bit desperately at her lower lip. A minute passed in silence, then stretched to two. When she finally spoke her voice was cracked and broken. 'You ask the impossible.'

'Promise me, Madeline,' he said again and took one last chance to inhale the warm orange scent of her. Her hair tickled against his nose as he awaited her reply.

A small sob sounded. The teeth bit harder against her lip. 'Very well,' she croaked, 'I promise.'

One last kiss from her sweet mouth, then Lucien turned and walked towards the door.

'My love,' she whispered as the door clicked shut. 'Oh, my love,' and pressed her fingers hard against her mouth to capture the sobs that threatened to burst forth. Nothing could still the shudders that wracked her body.

Madeline did not know how long she stood motionless, watching the door of the small drawing room. Perhaps she waited in case Lucien changed his mind. Or to see if the whole nightmare was real or just some awful joke that Lucien and his brother had contrived between them. She stood statue still, breath so light as to scarcely be there. Her eyes were red and gritty, her cheeks damp with saline. She stood until there were no more tears to fall. Alone in the small drawing room, while her husband rode out to meet his death, to save both her and his brother. What chance did he stand against Farquharson and his men? The clock marked the passing of the seconds. Each frantic tick taking Lucien further from safety, closer to his doom. Tick, tick, tick, tick. Faster and faster. Madeline walked towards the mantel, lifted the pretty clock into her hands, and threw it hard across the room. It landed with a loud thud. Silence hissed. And the spell that had frozen Madeline shattered.

There was a thud of footsteps, uneven, growing louder. The door burst open. Madeline's head jerked up in expectation, his name soft upon her lips. 'Lucien?'

Mrs Babcock's ruddy face appeared. 'M'lady! Such a terrible noise. I thought you might have tripped and fallen your length...' The small black eyes rested upon the remains of the clock close by the window. 'Ah,' she said. 'No harm done.'

No harm? Madeline felt the urge to laugh hysterically. 'No harm?' she said aloud.

'Come along, doe.' The housekeeper steered Madeline out of the drawing room and along to her bedchamber. 'Master Lucien said you was a bit upset, like. Don't you worry, Babbie's here. I'll make you a nice posset and tuck you up in bed, all safe and sound, until his lordship gets back.'

Madeline allowed herself to be guided by the older woman. Until his lordship gets back, Babbie had said. What would she say if she knew the truth? Lucien wasn't coming back, not tonight, not ever. Madeline looked up into the kindly old face...and could not inflict the hurt the truth would give. 'There's no need for a posset, Babbie, I'll sleep directly. I'm just a little worried for Lucien, that's all.'

'Aren't we all, m'lady, aren't we all? If you change your mind about the posset, just ring and I'll be here.' The housekeeper stroked Madeline's cheek. 'I know you love him, doe. Never thought to see him smile again, not after what happened, what with the dowager Countess and Lady Sarah and all them terrible things. But you've made him happy, real happy. I'm sorry I was snappy with you when you asked me them questions.'

'I should never have doubted him.' Madeline sat down upon the bed.

'You weren't to know, and he can be a bit of a surly old bear when he's got a mind to be.' Mrs Babcock gave Madeline a brief hug, then hurried away with a face flaming like a beacon. She paused briefly by the door. 'I'll send Betsy up to help you change.'

'No, thank you, I'd rather manage by myself tonight.' Madeline raised a small smile. 'Goodnight, Babbie.'

'Goodnight, m'lady, and may the good Lord bring Master Lucien back to us safe and sound.'

'Amen to that, Babbie.'

The door closed, leaving Madeline alone.

Lucien's eyes raked through the darkness. A full moon hung high in the sky, glimmering silver upon the expanse of rippling dark sea, casting the castle ruins up ahead as a sinister silhouette. Nelson trotted closer until Lucien reined him in and dismounted, preferring to lead the horse the rest of the distance.

Salt and seaweed and dampness hung heavy in the air, undisturbed by the wind blowing in from the sea. His hand touched briefly against the solid form of the pistol hidden deep within his pocket. He walked the horse up as close as he dared, tethering the reins on a scrubby bush by the final entrance to the site. He paused, instincts alert, face harsh beneath the pale moonlight, eyes scouring the castle walls that lay ahead of him, or at least what remained of them. No sign of Farquharson. The ground was solid beneath his feet as he slipped out from behind the cover of his horse, exposing himself to any shot that Farquharson might care to take. One step, and then another, keeping close to the shadow of the rising crag to his left, he edged round and climbed the steps to the upper ward. His gaze swept every ancient stone. The high place was empty. And that meant that Farquharson had to be in the island part of the castle. Lucien turned and headed towards the narrow winding pathway that would lead him there.

Lap and swirl of waves sounded against the rocks far below, crashing and frothing with a ferocity that contrasted with the tranquillity of the ocean beyond. The men that had built Tintagel Castle had chosen their site well. The castle straddled an unstable neck linking Tintagel Island with the mainland. The remains of the upper and lower wards lay on the landward side, the inner ward and chapel remnants on the island. A pathway connecting the two dropped away to sheer jagged rock. Frothy white water swirled below. A defence designed to thwart the best of attackers. Lucien knew that it was here on the pathway that he was at his most vulnerable. His heart thudded fast yet steady, waiting each moment for the hidden shot to ring from the castle ruins. The longest walk of his life. The slowest. And still the shot did not come. Every step taking him closer. Every breath buoying his confidence that he would make it. He was so close that he could see the individual-hewn stones that made up the thick walls, the ruined apertures of windows and doorways. So close. The path led him directly into what had been one of the castle baileys. He scanned ahead. Wind howled. Emptiness echoed. The hairs on the back of Lucien's neck prickled. Eyes searching, ears straining for the slightest hint of Farquharson's location. Nothing. No one. Lucien's fingers slipped into his pocket, closed around the pistol handle, extracted the weapon. He held it down low, brushing beside his thigh, all the harder for Farquharson to see it. He backed against the rear wall, poised, ready.

'Farquharson!' The wind snatched the shout, to carry it away unanswered. Sweat beaded upon Lucien's upper lip. 'Farquharson!'

A small scrunch of a sound from the other side of the wall.

Keeping his body close to the protection of the ancient stone structure, Lucien moved with stealth to the end of the wall. Readied the pistol, finger on the trigger. One swift lunge and he peered round the other side, pistol aimed with precision at the spot from whence the noise had issued. Bare soil and rock, a trickle of pebbles…a cat disappearing in the distance. Lucien's gaze drifted down from the wall, down to the abrupt fall of the cliff. A shiver tingled down his spine. Close by the solitary cry of a gull sounded. Distorted. Ghostly. A portent of doom. Icy foreboding gripped him.

He retraced his steps, covering the ground as fast as he dared, slipping from the cover of one wall to another, scanning each and every part of the ruin in turn, ever ready for the surprise assault that did not come. Empty. Back across the precarious pathway. Still no one. Still nothing. Chill grew greater. Alone. Blood ran cold. The seed of doubt germinated, grew, and blossomed to reveal the truth. The pistol uncocked, stuffed within his pocket. He ran back through the inner ward to where the great black horse stood, still tethered where he had left it. Didn't even break stride to swing himself up into the saddle.

Lucien rode like he had never ridden before, coat flying, throwing up mud and water in his wake. Through the streets of Tintagel village to Bossmey, then Davidstow, following the road down towards Camelford. Riding as if the hounds of Lucifer snapped at his heels, riding until his lungs were fit to burst and his muscles shook from the strain. Past the gloom of the great moor. Hoping. Praying. Knowing even as he did, that he would be too late.

The knowledge that Farquharson had tricked him was a bitter pill to swallow. For if Cyril Farquharson was not at Tintagel, there was as like only one other place he could be. What was it that Collins had said as he lay bleeding upon the entrance hall floor? *He asked us questions about this place…* The place that now lay unprotected. The place that held the one thing that Farquharson wanted above all else. The place in which Lucien had left his wife, thinking her to be safe. And that place was Trethevyn.

Chapter Fifteen

For all that Madeline had said to Mrs Babcock, she knew that she would not sleep that night. How could she, knowing what her husband was riding out to meet, knowing that Farquharson would kill both Lucien and his brother? She had seen what the scoundrel had done to Collins. She did not doubt how much worse he would inflict upon the man who had thwarted him. The knowledge caused her heart to freeze lest it shatter into a thousand pieces. The fire burned low within the grate, a few small flames licking around a glowing mass. Gooseflesh raised upon Madeline's arms. She had no awareness of the dropping temperature within the bedchamber, nor of the draught that flitted through the great window to ruffle the curtains that hung still drawn back to frame the paned glass. She blew out the candles and watched the wispy smoke, from their quenching, curl in the air.

The sky was an inky dark velvet decorated with a pearly white button moon and a scatter of stars that glittered like diamond pinheads. She stood in the darkness, a small solitary figure garbed in the plain white cotton of her nightdress, and stared out across the lawns that lay before Trethevyn. Lucien would be at Tintagel by now, walking straight into Farquharson's hands like a lamb to the slaughter. She did not allow her thoughts to stray to what that slaughter would entail. And through it all Madeline could not really believe that it was happening. Was it true what they said, that when a man's life ebbed away his soul leapt out and appeared to those he loved? Surely she would know if he were dead, wouldn't she? But Madeline felt nothing of that; indeed, she could feel very little at all due to the numbness that had spread throughout her body.

She turned Lucien's words over in her mind a thousand times, hearing the story of what Farquharson had done again and again. A devious man. A fox. A villain. A man that would always play dirty, for there was no other way of winning. She thought about Cyril Farquharson. She thought about Guy as his hostage. She thought about Collins's tortured body and the words that had strained from his lips. And amidst all of her thinking the truth made itself known to Madeline. It didn't strike like a bolt from the blue. It wasn't a blinding enlightenment. Instead, it just slipped into her head quietly and without any fuss. And she accepted the realisation without question.

A curious torpor settled upon Madeline, a sense of inevitability that stretched almost to relief. She should have been paralysed with fear and dread and terror. But she wasn't. Certainty filled her. Knowledge, even. Worry vanished. Madeline knew what was coming and she was glad, for it could mean only one thing: that Lucien was safe.

She fetched Lucien's knife from the drawer of his desk in the library and slid it, still sheathed, into the pocket of her dressing gown. Then she returned to her bedchamber and sat down in the small armchair in the corner. The knife lay heavy and reassuring against her thigh. Her fingers, hidden within her pocket, rested comfortably around the handle. The monster was coming to get her, yet Madeline was not afraid. It was her nightmare become reality, but Madeline was calm. For once in her life she would not flee. She refused to hide. She had done with running. As she had told Lucien, she could not live her life for ever looking over her shoulder; *they* could not live life forever looking over *their* shoulders.

She knew now that Farquharson would never leave them alone. He would pursue them for eternity. He had already taken Guy. It was just a matter of time before he caught her and Lucien. Madeline could not let that happen, for she loved Lucien above life itself. And all the while Farquharson breathed, Lucien would not be safe. She understood now why Lucien had been so vigilant. She could see now that what she had dismissed as an obsessive hatred had been a frank appreciation of the danger that Farquharson posed. Lucien had been right. He had not underestimated Farquharson. He alone had known of what the fiend was capable. And now Madeline knew. And she knew too that she had a chance to stop this madness. The time had come to face Cyril Farquharson.

The house was quiet with waiting, the servants about their chores or in their beds. There was no point in endangering their lives. It was Madeline that he wanted, and Madeline he would get, alone save for her husband's knife. Max made no sound in the small dressing room that lay beyond. And so Madeline sat and waited for the fox to come to her door.

Cyril Farquharson slipped into Trethevyn like a shadow, silent and unnoticed. The latch on the windowed doors that led from the front garden into the library was easily coaxed into submission. The door swung open beneath his touch. His red hair was paled by the moonlight. He moved without a sound across the floor, thankful that Varington's valet had been persuaded to share the details of the inner layout of the house. The clock on the mantel struck eleven. Anticipation coursed through him.

Of course Tregellas would have long since realised that he had been duped. How long had the Earl spent searching the ruins before he had known that he was there alone? All alone. Searching for a man that was not there. Three hours from home. A smile cracked Farquharson's face. It was not hard to imagine how Tregellas had felt in that moment of realisation. Rage, dread, fear. Excitement tingled deep within Farquharson's gut. Even now, Tregellas would be spurring his horse hard over the roads that led from Tintagel. Pushing himself to the limit, fighting against the inevitable. Three hours was a long journey to make, knowing all the while what was happening to your wife, and being helpless to stop it. In your own bed, with your own servants none the wiser as to what was happening so very close at hand. Farquharson almost sniggered aloud. Tregellas would arrive home just in time to play his part in the final stages of Farquharson's plan. And what a plan it was. Superbly crafted by a master. Executed stage by stage. Using Varington to lure Tregellas to Tintagel, Varington, with whom Farquharson would deal later. And the whole of it built on knowing Tregellas's character, knowing that the Earl would never take Madeline there, knowing that he would leave her here all nicely tucked up ready for Farquharson. Farquharson's thoughts flitted to the woman above, the woman who was no doubt sobbing herself to sleep at this very moment: Madeline.

She had defied him from the start, humiliated him in front of all London. And for that she would reap the punishment that he had promised. How many nights had he lain awake with its planning? For how many months had he waited and watched? Sowing his seeds, biding his time until the right opportunity arose. How very tempting it had been to have her taken that day upon the moor with the maid screaming that Harry Staunton was coming. Or the time she had gone alone to visit the sick old woman on the other side of the village. Not much had escaped Cyril Farquharson's notice, thanks to money and his paid spies.

He knew when Madeline walked in the gardens and when she sat with her needlework by her bedchamber window. Even her midnight sojourn to the library and the drunken harsh response of her husband had not escaped his attention. The faked letter had done its work well, driving a wedge of suspicion between Tregellas and the woman he had stolen. Farquharson remembered those light golden brown eyes, the dark blonde hair swept so primly back. Madeline Langley was no beauty, but she had everything that he wanted in a woman: innocence, modesty and, more importantly fear…and that was what Farquharson craved above all. She had a shy reserve that held her apart from the crowd. She did not chatter the inane nonsense of most of the young ladies of the *ton*. She did not pout or stamp her foot or dab at a tearful eye. Not Madeline Langley. She just melted into the background, and watched what was around her with those magnificent eyes of hers. A little wallflower that hid something beneath. Unless Farquharson was very much mistaken, what flowed in those frightened little veins of hers was a passion that had not yet been brought to life. He hardened at the very thought and moved with impatience steadily closer to Madeline's bedchamber.

Lucien gritted his teeth and rode harder. How the hell could he have been so stupid as not to realise that Farquharson would have double-crossed him? Didn't he know the man for the sly malevolent villain that he was? Now, because of his mistake, because he had allowed Farquharson to outwit him, Madeline would suffer. Lucien had been fully prepared to face his own death, not Madeline's. He pushed aside the thoughts of exactly what Farquharson would be subjecting her to, just harnessed the rage and focused it to carry him with speed in the direction of Trethevyn.

The moon, so clear and high above, lit his path, helping him push Nelson faster than he normally would have dared along the muddy road close by Bodmin Moor. But no matter how much he or his beloved gelding gave, nothing could diminish the distance that separated them from Madeline. Even illuminated as well as it was, the rutted road was too long, too slow. He was approaching Camelford when he found himself plunged headlong into a shroud of thick mist. No warning, just a blanket of low cloud that hid the road ahead. 'Hell, no!' Lucien shouted aloud and pulled Nelson up hard. Breath came in heavy pants and sweat dripped from his face. Every muscle fired with adrenalin. All around was the eerie silence of the moor.

Just a pocket of mist, he told himself. He need only pass through it. It would lift as suddenly as it had descended. 'Come on, Nelson.' He tried to coax the horse to walk on, steering with his knees, making the little clicks of reassurance that the gelding liked to hear. Nelson obstinately held his ground, apparently impervious to all means of persuasion. The gelding's ears flattened and his black eyes rolled to become edged with white. Hind legs stumbled back. Snorting breath muffled in the unnatural quiet that surrounded them. Lucien tried to calm the frightened horse, but to no avail. From somewhere in the distance came a whinny. Nelson's ears pricked up. Lucien backed him out of the mist, scanning the undulating moorland. There, up on the hill to the left, not so far away, outlined black and stark against the brightness of the moon, was a solitary rider on his horse.

Lucien's fingers touched to the heavy weight of the pistol hidden within his pocket. The figure beckoned. Another trap? Farquharson or one of his cronies? Across the distance the man looked to be wearing an old-fashioned cocked hat. The stranger's voice filled the space between them. It was a deep voice, thickly accented with the familiar Cornish lilt. 'If you've a mind to get anywhere fast then you'd best go over the moor, past Brown Willy, cross the main coaching road at Jamaica Inn, then on between the Downs. Could cross it in an hour…if you can ride well and know the land. Goin' that way myself, if you care to follow.' The great black horse reared up on its back legs and both man and beast disappeared over the brow of the hill.

For all his suspicion, Lucien knew the man to be right. He didn't trust him. The stranger might be a cut-throat or a high-wayman. It was a risk Lucien was prepared to take. If he didn't reach Madeline in time, none of it mattered anyway. A brief touch of a booted foot to Nelson's flank and they were off, following in the man's wake, galloping across the clear moonlit hills, crossing hedges and streams, kicking up great clods of mud and grass, pressing onwards at breakneck speed, struggling to maintain the distant figure in sight, breath strain-ing hard in a cloud of condensation. Rider and horse merged.

Urgent. Intent. Madeline. Madeline. Madeline. Her name sounded silently again and again amidst the pounding rhythm of hooves and hearts. Faster and faster, until the first faint sight of Trethevyn's lights appeared in the distance and the stranger was gone.

* * *

When at last Madeline saw the doorknob turn and heard the quiet click, she felt a peculiar sense of relief. The waiting was over. The door opened in towards her, sweeping silently across the floor to admit the shadowy figure that followed in its wake. She watched the man creep towards the bed. He seemed smaller than she remembered. A dark shape moving stealthily forward into the room. Even bleached and muted by the silver moonlight, his hair was still discernible as red. The skin on his face was illuminated an unearthly white. He hesitated by the bed, caught unawares by its empty state. Then, like a fox scenting its prey, he raised his head and looked directly at her.

Through the darkness she met his gaze.

He was wary, the situation not quite as he had anticipated. A furtive glance all around, trying to ascertain if she was alone or if he himself had just walked into a trap.

'You came at last,' she said. And her voice sounded strangely calm.

'Madeline,' he breathed, and she heard the promise in the word.

'I did not know if I could wait much longer.'

His steps paused. She could almost see the puzzlement upon his face. 'You knew I was coming?'

'You promised.' She unfolded herself from the chair and stood up.

His perplexity was so palpable as to reach across the distance between them.

'In your letter,' she said as if by way of explanation.

Farquharson made no move towards her, his body poised as if to take flight at any moment.

Her gaze sought his across the room. 'You said that you loved me.'

A sharp frown appeared. His eyes shot right, then left. His hand touched to the shape of a pistol hidden beneath his coat.

'Did you speak true?' The game she played was a dangerous one, but it seemed to be working. She had never seen him so discomposed.

Narrow eyes scanned the darkness. He twitched and glanced around him as if he did not entirely trust the situation into which he had just walked. 'Tregellas is at Tintagel.' It was not a question. Farquharson knew very well that the Earl was exactly where he wanted him to be. He had watched Tregellas ride out alone four hours ago, long enough to ensure that the Earl had not changed his mind *en route*.

'Yes, where you sent him. It was very clever of you. He really had no idea, you know.'

Farquharson could not suppress the smirk.

'Almost as clever as the letter that you showed to Lord Varington.' She tilted her head to the side, almost as if in quizzical admiration. 'How did you manage that, with the Tregellas paper and seal, and, of course, my own writing clear upon it?'

He opened his mouth to tell her, just as she had known that he would. 'The paper was easy enough. It did not take much to discover that Tregellas has always used Hambledon printers and suppliers of fine paper. A small bribe ensured a few sheets went missing from his last order. You, my dear, gave me the means to replicate the seal yourself, with the cold-hearted reply that you sent me. Before I broke the seal on your letter I had a friend of mine impress it in glazier's putty and use the relief to cast a new seal. Something of the detail is lost in the process, but not enough to be noticed when it is pressed roughly into molten wax.' His gaze broke from hers to scan around the room.

But there was more still to know and Madeline meant to learn it all. 'You then had someone forge my handwriting.'

'No.' He could not resist the invitation to brag. 'I have in my possession a copying machine, a so-called polygraph. A most ingenious invention by Mr John Isaac Hawkins. Not designed for forgery, but useful for that purpose all the same. A pen is inserted into one side of it. A second pen positioned on the other side of the mechanism mirrors the movement of the first, to reproduce the identical letters on a fresh sheet of paper. I merely rearranged the words written by your own hand to make them read quite differently, then traced the first pen across them. The result was a letter saying what I wanted, written in the exact style of your hand.'

'I see.' She sighed softly, knowing what it was she had to do.

He stepped back, his expression hardening. 'Enough of this chatter. Come here, Madeline.'

There was only one way she could hope to deter the man before her. He was so sure of her aversion, wanted her to cower and tremble before him, needed her fear. Madeline would satisfy neither his expectations nor his desires, but in order to act she needed him close. 'Will you not come to me?' She stood where she was.

He hesitated and glanced over his shoulder, as if he could not be sure that Lucien had not returned to Trethevyn by some secret route. He took first one step towards her, and then another, before stopping. 'What trickery is this?'

'No trickery, my lord.' She opened her palms, held them out for him to see. 'Are you afraid?' she said.

A moue of displeasure marked his mouth. 'It's not supposed to be like this.' His top lip curled. 'Come here!' And his voice was rough with menace.

A soft laugh escaped Madeline and she stepped back to lean against the wall, slipping her hands into the pockets of her dressing gown as she did so.

'No more of your games!' he snapped and made to catch her.

It seemed to Madeline that he moved in slow motion. She waited until he had almost reached her before withdrawing her right hand from its silky hiding place. She drove the unsheathed knife as fast and as hard as she could towards Farquharson's chest. She saw the blade glint as it arced through the moonlight. She heard his grunt of surprise as the tip of the knife found its mark. And just when she thought that she had him, Farquharson twisted away, grabbing her arm in the process, almost wrenching it from its socket. There was a sharp pain in her wrist where his fingers gripped, and the knife clattered to the floor. Farquharson retrieved it and then held her arms in a tight grip, pinning her against the wall while he stared down into her face. There was a snarl on his mouth, a feral darkness in his eyes. 'Little bitch!' he cursed. 'You would kill me!' He seemed genuinely shocked.

She said nothing. The breath was soft in her throat. She had failed. There was nothing more she could do. She knew her time had come. Farquharson would do to her what he had done to Sarah Wyatt. And curiously, now that she faced that which she most feared, she was not afraid. The fear had all been in the anticipation and the imaginings. The reality of the horror brought only a calm acceptance.

What was it that Lucien had said? *The villain thrives on pain. It gives him pleasure to watch others suffer.* Madeline understood in that moment exactly what Lucien had meant. Farquharson's hands curled tighter, biting into her skin as he dragged her across the room and threw her on to the bed. Still she felt neither pain nor fear. She looked up at the cruel contorted features. 'There's no more pleasure to be had for you, Lord Farquharson.'

He struck her hard across the cheek as she lay there. 'What do you know of pleasure and pain, Madeline?'

She didn't even flinch.

A bark sounded from the dressing room.

Farquharson glanced round to the closed door that separated the two rooms. 'The dog won't bother us from in there,' he said, 'and there's so much I have to teach you, my dear.' His hand wrapped around her throat and squeezed. The press of his arousal against her leg grew stronger.

It seemed that Madeline was not in the shell that she called her body, but had floated clear of it to rest somewhere up high beside the plasterwork of the ceiling. Was she really looking down at Farquharson throttling her? Even as she watched, he released his grip to straddle her. 'It's too late.' The words croaked hoarse and she saw that it was her own lips that moved. 'Your power is gone, my lord. I am not afraid.'

'Then let me rectify matters, Madeline.' He tore the dressing gown from her. His hands moved to grasp the neckline of her nightdress, ripping down through the stark white cotton to expose the pale flesh beneath. His mouth pounced like a savage upon her breasts.

Still Madeline did not cry out. 'All you are worthy of is pity, sir,' she said. 'You are a man incapable of receiving or giving love.'

Max gave a whine and scratched at the dressing-room door.

From above she felt Farquharson cease his movement upon her. Watched while he raised his face to look into her own. Saw the saliva moist upon his lips and the wetness that dripped to his chin. Looked deep into that dismal grey gaze. '*I do not fear you.*' Each word was dropped with clear enunciation into the space between them. She felt his interest shrivel.

He swallowed hard. 'Whore!' he said and drew Lucien's knife from his pocket. 'So thoughtful of you to provide me with your husband's knife. He won't wriggle out of prosecution so easily this time. Murder is a wicked crime, committed by a wicked man. First against his betrothed, and now against his wife. I named him well, did I not?'

Another bark, followed by some more scratching at the door.

'You can kill me, Lord Farquharson, but no one shall believe Lucien guilty of the crime. Why, all of London knows that we eloped out of love,' she taunted.

'Indeed?' His face was cold and hard. There was nothing of humanity in his eyes. A smile played across his mouth. 'I think you'll find that they believe Tregellas abducted you and forced a wedding. And as for motive, I shall feel it my civic duty to publish the letter that you sent me; the letter in which you beg for rescue from a madman, and speak of your love for me.'

'Lucien shall prove it for the fake that it is.'

'I don't think so, Madeline,' said Farquharson. He paused and watched her. 'They'll hang him, you know. And I shall be there to watch while he slowly expires.' He smiled and licked his lips. 'What better fun than killing you, then watching your husband die for the crime.'

'No!' Rage welled within her. 'No!' she cried again. 'Ever the coward's way, Farquharson. Ever cloak and dagger, and behind his back. You are not man enough to face him. You know he would best you a thousand times over!'

Max barked again, and from outside came the distant thud of horse's hooves.

Farquharson glanced nervously towards the windows.

Someone was riding hard and fast.

'It's three hours from Tintagel to here,' said Farquharson as if to himself.

   He touched the blade to her throat, and then in one move
gently stroked its cold sharp edge against her skin.

   Madeline felt its shallow bite and a wetness trickled down
the sides of her neck.

   The horseman was coming closer.

   'I've waited so long for this,' he said and, bending forward,
licked the dribble of blood from her skin and then covered
her mouth with his own. The metallic taste of blood touched
upon her tongue, and then his mouth was suffocating her.

   They heard the sudden crunch of gravel on the driveway
and knew the horseman had reached Trethevyn. Max began
to bark in earnest.

   Madeline's heart leapt. It could not be, could it?

   Farquharson scowled and clambered off her. Still clutching the knife, he stalked to the window that led out on to the
balcony. Up the gravel driveway came a solitary horseman,
riding as if his very life was at stake. The horse's eyes showed
white and his great black muzzle was flecked pale with saliva.
The man was leaping down from the saddle as the Baron
watched. And even through the darkness Farquharson knew
that it was Tregellas that had come. 'How the hell…?' But
there was no time for questions. He knew he would have to
act quickly.

   Madeline sat up and slowly, so as not to attract Farquharson's attention, slid towards the edge of the bed.

   Farquharson was still peering out of the window. 'He
arrives in time to spoil our fun but, Madeline, not in time to
prevent your death, for which he will take the blame. A crime
of passion. All of London knows what has gone on between
us three.' He turned then and looked at her. 'And this time he
shall not escape justice, earl or not. I shall toast you, my dear,
as I watch his neck being stretched by a rope upon a gibbet.'

The blade within his hand glinted in the moonlight. 'And now, my sweet Madeline…' He began to walk towards her.

Madeline sprang from the bed and, unmindful of her nakedness, ran towards the dressing-room door. She heard Farquharson's movement behind her, felt the sudden grasp of his fingers biting hard against her shoulder. She snatched at the handle and the door to the dressing-room opened. Max's frenzied barking grew suddenly loud. She felt the rush of something against her legs, but then Farquharson was wrenching her back, throwing her towards the bed. It all happened so fast that she did not know what was happening. Her head struck against the bedstead. Waves of dizzy nausea washed over her. She lay sprawled upon the floor, struggling to get back up on to her feet, but unable to stop the world tilting enough to do so. 'Lucien!' she cried, but her voice was weak and thick with confusion and no matter how hard she tried she could not see through the darkness that had descended upon her.

There was the thud of feet and the scamper of paws. Something moist snuffled against her face and she knew that it was Max. Madeline ceased the struggle to open her eyes and let her head rest back upon the rug.

The raucous barking had turned to a low-pitched growling.

Farquharson cursed and his boots scuffed away. She heard the opening of the window, and then the rapid sliding of its close.

And Madeline knew that she had failed, for Farquharson would escape. He could swing down from the balcony across to the roof of the front porch. And from there it was not so very far to the ground.

She pushed herself up until she was sitting. Spots danced before her eyes. Her stomach jiggled like a ship on a choppy sea. She looked up to see Farquharson out on the balcony and

Max growling with his nose pressed against the glass. A black paw scraped against the pane.

'Max,' she called. And Max ceased his noise and came to stand by her. He whined and licked her face. Her fingers caught in his smooth black fur. She eased herself back to rest against the bedstead, and shut her eyes.

There was the sudden loud crashing sound. A man cried out, followed by a bone-jarring thud. Then there was only silence.

Lucien was taking the stairs two at a time, leaving a trail of muddy footsteps behind, when he heard the cry and the sickening thud of a body landing hard upon the ground. His stomach turned over and the breath tore ragged in his throat as he ran full tilt towards Madeline's chamber. 'Madeline!' he bellowed, fearing what he would find, but charging onward regardless. The door reverberated from his onslaught, swinging back open and wide. Only then did Lucien pause. Madeline was sitting on the floor, leaning against the bed. Her eyes were closed and her face was so white as to appear lifeless. Blood trickled from a gash on her forehead, and blood was dripping down her throat. And she was naked. Max sat by her side. He looked up at his master and gave a whimper. Lucien thought that he was too late.

'Madeline,' he whispered and moved quickly to her side. Down below there were the sounds of feet running and doors banging and servants' voices. 'Madeline!' he said again and it seemed that his heart had stopped.

Her eyes flickered open, and she was looking at him, and he knew that God had heard his prayer. She was alive. His beloved Madeline was alive.

'Lucien, is it really you?' she whispered and reached for him.

He took off his coat and wrapped it around her and lifted her into his arms.

'Lucien!' She clung to him, her fingers touching gently to his mud-splattered cheeks. 'My love.'

He felt the slow trickle of blood back into his face. The crushing burden of dread crumbled and dispersed. 'You're alive. You're safe.' He stared at her, unable to comprehend how that could be. 'Farquharson…' And then he remembered the cry and the thud and looked towards the window that led out on to the balcony.

Madeline saw his gaze. 'He went out there, trying to escape,' she said. 'The railings…I think he fell.'

Lucien laid her gently on the bed, and then with Max at his heels he moved to the window, slid the sash up and stepped out on to the balcony. At the right-hand side the railings had given way completely. Lucien glanced down and over to the right to the roof of the porch. It was empty. He stepped closer to the edge of the balcony where there were no longer any railings. The drop was sheer. Below on the hard stone of the steps lay a man's broken body: Cyril Farquharson. It was over.

Madeline heard him come back into the room, felt him sit down on the bed beside her. 'He's dead,' he said.

'Then we're safe.'

He nodded. 'I thought…' She heard the crack in his voice and his eyes squeezed shut. When they opened again he seemed to have regained some measure of control.

'No,' she said, 'You came in time, you and Max.' And she told her husband what had passed between her and Farquharson.

He stared as if he could not quite believe it. 'I must fetch the doctor for you.'

But she stayed him with a touch of her hand. 'No. There's nothing that shall not mend. The blood makes it appear worse than it is. Stay. Please.' She wrapped her arms around him.

'Madeline!' Her name was a harsh expiration of breath and

in that sound was everything of relief and disbelief and love. He cradled her against him.

She kissed his chest, his arms, tilted her face up to press a myriad of butterfly kisses against his jaw. 'I thought I'd lost you,' she whispered.

'My love.' He stroked her cheek. 'I feared I was too late. I couldn't bear to lose you. You are my very life.'

'As you are mine,' she breathed.

'Madeline,' he said again and their lips met in joyous salvation. And Lucien held her as if he would never let her go.

It was half an hour later when Farquharson's body was being removed that Lucien undertook to search the villain's pockets. A handkerchief, a pocket watch, some calling cards, two dice, a purse full of money…and a sheet of neatly folded paper. It rustled between Lucien's fingers as he splayed it flat to reveal the drawing traced upon it.

'What is it?' Madeline peered over his shoulder.

'A map…' He moved the branch of candles closer, straining to read the small scribbled words amidst the sketch. 'Showing the mine shaft close by the Hurlers stone circles.'

Two heads raised. Blue eyes met brown.

'Collins said Farquharson took them somewhere deep under ground,' said Madeline.

'I think we may just have discovered where he's holding my brother.'

They looked at one another a moment longer, each knowing the other's thoughts, and fears.

'Pray God he's still alive.' Lucien dropped a hasty kiss to her lips and went to ready the men of Trethevyn.

'And pray God that you come back safely to me,' replied his wife softly as he closed the door behind him.

* * *

The night was well advanced when Lucien and his party crept silently through the shadows towards the tin mine. The moonlight revealed a large group of men loitering by the entrance to the engine house. There looked to be about ten of them, perhaps as many as twelve. Vicious-looking villains. The hired muscle of which Collins had spoken. Some were armed with wooden clubs. And on some the moonlight glinted against long knife blades. Tobacco smoke drifted in the air; the small orange glowing spots of clay pipes were visible through the darkness. Lucien gestured the advance sign to the men behind him and slowly they began to spread out and edge forward.

The men had clearly been there some time. Some were leaning their backs against the wall of the engine house, others were sitting on what looked to be boxes. A bottle was being passed around. The quiet burr of their voices carried in the night. Someone sighed his boredom and another sniffed the contents of his nose down his throat. One of them gave a soft throaty laugh. None of them suspected what was closing around them.

Lucien and the men of Trethevyn attacked without warning, running in fast, catching the ruffians unawares. Lucien felled one man with a well-aimed blow from the handle of his pistol. The villains fought back, shouting, swearing. All around was mayhem. A fist cracked hard against Lucien's jaw and he tasted blood against his tongue. He lashed out and the man punched no more. The Trethevyn men were well armed, and they were angry. The night re-sounded with the clash of cudgels and yelling and scream-ing. A man ran at young Hayley's back with a knife raised ready to strike. Lucien aimed his pistol and pulled the trigger. There was a roar of gunpowder and the man collapsed with a grunt and a wet darkness seeping from his shoulder. The ruffians were falling, and those that didn't, ran away. The rest were easily overpowered. One by one the ruffians were bound and gagged and left where they lay.

Lucien checked inside the building that housed the great steam engine. It lay silent; the pumps that drained the mines of water idle for once. The place was deserted: no more of Farquharson's ruffians hiding. Back out into the darkness, past the tall chimney stalk, he made straight for the mouth of the mine. The tinderbox was struck, the lantern held low. He poured some powder into the pistol's pan and also down its barrel, fitted a patch over the muzzle and rammed a lead ball down into place. He slipped the pistol into his pocket. Those in the mine would have heard his shot. They were warned. Lucien had to be ready.

He peered down the shaft. It was narrow and vertical, and far deeper than the lantern light illuminated. A pit of hell. And down there somewhere Guy was waiting. Lucien could only pray that his brother was still alive. A ladder leaned against the shaft's inner rim. He swung his legs over and, gripping the ladder, began to descend, as fast as he dared. In a matter of seconds he was swallowed down into the narrow well of darkness, to meet what waited below. Sweat dripped down his back, soaking his shirt.

Never once did Lucien falter, just climbed and climbed further, down into the bowels of the earth, while up above his men waited and the moon shone down on a silent landscape.

Madeline paced the library. The woman who had faced Farquharson without fear now found her body chilled with apprehension. She chided herself, reasoning that Farquharson was dead and that Lucien knew what he was doing. *But it is a mine shaft,* the fear whispered, *and you do not know what awaits him.* The thought made her feel queasy. She bit down hard on her lip and tried to calm her fluttering nerves. What of Lord Varington? She dared not dwell too much on that thought, only hoped and prayed that he would be safe. She forced herself down into the large wing chair so favoured by her husband and watched the hands of the clock creep slowly forward. Night had never seemed so long, waiting never so difficult. At last the crunch of hooves sounded upon the driveway gravel. A low murmur of voices filled the night air. Madeline shook off the sleep that hovered so beguilingly close, and ran. She did not stop running until she saw her husband across the hallway.

Lucien was on one side. John Hayley on the other. Between them they supported the weight of a man who was pale and blood-smeared, a man that looked back at her with eyes so like her husband's.

'It was about time you sent him to collect me,' he drawled. 'I was growing bored with the wait.' Something of the familiar arrogance sparkled in his eyes, but his voice was strained and weak.

'Lord Varington,' she said.

'Guy,' he corrected her. 'I owe you an apology, Madeline.'

She saw how swollen and split the lips were that formed those words. Bruising darkened bloodshot eyes. 'There's no need.'

'On the contrary, I must insist that there's every need.' He coughed and fresh blood speckled his lips. A ragged hand wiped them away.

'We'll discuss the matter later when you've rested.'

'No.' The word forced out guttural and loud, echoing in the hallway.

'Come on, Guy,' Lucien coaxed his brother. 'Let's get you cleaned up and attended to by a physician first.'

'Madeline didn't write that letter, the one Farquharson showed to me. He had a copy made of your seal, bribed your printer to obtain the paper, and forged her writing by means of a polygraph.'

'I know. Madeline learned of it from Farquharson himself this evening. He could not refrain from boasting of his sly scheme.'

Guy stopped, an indefinable expression frozen upon his face. 'He's here?'

'Oh, he's here all right.' Lucien regarded his brother. 'But I didn't lie when I said that he was dead. The High Constable will arrange for the body to be removed in the morning.' He tried to pull his brother forward, but, despite the fact that Guy was bone-weary and swaying from the blood loss, the younger man showed not the slightest sign of moving.

Guy held Madeline's eye. 'I shouldn't have doubted you. Should have realised that Farquharson was as devious as the devil and sought only to use me to get to you and Lucien… and I damn well let him, fool that I am. I can only plead your forgiveness, Madeline.'

Madeline gently touched a hand against Guy's sleeve. 'There's nothing to forgive, my lord…Guy. Farquharson tricked us all.'

Guy gave a nod of his head.

'And now, little brother, if you're quite finished setting yourself right with my wife, I must insist that you retire to the blue bedchamber.'

Between them Lucien and his footman helped the wounded man up the main staircase.

Two weeks later, and Madeline and Lucien stood on the steps of Trethevyn, waving goodbye to Guy.

'He's not recovered enough to travel yet and London is so very far. I wish he would have heeded you.' Madeline sighed. 'I mean, what if—'

Lucien touched a finger to her lips. 'No more "what ifs". Guy is as stubborn as a mule when it comes to getting his way in these things.'

'Is the country really so abhorrent to him?' A dove cooed from a nearby bush. The sky above was a clear bright blue. And the air was fresh and rich with the fragrance of spring. 'I cannot imagine anyone preferring the foul-smelling streets of London to this.'

'I think, perhaps—' his eyes held Madeline's '—that there are certain other matters to which Guy is keen to attend.' A dark eyebrow raised suggestively. 'My brother does have a certain reputation to maintain.'

A flush of delicate pink suffused Madeline's cheeks. 'Reputations can be misleading—why, sir, all of London is convinced that you're the Wicked Earl. I must rectify that rumour when we return there next.'

'Beginning with your parents.'

'Did I not tell you?' Madeline raised her eyebrows and drew him a small smile. 'My parents have suffered a change of heart. Angelina writes that Mama has discovered the merits of having an earl in the family and has become quite high in the instep about it. And Papa worries only for my happiness. He is happy as long as I am.'

'And are you happy, my love?'

'Never more so,' she laughed.

His hands slid seductively around her back. 'Am I not wicked? To have forced you to a marriage that you didn't want? To have exposed you to the worst of an evil villain who would have taken your life?'

'Extremely wicked,' she agreed and raised her lips so that they almost touched his.

'Did you believe the whispers that I was a wicked man?'

'Never.'

'How could you be so certain? You didn't know me, after all.'

'Instinct. Trust. I don't really understand it myself, but when I looked into your eyes the night you danced with me at Lady Gilmour's ball…' She shrugged her shoulders. 'I just knew. Besides…' she smiled and stole a kiss from his mouth '…anyone who saved me from Farquharson could not be at all wicked.'

With uncanny timing a black bobbing head appeared in the distance, scampering paws against gravel and barking fit to raise a riot. Max bounded up to where they stood.

'This old boy can chew as much of my footwear as he likes.' Lucien stooped to rub the dog's ears. 'Good dog!'

Madeline smiled. 'I did see him with one of your boots this morning.'

'Mmm.' Her husband's hands were busy plucking the pins from her hair, releasing it to tumble free down her back.

She held up her face to his and traced her tongue against his lips.

A low rumble sounded in Lucien's throat. The pins dropped to scatter upon the steps.

'Will you not tell me again how the ghost of Harry Staunton guided you back across the moor to Trethevyn that night?'

'Madeline…' he briefly covered her mouth with his own. One light kiss. 'There are no such things as ghosts.' A second kiss, harder, more thorough than the first, 'The man was likely someone from a neighbouring village.' When his lips claimed hers for a third time it was with a mounting passion that would brook no more talk of the ghostly highwayman. 'Did I tell you how much I love you?' He swept her up into his arms, his ice-pale eyes thawing to a blue smoulder. 'Or show you?'

'You know very well that you did only this morning, you wicked man!'

'Wicked by name, wicked by nature! Alas, my love, I find I've a need to show you again. And there's the small matter of the village sweepstake on our producing an heir…'

Together they laughed, and Earl Tregellas turned and carried his Countess over the threshold of Trethevyn.

Out on the moor, the figure of a masked man doffed his cocked hat and faded into the sunlight.

* * * * *

THE STEEPWOOD

Scandals

Regency drama, intrigue, mischief…
and marriage

VOLUME SEVEN

Mr Rushford's Honour by Meg Alexander

Gina, Lady Whitelaw left Steepwood as plain Gina
Westcott. Now, years later, she's returned home
– and has to face the man who stole her heart…

⚜

An Unlikely Suitor by Nicola Cornick

At three-and-twenty and a bluestocking to boot,
Miss Lavender Brabant feels her chance of marriage
has passed. But now she's met Barnabas Hammond,
a shopkeeper's son!

On sale 4th May 2007

A young woman disappears.
A husband is suspected of murder.
Stirring times for all the neighbourhood in

THE STEEPWOOD

Scandals

Volume 5 – March 2007
Counterfeit Earl by Anne Herries
The Captain's Return by Elizabeth Bailey

Volume 6 – April 2007
The Guardian's Dilemma by Gail Whitiker
Lord Exmouth's Intentions by Anne Ashley

Volume 7 – May 2007
Mr Rushford's Honour by Meg Alexander
An Unlikely Suitor by Nicola Cornick

Volume 8 – June 2007
An Inescapable Match by Sylvia Andrew
The Missing Marchioness by Paula Marshall

Victorian London is brought to vibrant life in this mesmeric new novel!

London, 1876

All her life, Olivia Moreland has denied her clairvoyant abilities, working instead to disprove the mediums that flock to London. But when Stephen, Lord St Leger, requests her help in investigating an alleged psychic, she can't ignore the ominous presence she feels within the walls of his ancient estate. Nor can she ignore the intimate connection she feels to Stephen, as if she has somehow known him before…

Available 20th April 2007

FREE

2 BOOKS AND A SURPRISE GIFT!

We would like to take this opportunity to thank you for reading this Mills & Boon® book by offering you the chance to take TWO more specially selected titles from the Historical Romance™ series absolutely FREE! We're also making this offer to introduce you to the benefits of the Mills & Boon® Reader Service™—

- ★ **FREE home delivery**
- ★ **FREE gifts and competitions**
- ★ **FREE monthly Newsletter**
- ★ **Books available before they're in the shops**
- ★ **Exclusive Reader Service offers**

Accepting these FREE books and gift places you under no obligation to buy; you may cancel at any time, even after receiving your free shipment. Simply complete your details below and return the entire page to the address below. You don't even need a stamp!

YES! Please send me 2 free Historical Romance books and a surprise gift. I understand that unless you hear from me, I will receive 4 superb new titles every month for just £3.69 each, postage and packing free. I am under no obligation to purchase any books and may cancel my subscription at any time. The free books and gift will be mine to keep in any case.

H7ZEE

Ms/Mrs/Miss/Mr..Initials ....

BLOCK CAPITALS PLEASE

Surname ....

Address ....

....

....Postcode ....

Send this whole page to:

The Reader Service, FREEPOST CN81, Croydon, CR9 3WZ